ISLAMIC

METALWORK

IN THE FREER GALLERY OF ART

ESIN ATIL

W. T. CHASE

PAUL JETT

FREER GALLERY OF ART
SMITHSONIAN INSTITUTION
WASHINGTON, D.C., 1985

Published by the Smithsonian Institution Press on the occasion of an
exhibition held at the Freer Gallery of Art, Smithsonian Institution,
Washington, D.C., September 27, 1985–January 5, 1986.

The paper in this book meets the guidelines for permanence and durability
of the Committee on Production Guidelines for Book Longevity of the Council
on Library Resources.

Produced by the Smithsonian Institution Press
Typeset (in English) by Monotype Composition Company, Inc., Baltimore, Maryland,
and (in Arabic) by National Graphic Center, Falls Church, Virginia
Printed by Schneidereith & Sons, Baltimore, Maryland
Edited by Jane McAllister
Designed by Stephen Kraft

For sale by the Superintendent of Documents,
U.S. Government Printing Office
Washington, D.C. 20402
Stock number: 047–001–00161–3

Contents

Foreword

Islamic metalwork was, relatively speaking, a latecomer to the Freer collections. Although Charles Lang Freer (1854–1919) included many important examples of Islamic drawings, ceramics, and manuscripts in his original bequest, the first significant piece of metalwork did not enter the collection until 1936, almost two decades after Mr. Freer's death. That first piece of Islamic metalwork was a thirteenth-century brass pen box inlaid with silver inscriptions (no. 14). It was purchased by John Ellerton Lodge (1878–1942), the first director of the museum. Mr. Lodge, who served as director for twenty-two years, from 1920 to 1942, was responsible for acquiring objects in many areas not fully represented in the original Freer bequest. In his decisions, Mr. Lodge drew upon detailed discussions with Charles Lang Freer regarding the future of the Freer Gallery.

The initial translation of the brass pen box's important inscriptions, giving the name of the patron and artist, and dated 607 A.H. (1210/11 A.D.), was made by Grace T. Whitney in 1936. Later that same year, Grace Dunham Guest (1872–1964), assistant director of the Freer from 1920 to 1946, provided additional annotation for the translation, as well as references to related objects in other collections. In 1936 Ernest Herzfeld (1879–1948) published an article about the Freer pen box in *Ars Islamica.* The precise terminology in Professor Herzfeld's translation of the inscriptions and the associated historical documents is characteristic of his extraordinary scholarship.

The collaboration of many scholars, as typified by the information regarding the inscriptions on the Freer pen box, is characteristic of the way in which we at the museum are learning more about individual objects in our collections. Throughout the more than sixty years of its history, the Freer Gallery has stressed the importance of research and scholarship, and the current exhibition provides an opportunity to present tangible evidence of what is now known about this particular group of objects in the collections.

The greatest number of objects in this exhibition of Islamic metalwork was acquired during the curatorship of Richard Ettinghausen (1906–1979), curator of Near Eastern art from 1944 to 1967. Dr. Ettinghausen's discriminating taste and scholarly research were instrumental in raising the Freer Gallery's Islamic collections to their present position of international eminence. Complementing the Islamic metalworks themselves, all of which are illustrated in this catalogue, are the comprehensive notes that Dr. Ettinghausen assembled in the research records of the Freer Gallery. Much of the documentation in those notes has been incorporated into the individual catalogue entries in this publication.

Information in the Near Eastern archives at the Freer Gallery continues to assist scholars in their research. The Herzfeld Archive consists of all the field notebooks, negatives, drawings, and plans of Professor Herzfeld, who spent his lifetime as an archaeologist in western Asia. The material was given to the Smithsonian Institution in 1946 with the provision that it be housed in the Freer Gallery; supplementary materials were added in 1951 and 1952. The Myron Bement Smith Archive is comprised of approximately eighty-seven thousand items assembled by Dr. Smith (1897–1970) during his forty-year career as a classical archaeologist, architect, and historian. The photographic materials, acquired from a number of private collections and consisting of sixty-four thousand negatives, prints, and color and lantern slides, provide a comprehensive visual documentation of a wide range of subjects relating to the anthropology, architecture, art, geography, and history of the Islamic world.

This special exhibition of Islamic metalwork was proposed by Esin Atıl, who guided the museum's Near Eastern collection from 1970 to 1984. She selected the objects for the exhibition and prepared the text for the catalogue. Dr. Atıl has already published significant portions of the Freer Gallery's Near Eastern collection. Those publications include *Exhibition of Twenty-Five Hundred Years of Persian Art* (1971), *Ceramics from the World of Islam* (1973), and *Art of the Arab World* (1975).

In preparation for this exhibition of Islamic metalwork, W. T. Chase and Paul Jett of the Freer Gallery's Technical Laboratory examined each of the pieces with regard to fabrication techniques and metallurgical composition. Their findings, which are included in the catalogue, provide new and important insights into the subject. This type of collaboration between Freer Gallery curators and scientists has already resulted in the two volumes of *The Freer Chinese Bronzes*, which appeared in 1967 and 1969. As a consequence of this latest collaboration, we are more keenly aware of every aspect of the Islamic metalwork collection in the Freer Gallery. We feel certain that the information assembled by the staff of the museum's Technical Laboratory will enable scholars to better appreciate the skill of Islamic designers and metalsmiths.

Thomas Lawton
Director

Preface and Acknowledgments

The purpose of this study is not to present a general survey of Islamic metalwork but to define the stylistic and technical characteristics of the objects in the collection of the Freer Gallery of Art and to show how they represent the traditions identified with certain periods and regions. A number of silver and gold pieces have been intentionally left out since they require further art historical and technical research to establish their authenticity and provenance. These are included in Appendix III together with other objects not discussed in the catalogue.

Any work on Islamic metalwork requires the collaborative efforts of experts in the fields of technical studies, epigraphy, and cultural history. Several scholars assisted in the reading and interpretation of the inscriptions, while others shared their research and expertise in the identification of problematic pieces. To the following friends and colleagues who willingly provided information and shared our enthusiasm for Islamic metalwork, we owe a special gratitude: David Alexander for confirming the Safavid provenance of the seventeenth-century dagger with the bifurcate pommel; Paul E. Chevedden and Ali Masud El-Baluch for correcting the reading of the inscriptions on the large twelfth-century candlestick assigned to Herat; Yousif M. Ghulam for reading the animated inscription on the canteen; Anatol Ivanov for reading the poem and deciphering the *abjad* dating on the Zand-period dagger and sheath; Marilyn Jenkins for helping with problematic pieces of jewelry; A. H. Morton for analyzing the *siyaq* script on the base of the late Timurid silver bowl; and Barbara Stowasser for checking both the Arabic and Persian inscriptions in the catalogue entries.

The authors were assisted in their technical studies by the other members of the Freer's Technical Laboratory, John Winter, Elisabeth FitzHugh, and Martha Smith. Martha Goodway, metallurgist of the Conservation-Analytical Laboratory of the Smithsonian, was very helpful, especially with the steel and iron objects. Paul Craddock of the British Museum Research Laboratory loaned us original printouts of his analyses of Islamic metalwork, and was forthcoming with helpful suggestions. The National Gallery of Art's Conservation Laboratory was extremely cooperative in letting us use their X-ray fluorescence analyzer; we would like to thank Victor Covey and Ross Merrill, successive laboratory heads, and Barbara Miller, chief of the Analytical Section there. We would also like to acknowledge the invaluable assistance of Patricia Bragdon, who oversaw the production of the manuscript and compiled the reference photographs.

Esin Atıl
W. T. Chase
Paul Jett

Introduction

The tradition of metalwork is the most representative of all the Islamic arts in that it reflects the tastes and demands of diverse social and economic classes, for objects were made for rulers and wealthy citizens as well as for humble households. Unlike illustrated manuscripts, which were produced exclusively for royal libraries and courtly patrons, and ceramics, which served more popular needs,[1] metalwork was commissioned and purchased by members in all levels of society. Imperial pieces were made of expensive materials and decorated with themes specified by the clients; the wealthy middle classes competed with the court and ordered equally sumptuous objects; and the public purchased items made from lesser metals and embellished with decorations of generalized subjects. Each piece, whether imperial or plebian, was designed and executed with care, revealing the expertise and pride of the maker.

A vast amount of metalwork has remained from the Islamic world in spite of the continuous political turbulences during which treasuries were confiscated and objects were melted down to be recycled into currency or fashioned into new pieces. Many objects made of copper alloys, including inlaid brasses, appear to have escaped destruction and been cherished throughout the centuries, although those made of silver and gold seem to have been less fortunate.

The production of Islamic metalwork reveals a fusion between art and craft. Some pieces are simple and traditional whereas others display an incredible technical virtuosity and originality. Their decorative repertoire employs both derivative and common themes and unique compositions; the designs can be either boldly executed or so highly refined that at times they rival the art of illumination. The artists generally concentrated on surface decoration and applied different materials to produce varied contrasts and coloristic effects, which tend to overpower and even camouflage the base metal. They relied on the techniques and materials employed in the past to create an extraordinary range of decorative themes. By combining diverse geometric, floral, and figural compositions with different styles of writing, the artists invested their pieces with mystical and symbolic meanings that required a highly sophisticated clientele.

The development of the decorative vocabulary of Islamic metalwork has not yet been established clearly. The structure of the workshops, the relationship between masters and apprentices, and the division of labor among the artists also are not properly known. In addition, there are no proper literary sources or archival documents to provide information on the location of major centers and the types of wares produced at different periods.

The most valuable information is found on the objects themselves. Although there are only a few signed and dated pieces, and even fewer examples that state where they were made, the inscriptions help to identify certain ateliers and centers in addition to the types of patronage. For instance, the inscriptions on the famous bucket (fig. 1) in the Hermitage, a key piece in the study of Islamic art, state that it was inlaid by Muhammad ibn Abd al-Vahed and made by Masud ibn Ahmad, who is called ''the designer of Herat.''[2] A division of labor obviously existed between the artist who conceived the shape and design of the piece and the one who executed the inlays. The inscriptions on the Leningrad bucket also state that it was made in December 1163 at the request of Abd al-Rahman ibn Abdallah al-Rashidi for Khwaja (title meaning

1. Bronze(?) bucket inlaid with copper and silver
Ordered by Abd al-Rahman b. Abdallah al-Rashidi for Khwaja Rukn al-Din Rashid al-Din Azizi
Made by Masud b. Ahmad and inlaid by Muhammad b. Abd al-Vahed, *al-naqqash-e Herat*
Afghanistan, dated 1163
(Leningrad, State Hermitage Museum, CA–12687)

11

religious teacher or leader) Rukn al-Din Rashid al-Din Azizi (or Harari), the son-in-law of Abu'l-Husayn al-Zanjani. Although the personages mentioned are unknown historically, one can surmise that the patron was wealthy or ambitious to have commissioned such a valuable gift. Moreover, the patron intended to impress the beneficiary, a man of influence and, more significant, one who would be appreciative of the technical and aesthetic qualities of an object as mundane as a bucket. The inscriptions also provide the date and the name of a city, Herat, with which one of the artists was associated.

Another clue to the labor division in an atelier is found on a Koran box (fig. 2) in Berlin, thought to have been produced in Cairo in the 1320s. The inscriptions state that it was made by Muhammad ibn Sunqur al-Baghdadi (of Baghdad) and inlaid by Hajj Yusuf ibn al-Ghawabi.[3] Once again, the artist who fashioned the box is differentiated from the one who executed the inlays.

This type of specific and detailed information is extremely rare in the history of Islamic metalwork. Most of the objects that bear the name of an artist are thought to have been constructed and decorated by the same person, as in the case of the pen box made by Shazi in 1210/11 (no. 14), the ewer made by Qasim ibn Ali in 1232 (no. 16), and the dagger and sheath made by Taqi(?) in 1777 (no. 35). It should be mentioned that these three examples not only were signed and dated but were produced for the court; they were commissioned either by a well-known sultan, a grand vizier, or a regent, and thus can be assigned a provenance. The dagger is one of the few examples that bears an inscription with the name of the city, Shiraz, in which it was made.

2. Brass Koran box inlaid with silver and gold
Made by Muhammad b. Sunqur al-Baghdadi and inlaid by Hajj Yusuf b. al-Ghawabi
Egypt, ca. 1320
(Berlin, Museum für Islamische Kunst, I.886)

The location and production of metalworking centers are not easily determined, possibly owing to the political fluctuations in the Islamic world and the migration of artists seeking better employment in different capitals. Certain ateliers can be identified, nevertheless, through a series of inlaid brasses that are inscribed by artists who use the same *nisba* (word denoting place of origin) attached to their name. The largest group of objects are signed by metalworkers with the *nisba* al-Mawsili, literally meaning "of Mosul." According to these inscribed works, the al-Mawsili artists were active in Iraq, Syria, and Egypt between the 1220s and 1320s, and produced more than thirty examples that are among the masterpieces of Islamic art.[4] It is doubtful whether all the members of this elite group of metalworkers could trace their origin to Mosul or were even associated with that city; they wished to be identified, however, with the al-Mawsili corps and maintained a consistent level of high-quality production and refined work-manship for more than a century.

In spite of the lack of comprehensive documentation, the development of certain stylistic and decorative features can be reconstructed from the dated pieces. Metalwork produced between the seventh and tenth centuries, the formative period of Islamic art, reveals the continuation of past traditions and the beginning of an interest in surface decoration. Preoccupation with surface embellishment reached its epitome from the eleventh to thirteenth centuries, the classical age of Islamic metalwork, during which an extensive decorative repertoire was developed and the technique of inlaying diverse materials was perfected. With regional variations these themes and techniques persisted throughout the history of Islamic metalwork.

FORMATIVE PERIOD: SEVENTH THROUGH TENTH CENTURIES

The Islamic era begins with the *hijra,* the celebrated flight of the Prophet Muhammad and his followers from Mecca to Medina in the year 622. Within a short time the teachings of Muhammad spread from the Indus River to the Atlantic Ocean, and Islam evolved as a major political and social power in the Eastern Hemisphere. This vast empire was ruled by the caliphs, the successors of Muhammad, first by the members of the Umayyads (661–750) of Damascus, then by those of the Abbasids (750–1258) of Baghdad, both dynasties professing the Sunni, or orthodox doctrine. By the tenth century the central authority of the caliphate was undermined by the governors of the eastern and western provinces who attempted to establish autonomous states. The Abbasids also were threatened by the Shiites, who claimed as the rightful successors of Islam the descendants from the line of Ali, Muhammad's son-in-law. The Shiite Fatimids

3. Bronze(?) ewer
Iraq(?), 8th–9th centuries
(Cairo, Museum of Islamic Art, 9281)
(left)

4. Bronze(?) ewer
Made by Yazid
Iraq(?), 8th–9th centuries(?)
(Tiflis, Museum of Arts, I/5)
(right)

(909–1171) succeeded in establishing a rival caliphate in Cairo, soon extending their influence from North Africa into Palestine and Syria.

Despite political fragmentation the world of Islam retained a remarkable unity through its singular faith, language, and administrative and legal system. The arts and sciences flourished, commercial activities increased, and the economy thrived. Through its rapid expansion Islam had been exposed to diverse cultures and began to assimilate these traditions to formulate its own artistic vocabulary. It is not surprising, therefore, that metalwork produced in the formative period of Islamic art reemployed the techniques and themes found in Roman, Byzantine, and Coptic art of the eastern Mediterranean, as well as those of the Sasanian objects made in Iraq and Iran. A number of pieces, such as the stand decorated with eagles (no. 1) and the pierced incense burner (no. 2) in the Freer Gallery, show the continuation of the traditions inherited by the artists and do not reveal a noticeable change in style.

The earliest datable objects that can be identified as Islamic are a series of ewers having various shapes. One type, the so-called Marwan ewer (fig. 3), identified as such because it was found near the tomb of Caliph Marwan II (744–50) in Fayyum, Egypt, shows a rounded body with a zoomorphic rooster-shaped spout. Assigned to Egypt, Syria, or Iraq and dated to the eighth to ninth centuries, it is representative of some half-dozen cast and engraved brass or bronze pieces with similarly shaped spouts.[5]

A second type of ewer lacks the independent spout but is embellished with a large palmette-shaped thumb-rest on the handle. This type is also dated to the eighth to ninth centuries but is attributed to Iraq or Iran. The most famous and controversial example is the Tiflis ewer (fig. 4), which has inscriptions stating that it was made in Basra in 686/87 or 688/89, a dating that has been contested.[6] At least six related pieces, some of which contain copper inlays, are known to have the same shape.

A third type, represented by a Freer ewer (no. 3), has no surface decoration; its handle terminates in stylized gazelle heads and attaches to the lip. Its pear-shaped body and extended lip forming a spout clearly reflect Sasanian prototypes. This type is thought to have been produced in Iran during the ninth to tenth centuries.

Also dating from the early Islamic period are a few bird-shaped vessels used as aquamaniles, the most important of which is the silver-inlaid example (fig. 5) in the Hermitage bearing the date 796/97.[7] This piece, together with the Marwan- and Tiflis-type ewers, indicates that by the eighth century different tools were employed to engrave and chase the designs, which included inscriptions; and silver and copper were applied as inlays, pointing to the beginning of an interest in surface decoration that was to dominate the future production of metalwork.

Even though relying on the techniques of production (casting and hammering) and those of decoration (chasing, engraving, and inlaying) established in the past, early Islamic metalworkers formulated several new trends that became widely used in the classical age. One of these was the production of zoomorphic vessels or appendages, such as the Hermitage aquamanile and the spout of the Marwan ewer; a second is the employment of epigraphy, which not only provides pertinent information about the piece but also decorates it; and a third is the attempt to create coloristic effects by applying different materials on the surfaces.

5. Bronze(?) bird-shaped vessel inlaid with silver
Made by Sulayman
Iran(?), dated 796/97
(Leningrad, State Hermitage Museum, NP–1567)

CLASSICAL AGE: ELEVENTH THROUGH THIRTEENTH CENTURIES

The beginning of the classical age coincides with the arrival of the Seljuk Turks from Central Asia in the middle of the eleventh century, at which time the Sunni Abbasid caliphate was revitalized and the central Islamic lands were reunited under one rule. The Seljuk sultanate (1038–1194) did not survive long, and by the 1150s the empire was divided among the members of the ruling house who established autonomous states in Iran, Iraq, Syria, and Turkey. In the twelfth century a number of Atabeks, or regents to the Seljuks, also rose to power and founded their own short-lived dynasties. The most notable among them were the Artukids (1102–1408) of southeastern Turkey and the Zengids (1127–1222) of Iraq and Syria.

The early classical period also witnessed the flowering of the Fatimid rule and its replacement by the Ayyubids (1169–1260), who eventually controlled Egypt, Syria, Palestine, and Yemen. Several other independent dynasties were ruling in Spain and North Africa in addition to eastern Iran, Afghanistan, and the Muslim regions of Central Asia and India. The political history of the age was further complicated by the Crusades, seven of which arrived in the central Islamic lands between 1096 and 1270. The Crusaders, who were fighting against the Muslims as well as feuding among themselves, established settlements that frequently changed hands. The arts flourished and reached a true classical age in spite of the political turmoil resulting from the rise and fall of dynasties and the endless alliances and battles among the local regimes and the newcomers. There occurred an unprecedented prosperity that affected both the patrons and the artists. Imperial and courtly patronage increased with the establishment of new states or principalities, each of which required possessions worthy of its status. The competition for power and the ambition among the administrative and military ranks to be a part of the ruling elite resulted in an equally strong demand for princely items. The affluent middle classes also desired ostentatious objects with which they could display their wealth.

The artists rose to the occasion and created extraordinarily refined objects for their patrons, who may have been sultans, aspiring bureaucrats, or wealthy merchants. The pieces dating from the classical age that are included in the collection of the Freer Gallery are representative of the patronage of the period and the economic prosperity of the middle classes: one piece (no. 18) was commissioned by a sultan, two (nos. 14 and 16) were ordered by statesmen, and the majority (nos. 4–13, 15, 17, and 19) were made for anonymous but wealthy patrons.

The production of metalwork, like that of the other Islamic arts, reached the epitome of technical and aesthetic perfection during the classical age. Artists produced a tremendous amount of wares throughout the Islamic world and employed a variety of techniques and materials both to shape and embellish the pieces. The majority of the objects were decorated with inscriptions, which became the most prominent characteristic of Islamic metalwork. Although the inscriptions generally repeat a series of good wishes and contain formulaic phrases, the contents of select examples provide important information that helps to determine the development of regional styles and themes.

Dating from the eleventh and twelfth centuries are personal ornaments made in gold and decorated with applied filigree, granulation, and twisted wire, and at times inlaid with niello, black organic compounds, and gems (see nos. 4–9). Fashioned into belts, rings, pendants, hair ornaments, earrings, or matching pairs of bracelets, these items reflect a flourishing, wealthy society. The key pieces in dating a series of similar objects are a pair of identical bracelets (one bracelet, fig. 26, owned by the Metropolitan Museum of Art and the other, no. 5, by the Freer Gallery), their clasps backed with discs struck from coins produced in Iran in the first three decades of the eleventh century. Their refined workmanship is also found in contemporary examples made in Syria (see no. 4 and fig. 25).

Other luxurious items, including the Freer bottle used for sprinkling rosewater (no. 10), were made in silver and embellished with gilding and niello. The bottle was among the last examples made in silver, which became scarce after 1100. Numismatic evidences indicate that the central Islamic lands were faced with a shortage of silver after the eleventh century. The "silver famine" also affected the metalworker, who was forced to use less-costly metals and reserve the precious silver for thinly applied inlays.

The predominant material used in the classical age was brass, shaped by diverse methods, such as casting, hammering, turning, and spinning; and decorated with thin inlays of silver, gold, and copper in addition to black organic compounds. Artists created a variety of forms by combining two or more techniques to construct the pieces. They made different types of zoomorphic vessels (see no. 11), incense burners (see no. 12), candlesticks (see nos. 13, 15, and 19), ewers (see no. 16), and basins (see no. 18), and such unusual objects as an oversized canteen (see no. 17).

Certain shapes and decorative features can be assigned to specific regions and even centers. A distinct group of candlesticks was produced during the second half of the twelfth century in an area identified as Khorasan, now divided between Iran, Afghanistan, and Turkmenistan. Represented by an example in the Freer Gallery (no. 13), this group reveals the artists' remarkable technical virtuosity in creating a large hollow shape from a single sheet of brass, with certain elements standing in high relief. The inscriptions on some seven pieces associated with this group are conventional and do not indicate when and where they were produced. Their provenance can be deduced from an ewer (fig. 6) in Tiflis decorated with similar elements: its inscriptions state that it was made in 1181/82 by Mahmud ibn Muhammad al-Haravi (of Herat).[8] Even though there is no concrete proof that the candlesticks also were made in Herat, the city is recognized as a center in which the production of such inlaid brasses flourished during the second half of the twelfth century. References to Herat are also found on other contemporary metalwork, the most renowned of which are the Hermitage bucket of 1163 (fig. 1) mentioned previously, which was signed by an artist from that city; and the pen box of 1210/11 (no. 14) in the Freer Gallery, made by Shazi, who has appended al-Haravi to his name on another piece.

The Hermitage bucket and the Freer pen box are among the most important pieces of Islamic metalwork because they contain extensive and informative inscriptions that help to determine when and where certain themes originated. They also provide insight into the types of patrons who desired such valuable objects: a wealthy but unknown bureaucrat or merchant ordered the bucket, and an intellectual and famous statesman commissioned the pen box. Both objects are decorated with a feature unique to Islamic metalwork: the animated inscription in which the vertical shafts of both cursive (naskhi) and angular (kufic) scripts terminate in human heads or torsos. The first appearance of the anthropomorphic inscription is on the Hermitage bucket; the same feature was employed some fifty years later on the Freer pen box and on several other contemporary objects attributed to eastern Iran and Afghanistan.[9]

During the second quarter of the thirteenth century the human-headed inscription moved westward and became fully animated, with the arms and legs of animals and

6. Brass ewer inlaid with copper and silver
Made by Mahmud b. Muhammad al-Haravi
Afghanistan, dated 1181/82
(Tiflis, The Museum of the History of Georgia, MC 135)

7. Brass footed-bowl inlaid with silver
Iran, ca. 1230
(Cleveland, The Cleveland Museum of
Art, 44.485)

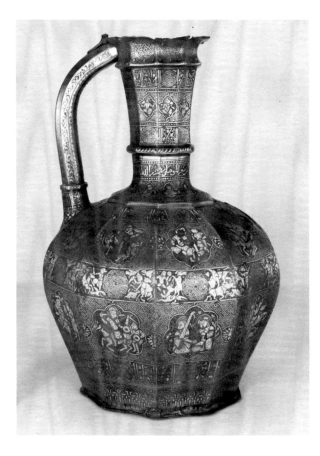

8. Brass ewer inlaid with copper and
silver
Made by Shuja b. Mana al-Mawsili in
Mosul
Iraq, dated 1232
(London, The British Museum,
66 12–69 61)

humans making up the letters, as seen in both the famous Wade Cup (fig. 7) in Cleveland, attributed to western Iran in the 1230s[10]; and the Blacas ewer (fig. 8) in the British Museum, made in 1232 in Mosul by Shuja ibn Mana al-Mawsili.[11] The latter work firmly establishes Mosul as a major metalwork center. It is one of those rare objects having an inscription that states where it was produced. The fully animated inscription, which flourished in the mid-thirteenth century, was applied to several extraordinary inlaid brasses made in Syria and Egypt, including the Freer canteen (no. 17); the basin (fig. 9) in Musée des Arts Décoratifs, made in 1252/53 by Davud ibn Salama[12]; and the incense burner (fig. 10) made for the Ayyubid sultan, al-Adil II, around 1238–40.[13] This remarkable and fanciful style of writing survived until the end of the thirteenth century and was possibly last employed on the Fano Cup (fig. 11) in the Bibliothèque Nationale, Paris[14]; and on a candlestick (fig. 12) made around the 1290s for Kitbugha, a Mamluk amir who later became a sultan.[15]

The fully animated inscriptions appear to have flourished in Iraq, Syria, and Egypt between the second and fourth quarters of the thirteenth century. Those with human heads and torsos, which originated in eastern Iran during the second half of the twelfth

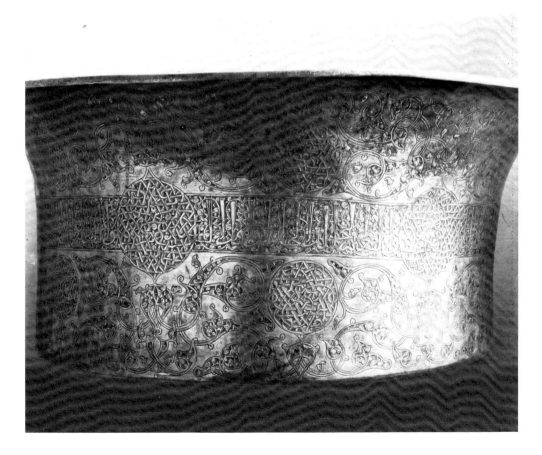

9. Brass basin inlaid with silver and gold
Made by Davud b. Salama al-Mawsili
Syria(?), dated 1252/53
(Paris, Musée des Arts Décoratifs, 4411)

19

century, continued to be employed in western Iran (see no. 15) and Turkey (see no. 19) throughout the thirteenth century.

The decorative repertoire of Islamic metalwork perfected in the classical age shows a countless variety of themes, some of which were shared by the other contemporary arts, including manuscript illustration and illumination, and ceramics. The objects were carefully designed, with the surfaces divided in units of threes and fours and linked either by formal devices (such as continuous and looping bands or repeated patterns) or by the sequential development of the chosen themes or narrative cycles. There was a definite progression in "reading" the decoration, which was in the same direction as the inscriptions, that is, right to left, or in the case of objects in the round, counterclockwise.

Inscriptions were by and large the most significant components of surface decoration. They were rendered in kufic, the angular script (see nos. 4, 5, 8–10, 12–14, 17, and 18), or in naskhi, the simplest form of the various cursive styles (see nos. 14, 16, and 19). Many objects combined several different styles of writing, such as kufic and naskhi (see no. 8); foliated kufic, in which the vertical shafts of the letters are transformed into floral elements, and naskhi (see no. 13); kufic with animated or human-headed naskhi (see nos. 17 and 19); plaited or knotted kufic with thuluth, a hierarchic version of the cursive script (see no. 18); and human-headed kufic and naskhi (see no. 14). The inscriptions on some pieces (nos. 11, 15, and 19) were either simulated or used for magical or talismanic purposes, and thus are not comprehensible today. The contents of the inscriptions on the courtly pieces (nos. 14, 16, and 18) frequently are highly informative, stating when, by whom, and for whom they were made; at times they even provide the name of the city in which the object was produced.

Metalwork made for noncourtly clientele contains, as can be expected, formulaic and generalized statements bestowing a series of good wishes and blessings to unidentified owners (see nos. 4, 8–10, 12, 13, 15, 17, and 19). Also inscribed on some pieces are statements that glorify the object and its qualities or refer to its function, such as on a wine cup or candlestick. Koranic verses and pious invocations generally were reserved for objects made as furnishings for religious monuments, including mosque lamps, Koran boxes, and chests.

Geometric patterns, used either to fill in the background of the main themes or serve as independent motifs, utilize a variety of shapes, some of which can be associated with solar symbols. Among the most popular were designs radiating from central stars or rosettes, representing the celestial light (see nos. 12 and 18); and geometric roundels symbolizing the sun (see nos. 17 and 19).

Floral themes were used also, both as background decoration and as individual motifs with symbolic meanings. Lancet leaves were associated with sun rays (see nos. 13, 15, 16, and 18), whereas the rosette represented the sun (see nos. 17 and 19). Often combined with related geometric motifs, these symbols of divine light were frequently

10. Brass incense burner inlaid with silver
Made for Sultan al-Adil II
Syria(?), ca. 1238–40
(Ham, Richmond [England], The Keir Collection)

11. Brass footed-bowl inlaid with silver and gold
Syria or Egypt, 13th–14th centuries
(Paris, Bibliothèque Nationale, Chabouillet 3192)

applied to lighting devices, such as candlesticks and incense burners (see nos. 12, 13, 15, and 19). Floral scrolls used in the background developed into several different types, which were used alternatively in adjacent units or were superimposed, with one scroll placed above the other. One of these was a tightly wound scroll with hooked leaves; another contained curving branches bearing stylized blossoms and buds. Both types appear on Ayyubid objects made in Syria or Egypt in the second quarter of the thirteenth century, as seen on the Freer ewer, canteen, and basin (nos. 16–18). The same two types also were employed on pieces made several decades later in Turkey (see no. 19), indicating the dispersion and popularity of this decorative feature.

The most sophisticated floral scroll is the animated type in which tendrils or branches terminate in animal or human heads. It first appears on objects made in Afghanistan and eastern Iran, as represented by Shazi's pen box (no. 14). The same type is found on mid-thirteenth-century brasses produced in Syria and Egypt (see nos. 17 and 18), its westward movement coinciding with that of the animated inscription. In contrast to the animated inscription, which is unique to metalwork, the animated floral scroll was employed in the other arts and became popular in later manuscript illumination. Frequently associated with the *waqwaq* legend in which Iskandar (Alexander the Great)

12. Socket and neck of brass candlestick inlaid with silver and gold
Made for Zayn al-Din Kitbugha
Egypt, ca. 1290
(Cairo, Museum of Islamic Art, 4463)

21

seeks the tree that prophesies the future,[16] the scroll has anthropomorphic or zoomorphic attributes and becomes a living entity. Similar to the animated inscription, this type of scroll survived well into the Mamluk period and was employed on fourteenth-century inlaid brasses made in Egypt and Syria.[17] The animated floral scroll appears to have been used originally as the main theme; it later became a part of the background decoration and often was placed under the inscriptions.

Animals and birds played an important role in the decorative repertoire and were used both as the main theme and as a part of the background. Certain motifs, particularly the lion and the eagle or hawk, were associated with royalty, while others had talismanic and protective attributes. Both real and fantastic animals were represented, including a variety of birds, four-legged predators with their prey, and such winged creatures as unicorns, griffins, harpies, and sphinxes. On many objects dating from the eleventh and twelfth centuries attributed to Iran and Afghanistan, animals were used as the main decorative theme. Winged sphinxes and griffins, and pairs of birds flanking a tree, as represented on a Freer bracelet (no. 8), contained auspicious messages. Animals depicted in combat or ferocious birds of prey or lions attacking weaker creatures, similar to those found on the bottle (no. 10), symbolized imperial power. Dating from the same period and region are zoomorphic vessels shaped like lions or birds (see no. 11), frequently used as incense burners or aquamaniles. Similar animals were fashioned into ornaments and jewelry (see nos. 6 and 7), used as finials (see no. 12), or rendered in high relief to decorate the pieces (see no. 13).

Friezes composed of real and imaginary quadrupeds, generally paired as predators and prey (see nos. 14 and 18), appear to have originated in the eastern Islamic lands and moved westward. Among the most characteristic imperial themes was a hawk attacking a bird, enclosed within a roundel (see no. 17), popularly used in Egypt and Syria in the thirteenth century.

Imperial themes were represented by figural compositions as well, with banquets and hunts symbolizing both earthly and paradisaic pleasures. Scenes depicting enthroned princes and courtly figures feasting and drinking while being entertained by musicians and dancers were fully developed by the thirteenth century (see nos. 15, 17, and 18). The decorative vocabulary included revelers holding beakers, surrounded by tall-necked wine bottles and bowls of fruit; musicians playing a variety of string, wind, and percussion instruments, such as lutes, harps, zithers, flutes, drums, tambourines, and cymbals; and hunters on horseback pursuing wild creatures, assisted by trained falcons and cheetahs. Princely cycles depicted on metalwork are also encountered on contemporary ceramics and other arts, reflecting the preoccupation with these themes during the classical period.

Figural compositions were fully exploited by the artists, who were technically competent enough to transfer easily any given subject onto the surfaces of their metal objects, thus rivaling the painters who worked with brushes on paper or on pottery.

Astrological themes were second in popularity to imperial subjects, and many pieces were decorated with the personifications of the seven planets and the twelve constellations of the zodiac,[18] depicted independently or in combination. There also existed cycles with the labors of the months or the heavenly bodies associated with the months, a theme unique to the metalworkers of Turkey, who represented them on a series of candlesticks (see no. 19). At times, incorporated into the decoration were select astrological symbols, such as the symbol of the moon represented either by a crescent or a figure holding a crescent (see nos. 16 and 17), or by the pseudoplanet Jawzahr, personified by a dragon (see no. 15).

In addition to the conventional repertoire, the metalworkers created original cycles and compositions for specially commissioned objects, although the individual themes employed were by no means unique to these pieces. The decorations of the Freer basin and canteen fall into this category. The patron of the Freer basin (no. 18), Sultan Najm al-Din Ayyub, must have requested both the polo game, his favorite sport, and the scenes from the Life of Christ together with the group of saints to be represented on his metalwork. The patron of the canteen (no. 17) is not recorded in the inscriptions, but he too must have specified the Christian themes and the portrayal of the tournament found on the piece. The basin and canteen belong to a rare group of some sixteen Ayyubid objects produced in the 1240s and decorated with Christian themes. Two of these are signed by al-Mawsili artists and two others bear the name of Sultan Najm al-Din Ayyub. It has been argued that the Christian themes reflect royal iconography and the taste of the Ayyubid court.[19]

The metalworkers of this period formulated a decorative vocabulary that became the most prominent characteristic of Islamic metalwork and was used with minor modifications up to the twentieth century. The decoration included inscriptions written in angular and cursive scripts, geometric and floral motifs reflecting solar symbols, animals denoting imperial themes, and princely and astrological cycles with paradisaic and cosmic interpretations. The diversity and wealth of innovative motifs and themes were never equaled, although certain elements would be refined in years to come.

POSTCLASSICAL PERIOD: FOURTEENTH THROUGH EIGHTEENTH CENTURIES

The classical age of Islamic art was brought to an end by the Mongol invasions from Central Asia that took place in the middle of the thirteenth century and annihilated a number of states and cultural centers, forcing a substantial percentage of the population to migrate westward to seek refuge in safer regions. The most valiant defenders of Islam against the pagan invaders were the Mamluks (1250–1517), who had replaced the Ayyubids in Egypt and Syria. The Mongol onslaught eventually came to a halt, and a branch called the Ilkhanids (1256–1353) settled in Iran, converted to Islam, and eventually adopted the local traditions. Economic stability was resumed, commercial activities restored, and the arts of Islam flourished once again.

By the middle of the fourteenth century, Ilkhanid power had disintegrated and the empire was divided among local dynasties, among which were the Muzaffarids (1314–93) and the Injus (1303–57), both of whom claimed the province of Fars in southern Iran.

At the turn of the century there occurred yet another invasion from Central Asia, this time led by Timur, who moved swiftly into the central Islamic lands and Anatolia. The Timurids (1370–1506) held court first in Samarkand, then in Herat, which became the most renowned cultural center after the 1470s. Herat was rivaled in the west by another newly established Islamic capital, that of İstanbul, which had become the seat of the Ottoman Empire in the middle of the fifteenth century. The Ottomans (1281–1923) had emerged from a small principality at the northwestern corner of Turkey, spread into Anatolia and Thrace, and conquered İstanbul, the former capital of the eastern Roman and Byzantine empires.

The political history of the Islamic world during the sixteenth century is dominated by powerful empires. The Ottomans were by far the strongest, their realm extending from western Asia to northern Africa and eastern Europe. The Safavids (1501–1732) inherited the lands of the Timurid empire, and ruled over Iran and Afghanistan, while the Mughals (1526–1858) succeeded in controlling India. These great empires established large and complex court ateliers that employed the most talented artists of the age.

The production of Islamic metalwork during the fourteenth century reveals a continuation of classical techniques and themes. The same repertoire of inscriptions, geometric and floral decorations, figural compositions, and imperial and solar symbols appears on brasses inlaid with silver and gold (see nos. 20–23). The inscriptions show a change in style and generally were written in thuluth, the hierarchic cursive style, which in time replaced figural compositions and became the major decorative element on metalwork.

Dated and inscribed examples indicate that the most prolific production of metalwork was sponsored by the Mamluks of Egypt and Syria, and the rulers of Fars in Iran. Mamluk artists reemployed the features perfected by their Ayyubid predecessors and created some of the most spectacular examples of Islamic metalwork. They excelled in rendering thuluth inscriptions and developed a circular composition in which the vertical shafts of the letters radiated from a central unit (see no. 22). The patrons were the ruling classes—the sultans and the amirs—who frequently employed their individualized blazons or heraldic coats of arms on their objects.

Metalwork produced in Fars, also made for the court and the wealthy elite, reflects the classical themes together with a preference for thuluth inscriptions and generalized princely subjects, including enthroned personages and hunters (see nos. 20 and 21).

Certain new solar motifs became widely used on fourteenth-century objects. The Mamluk feature of radiating inscriptions, which contain praises to sultans and to amirs identified by their masters, can be interpreted as both an imperial and cosmic symbol that associates the earthly king with the heavenly ruler. Other solar symbols include rosettes, often with swirling petals; and lotus blossoms and ducks placed in circular compositions, in addorsed and confronted pairs (see no. 22), which tend to carry esoteric and mystical interpretations. Another widely used decorative detail is the fish-pond theme depicting fishes and other marine creatures swimming in concentric patterns inside basins and bowls (see no. 20). The earliest dated use of this theme, which represents the manifestation of the sun in the water, is found on a bowl (fig. 13) in Galleria Estense in Modena, made in 1305 by Abd al-Qadir ibn Ahmad al-Khaliq al-Shirazi, an artist from Shiraz, the capital of Fars.[20] It was also used on contemporary and possibly earlier examples commissioned by the Mamluks, such as the late thirteenth- or early fourteenth-century bowl and basin (figs. 14 and 15) made by Muhammad ibn al-Zayn, both in the Louvre.[21] These two objects, thought to have been made in Cairo, contain exceptionally detailed figural compositions that recreate the activities of the Mamluk court. Their refined execution indicates that the Mamluk metalworkers not

interior

13. Brass bowl inlaid with silver and gold
Made by Abd al-Qadir b. Ahmad al-Khaliq al-Shirazi
Iran, dated 1305
(Modena, Galleria Museo e Medagliere Estense, 8082)

14. Brass bowl inlaid with silver and gold
Made by Muhammad ibn al-Zayn
Egypt, ca. 1290–1310
(Paris, Musée du Louvre, MAO 331)

only inherited the technical facilities of their Ayyubid masters but also superseded them.

Inlaid brasses made for the Mamluks and those assigned to Iran share a number of other features, including alternate use of geometric and floral designs in the backgrounds; friezes of running predators and prey; and such cosmic themes as sun rays, geometric roundels, lotus blossoms, ducks, and compositions radiating from central stars, which survived well into the seventeenth century (see, for instance, nos. 24, 26, 28, 29, 31–35, and 37).

Although a number of iconographic and decorative similarities exist between fourteenth-century pieces made in Egypt and Syria and those produced in Iran, the contents of the inscriptions show a variation. Objects from Iran (see no. 20) often include the phrase "inheritor of the kingdom of Solomon," a title used by the rulers of Fars who controlled Persepolis and Pasargadae, ancient sites associated with the patriarch Solomon.

By the middle of the fourteenth century the impact of the classical decorative repertoire began to wane and certain themes gradually disappeared. The most notable among these were figural compositions, and animated inscriptions and scrolls. The main decorative element came to be bold thuluth inscriptions, as mentioned earlier, although on some objects (see no. 23) a derivative version of kufic was still employed. Comparatively more naturalistic floral scrolls, their thin undulating branches bearing split-leaves and forming occasional knots and cartouches (see no. 24), were fashionable in the following century and influenced the group of metalwork identified with the school of Venice.

Metalwork produced in the fifteenth century reflects the lack of high-quality workmanship and harmonious use of silver, copper, and gold inlays that characterized the

15. Brass basin inlaid with silver and gold
Made by Muhammad b. al-Zayn
Egypt, ca. 1290–1310
(Paris, Musée du Louvre, LP 16)

interior

earlier pieces. Many objects were simply engraved with hatching, ring matting, or black organic compounds applied in an attempt to create texture or color as background to the main themes. A number of brass and copper pieces also were tinned, which produced a silvery effect. The few inlaid examples indicate that silver wire was preferred over the earlier practice of using precut thin sheets. This deterioration in Islamic metalwork may have been the result of dire economic conditions or merely a change in consumer taste; patrons were no longer interested in possessing metal objects and chose, instead, to commission manuscripts or purchase imported Chinese porcelain.

An exceptional series of jugs and vases (see no. 25), carefully executed and inlaid with silver and at times with gold, was produced in the Timurid capital of Herat in the last quarter of the fifteenth century. The series represented the new aesthetics in surface decoration that would continue to be influential for centuries to come. The design is rendered minutely and consists of floral scrolls, and of Arabic and Persian inscriptions written in naskhi or nastaliq, an elegant cursive style reserved for royal manuscripts. The Arabic inscriptions generally contain routine benedictory phrases, whereas the Persian inscriptions either repeat those given in Arabic or include verses composed by such great Iranian poets as Hafiz, Sadi, and Firdausi.

The decoration used on late Timurid metalwork shows a close relationship with the contemporary arts of the book and reflects the same styles of writing and refined floral decoration, including superimposed naturalistic and stylized scrolls, as those found in the imperial manuscripts. Among the best examples of this period style shared by several different Timurid arts is a superbly designed and executed small bowl (no. 26) in the Freer Gallery. This exquisite piece, decorated with a poem composed by Hafiz, was highly valued by its later owner, Aqa Rustam, the ruler of Mazandaran in northern Iran, and is inscribed with its weight and what was thought to be the relative amounts of silver and gold. Thus far, it is the only known Islamic example that attempts to provide this type of technical information.

The surface decoration of Timurid metalwork had a long-lasting impact on both Ottoman and Safavid examples. Ottoman metalwork was also influenced by the late Mamluk style in which the objects were engraved, with punches or hatched lines filling the background (see no. 27). In addition, tinning was applied to a number of engraved brass and copper pieces dating from the fifteenth and sixteenth centuries. A specialty of Ottoman metalworkers was gilded copper, which continues to be popular today. Brass and copper objects were basically utilitarian and served diverse levels of the society. The court, in contrast, commissioned silver and gold items lavishly decorated with rock crystal or jade panels and set with turquoise, rubies, emeralds, and various other gems. A metal exclusively used for imperial wares was *tutya,* or zinc, fashioned into various shapes, including jugs, bottles, and bowls (see fig. 16), and often encrusted with gems. This material, also used in the Iranian court during the early sixteenth century, appears to have had a limited popularity and disappeared after the seventeenth century.

Early Safavid metalwork maintained the decorative features found on late Timurid pieces, but silver and gold inlays were used more and more sparingly. The influence of the art of the book also is visible on courtly objects, the most interesting of which is a bowl (fig. 17) made in 1510/11 by Mahmud Ali, decorated with a poem composed by Hilali and rendered in nastaliq by Sultan Muhammad, who was most likely the esteemed calligrapher Sultan Muhammad Nur of Herat.[22] The date on this piece is given in digits, a practice begun in the Timurid period, as opposed to being written out, which was traditional in the classical age. The majority of Safavid objects were made of brass and copper, at times tinned, and decorated with naskhi or nastaliq inscriptions and floral scrolls that were often superimposed, the one bearing naturalistic blossoms and buds, the other bearing split-leaves. These decorations were also applied to iron and steel, frequently inlaid with gold, and fashioned into arms, armor, objects for personal use (see nos. 31–33), architectural decoration, and furnishings (see nos. 28–30).

During the sixteenth and seventeenth centuries figural compositions were revived, with animals and humans generally placed within a landscape. Courtly figures feasting, drinking, or riding, and mystics discoursing or contemplating, continued to be depicted on Iranian metalwork for centuries thereafter.

Objects commissioned by the Iranian court included ceremonial weapons, particularly daggers, which were made of precious materials and decorated with floral scrolls and nastaliq inscriptions, as represented by the two outstanding examples in the collection (nos. 34 and 35). The inscription on the dagger and sheath (no. 35) made by Taqi(?) establishes Shiraz as a metalworking center. The date was rendered in a highly sophisticated manner, using the *abjad* system in which the total of the numerical values of letters refers to the year the set was produced. The other dagger has a bifurcate ivory

16. A group of zinc vessels inlaid with gold and gems
Turkey, 16th century
(İstanbul, Topkapı Palace Museum, 2/2836, 2/2844, 2/2860)

17. High-tin bronze bowl
Made by Mahmud Ali and inscribed by Sultan Muhammad
Iran, dated 1510/11
(London, Victoria and Albert Museum, 1191–1854)

29

18. Bidri-ware water-pipe base inlaid
with silver and brass
India, 17th century
(London, Victoria and Albert Museum,
IS 27–1980)

handle thought to originate in India and thus reflects the close cultural exchange that
existed between the Mughal and Safavid courts.

Early Mughal metalwork relied heavily on Iranian techniques and themes, as observed
on copper or tinned-copper examples as well as on brasses, which are at times inlaid
with silver or simply engraved with black organic compounds applied to the background.
Floral motifs predominate the decorative repertoire of Mughal metalwork, although
animals and human figures are occasionally depicted within a landscape. A few of the
pieces are embellished with inscriptions based on Iranian prototypes.

A specialty of Indian metalworkers was *bidri* ware (see fig. 18), named after the city
of Bidar, where this technique was thought to have originated. This type of ware, which
became widely produced after the seventeenth century, was composed of an alloy of
zinc. The pieces were cast and inlaid with silver, at times also with brass and gold. A
coating of sal ammoniac created a matte black surface when removed and provided a
contrast to the bright inlays.

The Mughal court was renowned for its wealth and passion for precious objects, and
it commissioned large quantities of silver and gold items as well as those employing
jade and rock crystal, all frequently encrusted with gems and enamels. Also made for

the court were steel and iron arms and armor together with ceremonial swords and daggers, some of which have jeweled handles and sheaths (see no. 38).

Among the rare objects that reflect the continuation of traditional figural compositions is the zoomorphic flint striker (no. 37), decorated with ducks or geese and hawks attacking birds, indicating the persistence of imperial and solar symbols. Included in this group is a unique knife (no. 36), commissioned by Jahangir, made from a meteorite that fell in 1621. The nastaliq verses on the knife commemorate this event, which is confirmed by the memoirs of the ruler. Jahangir's knife, decorated with such imperial symbols as the royal umbrella and predators attacking prey, is among the rare pieces that have a history reconstructed both from contemporary sources and, more significant, from the contents of the inscriptions.

The Islamic metalworker relied upon the technology of his predecessors and created an extraordinary range of decorative themes and styles that became indigenous to his world. Surface embellishment was of primary concern, and the objects were invested with both epigraphical and pictorial messages and symbols that forced the beholder to search for their meaning. Thus these messages, at times intentionally obscured, offered an intellectual exercise and enhanced the intrinsic value of the pieces.

Needless to say, the study of Islamic metalwork relies heavily on inscriptions that not only decorate the pieces but also provide the most important documentation for the identification of artists, patrons, dates, and provenance, thus enabling art historians to trace the stylistic and technical developments in diverse regions. As more of the inscriptions are studied and published, it is hoped that our knowledge of regional workshops will increase and we will be able to identify the individual styles of the artists who created some of the most spectacular objects in the history of Islamic art.

Studies on technique, iconography, and provenance are essential for the understanding of the evolution of Islamic metalwork, but its primary purpose, that is, its function, should not be overlooked. Each piece was designed for personal use and served a specific need; some held candles, liquids, incense, or writing implements whereas others were used as weapons or body ornaments. These functional objects were transformed into works of art through the technical virtuosity and refined aesthetics of their makers.

Notes

An abbreviated format is used for references. A complete list of sources begins on page 233.

1. The only exception would be minai and luster wares, which appear to have been commissioned by or made for the members of the wealthy middle classes and provincial courts.
2. This piece, cast in bronze or brass and inlaid with silver, copper, and niello, has been published in several sources, including Ettinghausen 1943a; Mayer 1959, pp. 61–62; and

London 1976, no. 180. The inscriptions have been deciphered a number of different ways. For the latest reading see Melikian-Chirvani 1982, pp. 82–83, note 61.

3. This large box made in sheets of brass mounted on a wooden core is inlaid with silver and gold. Berlin 1971, no. 19; and London 1976, no. 214.

4. One of the ateliers active circa 1220–50 is analyzed in Rice 1957a. For later artists who worked under the Mamluks, see Atıl 1981, p. 51.

5. Sarre 1934. See also Fehérvári 1976b, no. 2; and Baer 1983, figs. 65–66, for examples of this type.

6. The ewer is published in Marshak 1972, in which it is proposed that the piece is dated to the ninth century. For other related pieces see Pinder-Wilson 1967; Fehérvári 1976b, no. 1; Melikian-Chirvani 1982, no. 1; and Baer 1983, figs. 63, 113–14, and 166.

7. Sourdel-Thomine and Spuler 1973, pl. XVI. Another undated example is published in Berlin 1971, no. 234.

8. Giuzalian 1938; and Mayer 1959, p. 59.

9. The most notable among them is an ewer in the British Museum, dated circa 1200 (Barrett 1949, pls. 6 and 7); and an inkwell, a stem bowl, and a second ewer in the Es-Said Collection, London (Allan 1982a, nos. 2, 3, and 5).

10. Rice 1955b; and Ettinghausen 1957 and 1959.

11. Barrett 1949, pls. 12 and 13.

12. Paris 1971, no. 157; and Paris 1977, no. 156.

13. Fehérvári 1968, and 1976b, no. 129.

14. Rice 1955b, pl. XV; Paris 1971, no. 171; and Paris 1977, no. 321.

15. Atıl 1981, no. 15.

16. One of the earliest representations of this episode is found in a painting from the so-called Demotte *Shahnama* owned by the Freer Gallery, acc. no. 35.23. Grabar and Blair 1980, pl. 38.

17. See, for instance, the pen box dated circa 1320 in the Museum of Islamic Art, Cairo; and the basin dated circa 1330 in the British Museum. Atıl 1981, nos. 24 and 26.

18. According to Islamic astrology the seven planets were the sun (radiant disc, often with facial features), the moon (figure holding a crescent), Mercury (figure with a book, pen, and/or scroll), Venus (figure with a lute), Mars (helmeted figure holding a sword and severed head), Jupiter (figure with a bottle or fish), and Saturn (bearded figure with a pickaxe or bucket). There was also an eighth but pseudoplanet named Jawzahr, represented by a dragon and thought to be responsible for the eclipses of the sun and moon. The signs of the zodiac were Capricorn (an ibex), Aquarius (a well or bucket), Pisces (a fish), Aries (a ram), Taurus (a bull), Gemini (twins), Cancer (a crab), Leo (a lion), Virgo (leaves or corn), Libra (scales), Scorpio (a scorpion), and Sagittarius (a centaur with bow). The symbols of both the planets and constellations were based on Hellenistic models.

19. This subject is discussed in Katzenstein and Lowry 1983. See also discussion and notes in no. 17 in this catalogue.

20. Scerratto 1966, pl. 47; Baer 1968, pls. I–VI and figs. 1–8; and Baer 1983, fig. 169. See also Baer 1968 for a study of the fish-pond theme.

21. Atıl 1981, nos. 20 and 21. See also nos. 26–29 in Atıl 1981 for other Mamluk examples that depict swimming fish inside the bowls and basins.

22. This bowl is made of high-tin bronze (22% tin), a rare material for the period, and must have been commissioned by the court. Melikian-Chirvani 1982, no. 117.

Techniques and Materials

The subject of Islamic metalwork is one area of art history in which little technical or scientific information is available. This is partially owing to a general lack of published studies about Islamic metalwork. It is understandable that technical data is sparse, considering that the first fully illustrated catalogue of a collection was published only in 1976.[1]

The technical and analytical study of Islamic metalwork has a rather long history, although it is one of isolated and limited events. The damascened, or watered, steel of the Islamic lands has excited interest and investigation for generations.[2] Most of the early studies were inspired by the practical benefits that this superior steel was believed to offer, and research has contributed much to the understanding of the material and to an appreciation of its inherent beauty. In the study of bronze and brass metalwork, elemental analysis has been undertaken sporadically for a number of years. One of the first reports of analytical results was published by Roberts-Austen in 1892.[3] More recently, Iranian metalwork of the formative and classical periods has received a noteworthy technical review,[4] and results of studies carried out at the British Museum are currently beginning to be published.[5] Thus, there appears to be a slow but increasing growth in the number of technical and analytical studies of Islamic metalwork.

It is appropriate to present the results of technical examinations of Islamic metalwork in the Freer Gallery in particular, because many of the objects are widely known and referred to in the study of Islamic art; the technical information provided here will be useful to their study and understanding. Moreover, a number of these objects were jointly examined by the late Herbert Maryon and the late Rutherford John Gettens, pioneers in the study of ancient metalwork, whose notes have provided a wealth of information for the staff of the Freer Gallery over the years. The observations made by Maryon and Gettens have served as a well-founded starting point for the more recent and far more extensive examination of these objects.

As with any specialized field, metalworking has its own vocabulary. Even within the area of metalworking, some very different operations and materials are referred to with the same terms. A glossary has been provided on pages 44–51 in order to define the various words used in this publication to describe the properties of Islamic metalwork.

Each catalogue entry contains a section of technical notes following a standard format: first, the construction of the object is discussed and observations on the method of decoration are given; a statement about the present condition of the object follows; finally, the analytical results are presented. We have attempted to provide the necessary information without giving excessive detail. The technical notes are intended to define the materials used in the objects and to explain how the craftsmen made them. For those interested in particular information not given in the catalogue entries, details are in the files of the Freer Gallery's Technical Laboratory.

With the exception of the most recently acquired dagger (no. 38), all of the objects have been extensively analyzed by X-ray fluorescence applied to the unprepared surface. Details of the analytical method appear in Appendix I. Although X-ray fluorescence as applied here can give only semiquantitative answers, the analyses have been helpful in grouping the objects.

MATERIALS EMPLOYED

The thirty-eight objects discussed in this publication may be conveniently divided into four groups according to the type of metal predominently used in their manufacture. Six objects are constructed of gold, three are of silver, eighteen are basically of copper alloys, and eleven are mainly of iron or steel. It will be helpful to consider each group separately below. The following brief discussion of each group serves as an introduction to the technical notes for the individual objects, shows the similarities and differences in the use of materials in each group, and illustrates general trends in Islamic metalwork.

Gold

The six pieces of gold (nos. 4–9) are all articles of jewelry. Although five of the six are thought to be from the same general period and region, there is a wide range of compositions among the pieces. All, however, share a characteristic structure in which many separate pieces of thin sheet are joined to form the body of the work. Additional decorations with chasing, filigree, twisted wire, niello, set stones, or granulation complete the objects.

It is interesting that cadmium, a material that recently has begun to be found in antique jewelry,[6] was detected by X-ray fluorescence only in the pair of lion earrings (no. 7).

Silver

The three objects of silver (nos. 1, 10, and 26), other than being of the same basic material, have little in common with one another. They differ in type, provenance, method of manufacture, and composition. Thus, these three objects cannot be studied as a group. Each of the three, however, displays an elaborate and interesting construction technique.

Copper Alloys

The group comprising the eighteen copper-alloy objects (nos. 2, 3, 11–25, and 27) offers the most possibilities for useful comparison. These objects, described in the headings of the catalogue entries as being made of brass, can easily be further divided into three distinct groups according to their composition and method of construction. The three groups are clearly apparent in a three-dimensional representation of composition (diagram 1) as well as on a graphic plot by ratios of the alloying elements (diagram 2).

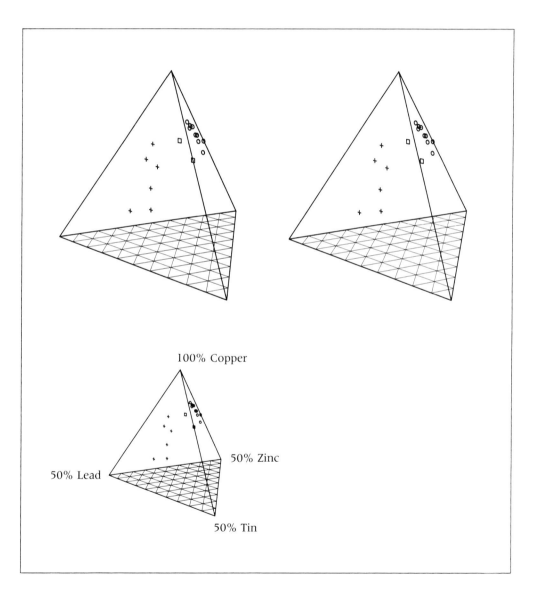

Diagram 1. The distribution of compositions of brass objects as shown by a stereo-pair representation of a quaternary diagram. One hundred percent copper is at the top of the diagram, with 50% tin at the forward corner and 50% lead and zinc at the rear left and right corners respectively (see small diagram).
Crosses denote the cast, highly leaded pieces. Turned or spun pieces are represented by squares, and the circles represent pieces made from sheet.

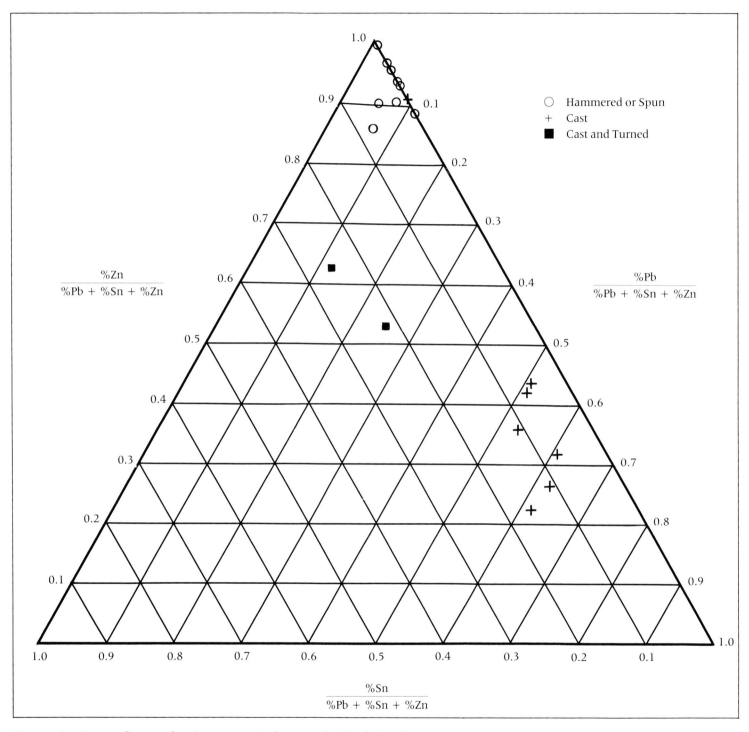

Diagram 2. Ternary diagram showing the distribution of the brass objects by the ratios between their lead (Pb), tin (Sn), and zinc (Zn) contents.

One group, composed of ten of the objects (nos. 13, 16–18, 20–24, and 27), might be called "pure brasses." Their compositions consist of about 15% zinc, 1–2% lead, and 1% or less tin. Nine of these objects have been formed by hammering or spinning; one (no. 27) was cast. The second group, which numbers six objects (nos. 2, 3, 11, 12, 14, and 15), are all cast. These six may be called "leaded brasses." Their compositions contain 6–18% zinc, more than 13% lead, and 1–5% tin. The third group consists of only two objects (nos. 19 and 25) that have compositions with 11% or more zinc, 4–5% lead, and 5–6% tin. These two objects are the only ones in which the tin content strongly appears to be more than accidental,[7] and also the only ones made from a combination of casting and turning. A specific four-part alloy may have been used for these two objects, but they are referred to as brass because of their large zinc content.

It is clear from our analyses that the Islamic metalworker knew the properties of the various alloys and how they could be worked. With the exception of the Ottoman candlestick (no. 27), the pure brasses with a lead content below 3% were used for sheet work, for which the metal had to be malleable and ductile. In contrast, leaded brasses of highly variable composition were used when the object was only to be cast and finished. The brittleness that results from a high lead content was not a drawback, as hammering was not used in the shaping of these objects. The two objects in the third group were finished on a lathe, by turning, and the alloy selected is one that, even today, is used for machining.[8] The selection and understanding of copper alloys by the Islamic metalworker is shown even more clearly by the "white bronzes," or hot-forged, high-tin alloys; no examples of these exist in the Freer's collection.[9]

Alloying and Zinc: All of the copper alloy objects in this catalogue can fairly be called "brasses"; they contain more zinc than tin. None of them, however, contains more zinc than can be alloyed with copper by the "cementation" process. In cementation, copper (more or less finely divided) and zinc (either in the natural ore form of calamine [smithsonite, zinc carbonate] or in the form of zinc oxide that has been purified from calamine by sublimation) are combined by heating them together in a sealed crucible. The method was used in medieval times both in Europe[10] and western Asia.[11]

Zinc can be alloyed with copper in at least three ways to produce brass. The cementation process yields alloys of up to approximately 28% zinc; the usual alloy yielded by the cementation process was between 22% and 28% zinc.[12] In 1723 an improved cementation process was patented, which, by increasing the surface area of the copper by granulation, enabled one to obtain a zinc content up to 33%.[13] Any alloy with a higher zinc content must have been made by the direct addition of metallic zinc to copper.

Metallic zinc is of particular interest in Islamic metalwork because it is found in a remarkable set of vessels made for the Ottoman court in the sixteenth century. These vessels are called *tutya*, which is another version of the Persian *tutiya*, meaning zinc oxide or zinc oxide vapor.[14] The name implies that they are zinc, and an analysis (done by W. T. Chase and E. W. FitzHugh of the Freer Gallery and Walt Brown of the National Museum of Natural History, Smithsonian Institution, using a scanning electron microscope with an energy-dispersive X-ray analyzer) performed on a small fragment shows it to be mostly zinc with traces of tin, iron, and copper.

Most of the *tutya* vessels seem to come from the sixteenth-century Ottoman court and from Iran,[15] but the shapes of the Ottoman vessels suggest some connection with metalworking centers in Herat. Incrusted with gold and gems, the vessels look similar in style and shape to those made of gold, jade, and rock crystal, clearly in the sumptuary tradition of Islamic crafts. The use of zinc for court vessels seems to begin and end suddenly during the sixteenth century, although it does persist in India, where zinc was being produced on a grand scale.[16] Is it possible that the sumptuary use of zinc during the sixteenth century stems from its introduction at that time from China or India through Afghanistan, Iran, and Turkey into Europe? These *tutya* vessels may be revealing to us the date of the introduction of metallic zinc in large quantities in Europe. People have always employed new materials for sumptuary or artistic purposes, and the use of *tutya* (a material that tarnishes easily and has little inherent strength) for making heavily ornamented vessels may be simply another example of the craftsman's search for novelty.[17]

If metallic zinc were newly introduced into the central Islamic lands during the first half of the sixteenth century, one should see some increase in zinc content in European brasses shortly thereafter. Indeed, this is the case; Cameron (1974) shows that the zinc content of English monumental medieval brasses increased to about 33% only after 1550; Pollard (1983) shows a similar increase in instruments (such as astrolabes) between 1565 and 1600; Craddock (1981, p. 22) shows a similar increase in zinc content of Tibetan sculpture in the sixteenth century; and Werner (1972) shows a similar increase in India. By the early 1600s zinc was being exported in large quantities from China and India to England,[18] and by 1712 large quantities were being used for brass-making in China, where the cementation process, although remembered, was no longer being practiced.[19] The *tutya* vessels form an important link in the story of the use of zinc.

Brass Fabrication Techniques (Casting, Hammering, and Spinning): Some of the cast pieces in this catalogue show inadequate mastery of casting techniques. In casting, when a thick section to be cast does not have adequate metal feeding into it as the metal solidifies, an internal shrinkage cavity is formed from the contraction of the liquid metal. Proper casting technique will allow for the contraction by having a sprue running to the thick section in the mold, to feed in more liquid metal as solidification is taking place, or by using a mold designed to make the section to be cast of more even thickness. Shrinkage cavities of this type can be seen on X-radiographs of the bird-shaped vessel (no. 11) and the handle of an ewer (no. 3). They are not seen on later castings.

The brasses worked up from sheet and the two cast pieces that were turned (nos. 19 and 25) present particular problems in ascertaining the method of fabrication used. Some of the sheet vessels were clearly hammered out of sheet; hammer marks can be seen on the X-radiograph of the large candlestick (no. 13), for example.

Others do not show individual hammer marks, but show large bands of lighter and darker areas. An example is the X-radiograph of the Iranian ewer (no. 16). Some regular deformation of these marks in a circular direction can also be seen, and we take this to be evidence of spinning, following Craddock and Lang (1983). Both spinning and turning will leave circular marks on an object; in spinning, however, the metal is actually moved upward over a form or chuck by the application of a large amount of pressure while the object is rapidly rotating. In turning, metal is removed or cut away. The amount of force in spinning must be quite large; turning can be done with less force. Wulff, in observing the coppersmiths of the īsfahan bazaar in 1963, saw turning used as a finishing technique for round vessels.[20] He describes the lathe in some detail. It does not look as though it would be adequate for spinning, and it is clear from Wulff's description that he did not see spinning employed. Nevertheless, some of the objects in this catalogue look as if they have been shaped by spinning. Perhaps more evidence will become available in the future.

Metal Inlays: While there are differences in composition and manufacture among the brass objects, many of them share in common the extensive use of inlay. Silver inlay predominates, although copper and gold are also frequently found. In addition to these materials, black organic compounds are used extensively.

The basic type of silver-inlay technique is one that has been observed numerous times before. A series of punch marks is made to outline the area to be inlaid. Within the outline, the body metal often is prepared to accept the inlay by being cut out or chased to form a shallow depression. The silver inlay is then cut to size and set into the depression.

For the narrow lines of silver inlay, the most common method observed in these objects is the application of a double row of chased punch marks into which thin wire or strips of silver were then impressed. The resulting line has a contour that reflects the shape of the end of the punch used to make the depressions. Thus an oval-ended punch yields a line with a contour resembling that of a rope, whereas a rectangular-ended punch gives a line with a stepped edge. To the naked eye, these different contours are rarely apparent. When inlay of narrow copper lines are used, one often sees the use of engraved depressions for securing the inlay, though punch-mark depressions are also commonly found.

While the regularity of the use of these techniques over such a large region and time period is impressive, there would still seem to be enough variation in working methods to allow one to distinguish between the products of various schools or regions. Subtle differences in the use and type of tools can be discerned from the tool marks that remain.

One of the more obvious differences, for example, is the preparation of the depressions for the application of the wider areas of inlay. Among the devices used are the following: a relatively deep recess, which allows for rather thick silver sheet to sit flush with the surface, as on the pen box by Shazi (no. 14); recesses made deeper toward the edge and quite shallow toward the center, as seen on the Mamluk plate (no. 22); and those in which only the punch-mark outline is recessed and punch marks are applied on top of the inlay to help secure it, as on the Veneto-Islamic bucket (no. 24).

Black Inlay: At the outset of this study, the black inlay found on brass objects was given particular attention. It was hoped that the composition of this material could be determined. In the literature, one often sees the black inlay on brass vessels identified as a number of different materials. Chiefly, it is called bitumen; other descriptions refer to it as enamel, black mastic, black paste, or pitch. In the course of preparing the metalwork for this exhibit, samples of black inlay were examined by X-ray diffraction, infrared spectrophotometry, microscopy, and solubility tests. Niello was found only on the metalwork of gold and silver. On the brass objects, no niello was found. With these objects, the "black" inlay varied in color from a deep black to a light brown. The analyses suggest that a number of organic media were used, often in combination with various inorganic fillers, such as quartz and calcite. The black materials varied in solubility from those that were insoluble in a wide range of solvents and required acid solutions for dissolution, to those that dissolved in common solvents such as toluene. Definitive analyses of these various compounds were beyond the scope of this study, but the tests conducted here suggest that promising results might come from analytical efforts to determine the various compositions of the organic black inlays. Given that there were a number of different organic materials used as black inlay, the identification of the materials might aid in establishing the provenance of objects.

Iron and Steel

The eleven works composed of iron and steel make up the last group. Most notable among these are the axe head (no. 31), the knife (no. 36), and the three daggers with patterned steel blades (nos. 34, 35, and 38). The knife (no. 36) was pattern-welded from steel containing nickel, probably of meteoritic origin; the others are described as watered steel, also known as the famous "Damascus steel." The descriptions of the methods of manufacture for the axe head, knife, and daggers are based on the theories of Smith and Maryon concerning the making of patterned blades.[21] The visual features of these five weapons seem to reflect closely the structures described by those two authors. But there are other interpretations of the structures of blades of this type and how they were accomplished.[22] Although there appears to be general agreement concerning the making of pattern-welded blades, the composition and method of manufacture of watered-steel blades are still subjects of current interest, in spite of the great amount of research that has been carried out in the past.[23]

The other ferrous objects in the Freer's collection do not have a pronounced surface pattern; one cannot tell by eye if they are watered steeel, hard steel, mild steel, or wrought iron. Since steel is harder than iron, microhardness measurements were made with a diamond pyramid hardness tester to determine whether or not these objects are steel.[24] The two comb backs (nos. 32 and 33) have the lowest hardness in the group (D.P.N. 175 and 182) and are probably a low-carbon steel. The flint striker (no. 37) has an intermediate hardness (D.P.N. 326), and is a mild steel. Although one plaque (no. 30) could not be tested because of its curved shape, it seems similar to a second plaque (no. 28, D.P.N. 387) from a scratch test; these are also mild steels. The hardest piece tested was the small, rectangular plaque (no. 29, D.P.N. 502); it is a hard steel. The plaque is so hard that it must have been quite time-consuming to cut and finish.

One other finding from the technical analyses of the iron and steel objects should be mentioned. The nondestructive method of elemental analysis (see below) gave relatively little information about the ferrous metals. The major alloying element of interest, carbon, could not be detected. Moreover, other elements of interest that may be present in small amounts generally were not detected, or at most their presence was only indicated and could not be quantified. The instance in which the X-ray fluorescence method was most useful in the examination of the iron and steel objects was on the meteoritic knife (no. 36). By detecting more than trace amounts of nickel in some of the layers of the pattern-welded blade, the analysis supports the opinion that some of the iron in the piece actually was of meteoritic origin.

METHODS OF EXAMINATION AND ANALYSIS

In the technical examination of the metalwork, the major goals were the determination of the method of manufacture and the identification of the materials used, particularly the alloys used to form the bodies of the objects. The most useful techniques for determining the method of manufacture were microscopic examinations using a stereo-binocular microscope and X-radiography. The identification of the niello, gems, corrosion products, and accretions was accomplished using microchemistry and X-ray diffraction analysis.

For the identification and quantitative measurements of the metals, most of the results were obtained by surface analysis using energy-dispersive X-ray fluorescence. The presence of clean, corrosion-free areas on nearly all these objects suggested the possibility of fairly accurate quantitative analyses without disfiguring surface preparation or removing samples. Given the diversity of objects, materials, and construction techniques of one or many parts, this seemed the best initial approach. The results from X-ray fluorescence can be used to make better-informed choices in later sampling and more exact analysis.

The areas chosen to be examined were those judged to be most free of corrosion, inlay, solder, or accretions that would interfere with a representative measurement of the body metal. Finding areas to meet those requirements was occasionally difficult, in which case only a small number of measurements could be taken.

In the technical notes for individual objects in the catalogue entries, the compositional figures quoted are, in most cases, an average of a number of measurements. The number of measurements made, and any qualifying considerations that should be taken into account, are given before the composition is described.

In most of the catalogue entries, the compositional figure is followed by confidence limits in parentheses. The confidence limits are based on the differences in multiple analyses of the same object, and give the range within which the correct compositional figure probably falls. Appendix I gives experimental details of the X-ray fluorescence equipment used, together with details of the data-reduction procedure, formulas for the calculation of confidence limits, and examples showing precision and accuracy.

When no figure follows the composition percentage, either only one measurement was made or the percentages quoted are from previous analyses that did not include an estimate of precision. The word "trace" given as the quantity means that the element was present but in amounts less than 0.5%. The term "not detected" is used when a particular element was sought but not found.

Comparisons were made between the results of the X-ray fluorescence analyses and the quantitative results previously obtained for some of the objects through other methods. The findings suggest that the different analyses of objects that have suffered less corrosion (such as the canteen, no. 17) are in close agreement. Conversely, heavily corroded objects have a surface composition that poorly reflects the overall composition of the metal. Only five of the objects analyzed appear to have been corroded to this extent. For two of the five (nos. 1 and 2), the results of analyses by other methods are available. For the other three (nos. 3, 11, and 12), surface analysis has yielded erratic results, which are reflected in the very high figures given for the confidence limits for those percentages. About these three, the analyses allow one only to say that they are highly leaded brasses. All three are cast pieces, and cast copper alloys with high lead compositions are extremely prone to segregation of the lead during the casting process. An accurate analysis by any method would be complicated.

For the brass objects, further analytical work is planned. This will include lead isotope ratio analyses to see if ore sources or, possibly, workshops can be distinguished, and spectrographic analysis to achieve greater quantitative accuracy on a broader range of elements.

Notes

1. Allan 1976, p. 299.
2. For one of the early published studies on this material, see Belaiew 1918.
3. Roberts-Austen 1892.
4. Allan 1979.
5. Craddock 1979; and Craddock and Lang 1983.
6. Demortier and Hackens 1982.
7. Craddock 1979, p. 73.
8. Copper Development Association 1978, p. 68, alloy #C84800, leaded semi-red brass, 76–3–6–15.
9. Allan 1979, p. 48ff; and Melikian-Chirvani 1974d.
10. Cameron 1974, pp. 221–25; and Pollard 1982, p. 2.
11. Allan 1979, pp. 42–46; and Craddock 1979.
12. Craddock 1979, p. 70; and Werner 1970, pp. 266–68.
13. Pollard 1983, p. 2; and Shaw and Craddock 1984.
14. Allan 1979, p. 42; three of the vessels are illustrated in İstanbul 1983, nos. E95–96 and E215.
15. Harari 1964–65, pl. 1380.
16. London 1982, no. 342; and Craddock 1984.
17. Smith 1972, passim.
18. Bonnin 1924, p. 3.
19. Needham 1974, pp. 212–13; and Chase, Bene, Zycherman, and Westley 1980, pp. 212–13.
20. Wulff 1966, pp. 26–27.
21. Smith 1960; and Maryon 1960a and 1960b.
22. Tylecote 1976, pp. 66–67; and Untracht 1982, pp. 364–65.
23. Yater 1983; and Sherby 1979.
24. Tests were performed at the Conservation-Analytical Laboratory and U.S. National Museum with the assistance of Martha Goodway. A Vickers-style diamond pyramid indenter was used, with 100- and 500-gram loads; hardnesses are given in diamond pyramid numbers (D.P.N.). Avner 1974; see also Tylecote 1962.

Glossary of Technical Terms

ALLOY: a substance of two or more metals, intimately mixed and united, usually by being fused together and dissolving in each other while molten; as, brass is an *alloy* of copper and zinc. Also applied to a similar substance composed of a metal and a nonmetal; as, steel is an *alloy* of iron and carbon.

BASE: See "Metals."

BLACK ORGANIC MATERIAL: a material applied to sunken areas, generally on the background of Islamic brass metalwork, to produce a black color resembling niello. It is often identified as a mixture of hydrocarbons, such as tar, bitumen, and mastic.

BRASS: an alloy of copper with zinc as the principal alloying element. Other metals such as lead occasionally may be added, to produce, for example, "leaded *brasses*." Past use of the term included the copper-tin alloys now referred to as bronzes.

BRONZE: when used to describe ancient metalwork, an alloy of copper and tin. Often other metals, particularly lead, are added as well. Modern usage has broadened to include any copper alloy in which the major alloying element is one other than zinc or nickel. The term is now generally used with a modifier, as "tin *bronze*," "aluminum *bronze*," or "leaded phosphor *bronze*." Whether one calls a particular copper alloy containing both tin and zinc a "*bronze*" or a "brass" is determined by whichever alloying element predominates. Correct terminology for candlestick no. 15 (74% copper, 6% zinc, 4% tin, and 16% lead) is "leaded tin brass."

CASTING: the process of making a metal object by pouring molten metal into a refractory void, or hole, and allowing it to solidify. The refractory void is usually contained in a mold. A core is necessary if the cast metal object is to contain a hollow space. Methods of *casting* include the use of open-face molds, sand molds, *cire-perdue* (or "lost-wax" investment molds), and piece molds made of refractory material (such as ceramic or stone) fitted together. A piece of metal that has been cast is also called a *"casting."*

CHAPLETS: in casting, pieces of metal that extend from the inner core into the outer mold to prevent the movement of the core and the resulting obstruction of the casting space and bad register, uneven wall thickness, or voids in the finished casting. *Chaplets* can be made from metal similar to that of the finished casting, in which case they can be finished and left in place, or made from a different metal, which can be removed and the holes plugged after casting. They can also just fill the casting space and butt up the mold and core walls, or be inserted like a spike into the walls.

CHASING: decorating the metal by hammering from the front or exterior surface of the object, employing variously shaped punches, tracers, chisels, and the like. The metal vessel or sheet is often backed with pitch or tar to support it during the chasing operation.

CHILLS: pieces of metal inserted into the casting mold that act to cool rapidly, or *chill*, the molten metal as it runs in. These serve to initiate the solidfication (freezing) of the molten metal at a particular spot, so that the founder can control the way the metal sets in the mold. *Chills* can be made from the same types of metal that chaplets are made of, and can be difficult to distinguish from chaplets.

CORROSION: gradual wearing away, decomposition, or disintegration by chemical processes; in metals, oxidation (as the rusting of steel) is an example of *corrosion*.

DAMASCUS STEEL: See "Watered steel."

DAPPING: creating domed forms in metal sheet by the use of a hammer and punches (which have hemispherical heads) called *dapping* punches, and/or a block with hemispherical depressions, called a *dapping* block.

ENGRAVING: a decorative technique in which metal is removed by cutting into the surface with such tools as gravers, burins, or scorpers. The typical *engraved* line has a tapered lead-in (where the graver digs gradually into the metal) and an exit (where the graver leaves the metal) or an abrupt end (where the chip raised by the graver is broken off). A good example of an *engraved* hatched background can be seen on canteen no. 17.

ETCHING: the production of patterns on a surface by the use of a corrosive chemical agent. As used here in describing the finishing treatment of steel, the application of a chemical solution (usually acidic) to bring out different structures in the steel by preferential removal or coloring of one constituent in order to achieve a surface pattern or design (see "Watered steel").

FILIGREE: decoration by means of wire, usually small, thin, twisted wire soldered together into an openwork structure. *Filigree* also applies to separate wires applied to a surface; the technique is used predominantly on gold and silver jewelry.

FORGING: the shaping of metal, usually steel and iron, by hammering while the metal is hot.

FORGE-WELDING: welding two pieces of metal, usually iron or steel, by heating them in a forge and hammering them together.

GILDING: the application of a thin layer of gold to a surface. This may entail the use of gold sheet or, as in *fire gilding* (also called *mercury amalgam gilding*), the use of a pasty amalgam (mixture) of mercury and gold that is applied to the cleaned base metal surface and then heated to drive off the mercury. Other techniques (such as *oil gilding* and electroplating) may be employed as well.

GRANULATION: decoration by means of small spheres (granules, balls, grains) of gold, usually attached to a gold sheet. The attachment can be made either with solder or by the ancient method of colloidal hard soldering (see "Soldering"). *Granulation* is used predominantly on jewelry.

HAMMERING:	shaping sheet metal by repeated blows of a hammer.
HARD SOLDER:	See "Soldering."
HATCHING:	parallel striations chased or engraved in a surface.
INCISING:	decoration from the front, or outside, by drawing a pointed instrument across the surface to produce a scratched line; also called "inscribing"; the pointed instrument may be called "a scriber or scribe."
INLAYING:	decoration of a surface by the insertion of one material into a ground of another; as applied on Islamic metalwork, the process usually involves chasing or cutting grooves into the metal surface of the object and forcing gold, silver, or copper into the grooves. Jewels, enamel, niello, and black organic material are also employed as *inlays.*
IRON:	See "Steel" and "Metals."
METALS:	elements or mixtures of elements (see "Alloy") that possess high electrical conductivity and a lustrous appearance in the solid state. *Metals* are usually divided into two groups, ferrous, or steel and iron, and nonferrous. The nonferrous *metals* can be subdivided into the *noble,* or *precious, metals* (gold, silver, and the platinum group), and the *base metals* (such as copper, lead, mercury, nickel, tin, zinc). The *noble metals* do not corrode nearly as rapidly as the *base metals* do.
MOLD:	a form containing a refractory void (*mold* cavity) into which molten metal is poured during casting.
NIELLO:	a black inlay material with a metallic luster, made of a mixture of silver, copper, gold, and/or lead sulfides. *Niello* is usually fused with heat into grooves cut into a metal surface; the surface of the *niello* and metal substrate is then finished with abrasives.
NOBLE:	See "Metals."
OVERLAYING:	decoration of one material by surface application of another;

47

gold was often *overlaid* onto cut grooves in the surface of steel ornaments (see no. 30).

PATTERN-
WELDING:

where strips, coils, or rods of iron and steel are forge-welded with hammering to make a piece of metal with a particular structure or surface pattern.

PIERCING:

making holes in a metal object by the use of tools such as punches, files, saws, or drills.

PREFERENTIAL
CORROSION:

corrosion or removal by chemical means of one phase or constituent in an alloy, leaving another behind. Usually, the most noble constituent remains. This leads to a phenomenon called surface enrichment, by which the surface of an object is enriched in the more noble constituents. For example, the silver-copper alloy of the eagle stand (no. 1) contains a large amount of copper; at the surface, the copper corroded preferentially, leaving the silver behind. After cleaning and removing the overburden of copper salts, the surface was seen to be depleted in copper and enriched in silver.

PUNCH:

a tool for surface decoration of metal (or other material such as leather or wood), usually made from a small, rectangular bar of forged steel. Punches can have ends of almost any shape; round, square, oval, and ring-shaped ends are common. They are used for *punching* or chasing by being placed against the surface of the metal to be decorated and struck with a hammer.

RAISING:

hammering a flat sheet of metal into the shape desired by placing the sheet against an anvil and striking it with a hammer. In forming a bowl, ewer, or other closed shape, the sheet is usually rotated around its major axis as the hammering proceeds, and the remains of the hammering usually can be seen on the less-finished inside as *"raising courses."* The metal of the sides is stretched outward or brought inward as *raising* progresses.

REPOUSSÉ:

hammering from the inside of a vessel or back of a sheet to produce raised areas on the outside or front; *repoussé* is often

48

combined with chasing, its opposite in technique. *Repoussé* serves to define the larger masses of the design, and chasing refines the relief and sharpens the contours.

RING MATTING: an overall surface decoration or texture made by chasing, using a ring-shaped, or annular, punch. These punches leave a ring-shaped depression in the surface; they can be made with more than one ring on the end of the punch, if desired. The usual method of making a punch for *ring matting* is to take a small, round-ended punch, hit its end with a sharp pointed punch (making a round hole in the end of the punch), and then filing the outside to shape.

RIVET: a headed metal pin used to join together separate pieces of metal. The *rivet* is applied through holes and secured by forming a head on the other end.

SCREW: a rod of metal, usually headed, with a helical land running around it such that the rod, if turned, will be slowly drawn into a hole with a matching groove. The *screw thread* is the helical land, so called because it originally was made by carefully wrapping a *thread* of metal around the *screw* and soldering it in place. By extension, *thread* also applies to the groove that engages the helical land.

SINKING: shaping metal sheet by hammering it into a depression. The depression is often in a large block of wood. In *sinking,* the hammering is done from the inside of the piece, whereas in "raising," at least at the beginning stages, it is done from the outside.

SOFT SOLDER: See "Soldering."

SOLDERING: the joining of metals by the use of *solders,* alloys that flow at temperatures lower than the metals being joined and achieve a joint by wetting and adhering to the metal substrates. *Solders* can be divided into two distinct classes, *soft solders* and *hard solders. Soft solders* are basically lead-tin alloys that melt at a relatively low temperature (below 300°C). *Hard solders* for gold and silver alloys usually contain mixtures of those metals (commonly with the addition of copper) to give a *solder,* which has a melting point close to that of the metals being joined. For the *soldering* of granulation, where normal *solder* would flood the interstices between the grains, a technique known as *colloidal hard soldering* is often used; a metal salt, traditionally of copper, is mixed with an aqueous organic binder. This mixture initially holds the grains to the substrate. As the work is progressively heated, the binder burns off, the metal salt is reduced to metal, and the metal then fuses with and *solders* together the parts to be joined.

SPINNING: shaping metal sheet into vessels or other round shapes by forcing the sheet, while it rotates on a *spinning lathe,* against a metal or wood form called a chuck. The chuck can be made in a number of pieces for removal from the finished shape. *Spinning* requires a great deal of force, especially for objects of appreciable thickness.

STEEL: an alloy of iron and carbon, with a carbon content between about 0.1 and 2.0%. Modern alloy *steel* can include even more carbon, as well as a number of metals, such as chromium, nickel, manganese, titanium, vanadium, and others. Ancient *steel* can contain small amounts of some of these metals as impurities. Most notable of these is nickel, which can have a beneficial effect, and when found in appreciable amounts has been taken to indicate that the source of the iron was a meteorite (see no. 36). *Steel* is distinguished from wrought or cast iron by its carbon content; wrought iron has less carbon than *steel* (0–0.2% carbon), whereas cast iron has more (1.5–5%). Cast iron can be made into *steel* by removing carbon, and wrought iron can be made into *steel* by adding it, as in the wootz process (see "Watered *steel*"). In practical use, however, steel is defined by the blacksmith as any iron alloy that hardens when it is heated and quenched.

SURFACE ENRICHMENT: See "Preferential corrosion."

TURNING: shaping or finishing metal by cutting it away while the metal object is rotating. Horizontal lathes (like the modern lathe) or vertical rotation (like a potter's wheel) can be used, together with various types of tools (such as chisels, scrapers, or knives).

WATERED STEEL: steel with a fine surface pattern resembling waves or ripples in water. In our usage *watered steel* is synonymous with "Damascus" steel. *Watered steel* is made from wootz, a type of crucible steel that originated in India; wootz is made by putting wrought iron together with vegetable material in a crucible and heating it for a prolonged period. The steel that emerges is especially high in carbon (approx. 2%) and crystallizes on cooling with a pronounced structure. After etching, the pattern of bright, silvery areas (cementite, iron carbide) and dark brownish gray areas (pearlite, a mixture of iron and iron carbide) is revealed. The axe head (no. 31) is a particularly good example of a *watered steel* pattern that is not far removed from the original wootz cake. As the cake is forged out into a blade, the pattern is elongated and flattened out; it takes on an appearance like wood grain (see nos. 35, 36, and 38). *Watered steel* is different in origin from "pattern-welded" steel; in the first, the pattern comes from crystallization phenomena inside the metal; in the latter, it comes from the welding together of different types of steel.

WELDING: the joining of two pieces of metal at a temperature close to their fusion point. The ideal of *welding* is to form as homogeneous a joint as possible. *Welding* requires that the surfaces to be joined either melt or reach a plastic state, unlike soldering, in which the solder melts and wets the surfaces to be joined, holding them together by adhesion. With iron and steel, *pressure welds* between separate pieces can be achieved by heating and hammering them together (see "Forge-welding" and "Pattern-welding").

WIRE: a piece of metal of great length relative to its thickness, often round in cross section. *Wire* may be made by many different techniques, such as cutting thin strips from a sheet and twisting them, swaging (repeated hammering of strips into a block with a groove cut in it), or drawing (pulling the *wire* through a draw-plate with a graded series of holes down to the desired size).

Catalogue

1. Stand with Four Eagles

Silver: cast in sections and chased

Iran(?), 7th–8th centuries

Height: 8.5 cm. (3⅜ in.); diameter: 17.8 cm. (7 in.);
 weight: 1,537.0 gm. (54.2 oz.)

53.92

The stand is made up of a round ring or collar that rests on eight round posts; between every other post is an eagle; the posts and eagles are attached to a flat base with a circular opening in the center. The eagles are crisply modeled and have sharp features; their wings are folded at the back and their legs form the feet of the stand. The feathers of the wings are indicated by deep lines that meet at the back and form chevrons; a series of diamonds filled with strokes accentuates the chests.

Representations of eagles are frequently encountered in ancient western Asian art. They appear in Achaemenid, Parthian, and Sasanian seals, coins, and crowns as well as on silver or gold plaques and vessels. According to the Zoroastrian tradition, the eagle possessed magical qualities and had royal and divine implications; gods of victory and good fortune often transformed themselves into animals and birds such as eagles. In the Sasanian repertoire, eagles were also used as supports for thrones[1] and fire altars. This bird plays a prominent role in Roman, Coptic, and Byzantine art as well. It is associated with imperial power and appears on standards, seals, textiles, and sculpture. In Christian iconography the eagle symbolizes the Resurrection and is the attribute of Saint John the Evangelist. There are several Byzantine eagles in the round, some of which are in bronze and terra-cotta.[2] The eagle generally is represented frontally with wings displayed, or in profile with addorsed wings; the bird is also shown attacking prey. The Roman and Byzantine eagles tend to be shown with both folded and displayed wings.

The eagles on the Freer stand can be traced to late antique as well as ancient western Asian traditions. The stand must have been made to hold a medium-sized ovoid jar or vase, examples of which exist in Sasanian art. Stands with rings resting on posts or figures were produced before the Sasanian period and continued well into the medieval age. It is difficult, therefore, to assign a date for this piece. There are no other comparable examples, and the only other related piece is a single eagle (fig. 19), cast from a similar mold, now in the Brooklyn Museum.[3]

The coarse execution of the eagles suggests that the stand is either provincial Sasanian or dates from the early Islamic period during which past traditions were reemployed. The eagles here are used decoratively and appear to have lost any heraldic, royal, or divine meaning, which tends to support an early Islamic date. It is also possible that the stand was produced in an area influenced by Byzantine traditions, such as Egypt, Syria, or Turkey.

Technical Notes

The stand is made up of a number of separately fabricated parts soldered together. The eagles are apparently all cast members. Each is unique and not cast from the same model; some of the details are chased. The posts are soldered to the top ring and the base. The lower ends of the posts have been thinned down and fitted into holes in the base, hammered over, and soldered in place. The base appears to be cast; no join lines are apparent to suggest that it was a straight band bent into a circle. Also, some porosity is apparent in X-radiographs of the metal. The top ring is a rod bent into a circular shape. The ends of the ring are soldered together just above the point where one of the posts meets the ring. Hard solder was used for all the joins.

When acquired, the object was covered with copper corrosion products, probably malachite. Light cleaning was sufficient to remove most of the green material; the cleaning was followed by light polishing and lacquering. Except for a few cracks in the bottom band, the piece is in very good condition; all of the solder joints are still sound.

The presence of copper corrosion products is not surprising, considering that the silver is quite base, that is, alloyed with a high percentage of copper. This is true of the various parts of the stand. Neutron activation analysis[4] of two drilled samples gave the following results for the major and minor elements:

	Silver	Copper	Gold
Bottom of base	53.4%	46.5%	0.1%
Bird	61.3%	38.6%	0.1%

X-ray fluorescence analysis of the surface indicates a silver content ten to twenty percent higher than that of the drilled samples, with the majority of the remainder of the alloy made up of copper with small amounts of gold and lead. The difference can be explained by surface enrichment resulting from the preferential corrosion of the copper in the alloy as indicated by the green corrosion products formerly on the stand. The copper in the surface of the piece, being less noble, corroded preferentially out of the surface and formed a superficial coating of green copper salts. This process left the surface of the object enriched in silver and depleted in copper.

The hard solder at the joints appears to be close to a eutectic (lowest-melting) mixture of silver and copper. The hard solder was investigated by X-ray fluorescence. Making allowances for the surface-enrichment effects, the solder is more noble than the metal of the stand (approximately 72% silver versus approximately 60% silver). Modern hard solders often contain cadmium, none of which was detected in the solder of the stand.

19. Silver eagle
Iran(?), 7th–8th centuries
(New York, The Brooklyn Museum, 50.91)

Provenance: Purchased from Heeramaneck Galleries, New York, 1953.
Published: Atıl 1971, no. 46.

Notes:

1. One such support is published in Melikian-Chirvani 1969f. For its representation on a silver vessel, see Ann Arbor 1967, no. 16.
2. A bronze finial in the form of an eagle in the Seattle Art Museum is published in *Art Quarterly* 1969. For a large terra-cotta example see Dumbarton Oaks 1967, no. 304; a unique lapis lazuli example is illustrated in Walters Art Gallery 1947, no. 544.
3. This piece was once thought to be East Roman and is now classified as Sasanian.
4. These analyses were performed at the Brookhaven National Laboratory, Upton, New York, by Pieter Meyers.

2. Incense Burner

Brass: cast in sections; pierced and chased or engraved

Egypt, 8th–9th centuries

Height: 31.5 cm. (12⅜ in.);

   length (including handle): 40.8 cm. (16¹⁄₁₆ in.);

   width: 21.2 cm. (8⅜ in.); weight: 4,078.0 gm. (143.8 oz.)

52.1

The incense burner is made up of three parts, which were cast separately: the top half with five domes, the bottom half with four legs, and the long handle. The piece resembles a square structure surmounted by a large dome flanked by four smaller ones; it rests on legs adorned with animal masks and paws. Each of the domes was embellished originally with an eagle that stood on a lobed pedestal. The birds on the large and two smaller domes, and one of the pedestals have been broken off. The rectangular handle terminating with a crouched antelope or gazelle has been reattached; the front legs of the animal are missing.

The piece is elaborately decorated, with pierced floral and geometric motifs covering the entire surface. Two rows of leaflike crenellations encircle the upper and lower edges. The side panels on each half bear a braided pattern framed by strips with beads or diagonal lines. The back has two hinges with iron pins that join the two halves; a projection on the front allows the top to be lifted open. The bottom of the lower half is completely sealed; there is a large quatrefoil opening beneath the domes on the upper half.

The domes are decorated with large floral scrolls bearing leaves or blossoms; the large central dome has two additional concentric bands at the top adorned with leaves.

The four splayed feet ending with large masks of either lions or griffins terminate in heavy animal paws or claws. A leaf scroll identical to the one seen above the central dome appears on top of the handle; the sides have a chevron pattern. The horned animal at the end is well modeled, with its facial features carefully marked. This animal together with the eagles and the legs are the only parts of the incense burner that are not pierced.

The shape of the incense burner is highly unusual although the decorative themes— such as the large scrolling vines, eagles with displayed wings, and animal masks and paws on the feet—are commonly found on Byzantine and Coptic incense burners (see fig. 20) dating between the fifth and ninth centuries.[1] Almost all of these examples are cylindrical with domical lids, or they are square with pyramidical covers. The model for the Freer piece is thought to be either a contemporary building or a church furnishing such as a ciborium. A type of a square structure surmounted by a large dome with smaller domes on four corners is known to have been used in Byzantine architecture after the ninth century and may have existed even earlier, as suggested by the shape of this incense burner. It has also been argued that the shape of the square and domed early Islamic incense burner was inspired by the Buddhist stupa architecture of Central Asia and India.[2]

The Freer incense burner forms a link between the late antique and Coptic traditions (possibly also those of Central Asia) and early Islamic art. The shapes used in the early Islamic period tend to be both cylindrical and square, and were popularly employed from Afghanistan to Spain.[3] Classical Islamic incense burners generally follow the cylindrical type and are inlaid with silver, copper, and gold.[4]

20. Bronze(?) incense burner
Egypt, 9th century
(Paris, Musée du Louvre, E 11708)

In the casting of the incense burner, all the appendages on the three separate pieces were integrally cast with the respective piece. Thus, the domes, birds, and flanges were all cast as one with the rest of the lid. No joins are evident that would suggest otherwise.

Technical Notes

Also, sprues extend down from the tails of the birds to the hemispheres, indicating that the lid was cast upside down. Similar sprues are found extending down from the bottom of the incense burner to the legs. The flanges on the top and bottom pieces all differ slightly from one another in shape, suggesting that these were not reproduced from the same model but rather that they were formed individually. The casting of such intricate pieces seems to have proved difficult, as there are a number of flaws where the metal failed to fill the mold entirely. These are shrinkage cavities where the caster has attempted to cast too thick a section; some flaws of this type can also be seen in the upper portion of the handle by X-radiography.

The incense burner is decorated with openwork and recessed lines. The openwork on the hemispheres, the sides of the incense burner, and the handle appears to have been executed, or at least accentuated, by tooling, after casting. Sharp, slight ridges along the edges of the openwork can be seen, together with striations that run across the flat edge of the openings, presumably caused by the cutting tool used to make the openings. The recessed lines were cast in place; this is demonstrated by the casting flaws where the metal failed to fill the mold and thus interrupted the course of the lines. In some cases, however, the lines may have been further defined by chasing or engraving.

The incense burner has suffered over the course of time. As was mentioned previously, various elements have been lost from the top and handle. The top and bottom, attached to one another by hinges, have corroded firmly together. Corrosion covers the entire surface, particularly on the bottom, where a somewhat unusual copper corrosion product, chalconatronite, is found.[5] The handle has been recently reattached, and losses in this area were filled.

Samples were taken from the handle and body of the incense burner in 1972. Analysis by wet chemical methods[6] gave the following results:

	Copper	Zinc	Lead	Tin	Iron	Total
Body	75.0%	6.6%	12.8%	1.9%	0.7%	97.0%
Handle	68.9%	12.3%	16.6%	0.6%	1.3%	99.7%

Although the body and the handle are not cast from the same metal, there is no reason to assume that they are not original, given the similarities between the two parts.

X-ray fluorescence analysis showed a highly variable composition, especially in areas with heavy patination. The figures from X-ray fluorescence are a less reliable indicator of composition than those from wet chemistry; the large confidence limits confirm this fact. In particular, the lead content as given by X-ray fluorescence is questionable and probably much too large. The average of four determinations is as follows:

Copper	Zinc	Lead	Tin
63% ($\pm$15)	6% ($\pm$4)	22% ($\pm$14)	7% ($\pm$5)

These average figures are very similar to those for the Iranian ewer (no. 3). While the lead is probably overestimated, in both cases the objects can be seen in X-radiographs to be heavily leaded. The casting technique of both pieces is rather rough and unskilled. The evidence suggests that the two pieces may have a more similar origin than we have previously assumed.

Provenance: Purchased from Mallon, New York, 1952.
Published: Atıl 1975, no. 8.
            Baer 1983, fig. 32.

Notes:
1. See, for instance, examples published in Weitzmann 1979, no. 323; Aga-Oglu 1945, figs. 1 and 2; Essen 1963, no. 171; and Paris 1977, no. 19, illustrated as fig. 20 in this catalogue.
2. Baer 1983, pp. 46–50, in which eastern Iran is suggested as the provenance of these pieces.
3. For a cylindrical one from Afghanistan, see Melikian-Chirvani 1982, fig. 7; a square example from Spain is in Jenkins 1983, pl. 40. Other incense burners are published in Aga-Oglu 1945, figs. 3 and 4; Harari 1964–65, pls. 1278B–C; and Baer 1983, fig. 33.
4. Aga-Oglu 1945; for a spectacular fourteenth-century example, see Allan 1982a, no. 15.
5. Gettens and Frondel 1955, pp. 64–75.
6. The analysis was performed by I. V. Bene, formerly of the Freer Gallery's Technical Laboratory.

3. Ewer

Brass: cast

Iran, 9th–10th centuries

Height: 43.7 cm. (17³⁄₁₆ in.); diameter of body: 16.5 cm. (6½ in.);
  weight: 2,255.0 gm. (79.5 oz.)

45.13

The ewer with a pear-shaped body, high neck, and curving handle has been restored; a part of the high, splayed foot is a later addition. A portion of the body was damaged and a fairly large section has been filled in. Its only decorations are molded rings at the narrow and extended spout, lower neck, and upper foot; the handle, which terminates in highly stylized antelope or gazelle heads, bears a thumb-rest shaped as a cube with its corners cut out.

This elegant and understated piece belongs to a group of undecorated ewers, each bearing almost the same shape with minor variations in their proportions. The most spectacular among them was made of gold (fig. 21) and is now in the Hermitage.[1] The Hermitage ewer, assigned to the late Sasanian period, or about the seventh century, has more pronounced rings, a shorter handle with more naturalistic animal heads, and a lower foot. The remaining ewers are thought to be made of bronze and are attributed to the "post-Sasanian" period.[2] Their shapes are very close to that of the Freer example, but almost all of them have a lower foot. It is quite possible that the original foot of the Freer ewer was also fairly low. Another similar vessel made in pewter lacks the foot altogether.[3]

A related series of ewers (see fig. 22) with pear-shaped bodies, extended lips forming narrow spouts, high feet, and animal-headed handles were made of silver or bronze and decorated with engraved, carved, or repoussé animals, mythological creatures, or Dionysiac scenes.[4] These are generally dated toward the end of the Sasanian period, to the sixth or seventh centuries. A second series of pear-shaped ewers (see fig. 23) do not have spouts, but the handles are embellished with a large palmette. These are identified as being among the earliest Islamic bronzes and are assigned to the eighth or ninth centuries.[5] Included in this is the only dated example: the ewer (fig. 4) in the Museum of Arts in Tiflis inscribed with the date 686/87 or 688/89 but attributed to the ninth century, based on its style of decoration and script.[6] These late Sasanian and early Islamic pieces are thought to have originated in Khorasan and Transoxiana, regions extending from eastern Iran to Uzbekistan.

The same provenance generally is accepted for the group of undecorated ewers having shapes based on the more elaborate pieces produced in the late Sasanian period. Their simple but graceful shapes also can be seen on the high-tin bronzes of the early Islamic period. Among this type of ware is an ewer with a shape reminiscent of the Freer example, although it is considerably squatter because of its shorter neck and foot.[7]

It should be mentioned that single-handled ewers with extended lips forming narrow spouts also are represented in several early Islamic silver plates based on Sasanian prototypes. One example shows an ewer embellished with arches; another (fig. 24) depicts an undecorated type.[8]

21. Gold ewer
Iran, 7th century
(Leningrad, State
Hermitage Museum,
Z–524)

22. Silver ewer, partially gilt
Iran(?), 6th–7th centuries
(New York, The
Metropolitan Museum of
Art, 67.10)

23. Bronze(?) ewer inlaid
with copper
Iran(?), 8th–9th centuries
(Baltimore, Walters Art
Gallery, 54.457)

24. Silver plate, partially gilt
Iran(?), 7th–8th centuries
(Lugano [Switzerland], Marion
Hammer Collection)

The ewer was cast, seemingly in its complete form. No joins can be seen where the handle meets the body, and radiographs of this area appear to show a continuous flow of metal between the two parts. As was mentioned, the foot has been repaired, but the stem of the foot is original; where it meets the body, no joins are apparent.

There are a number of fills in the metal that would appear to have been executed to correct casting flaws and to fill in the holes created from the use of chaplets. Around the widest point of the ewer, two fills are present that are circular in cross section and

Technical Notes

measure 4.7 millimeters (³/₁₆ inch) in diameter. The location and shape of the fills suggests that chaplets were used in this area. On the neck, in the area where the handle is attached, a row of circular fills is apparent. These fills may have been necessitated by a great deal of porosity in this area or the failure of the metal to fill the mold at this point.

The repairs to the foot and the body are extensive and appear to be relatively recent. Yet, in spite of its condition, the vessel has retained its basic shape. The heavily corroded surface has a mottled appearance that is green, red, and brown in color.

Because of the condition of the ewer, only a rough approximation of the composition of the metal could be made by analysis of the surface; the large figures for the confidence limits indicate the wide variation between the separate measurements. In particular, the percentage given for the lead content is questionable and probably much too large. The average of seven measurements taken at various areas is as follows:

Copper	Zinc	Lead	Tin
57% ($\pm$14)	10% ($\pm$2)	27% ($\pm$14)	5% ($\pm$1)

The X-ray fluorescence analysis results are similar to those of the incense burner (no. 2).

Provenance: Purchased from Brummer Gallery, New York, 1945.
Published: Ettinghausen 1943b, no. 1.
Ettinghausen 1956, fig. 3.

Notes:
1. This famous ewer, part of the Poltava Treasury, has been published several times in, among other sources, Orbeli 1964–65, pl. 234A.
2. See, for example, ibid., pls. 243A–B; Marshak 1972, pls. 12 and 13; and Melikian-Chirvani 1982, fig. 2.
3. Harper 1978, fig. E.
4. Examples from this series are published in Smirnov 1909, pls. XLIX–LI; Orbeli and Trever 1935, pls. 48, 49, and 70–72; Orbeli 1964–65, pls. 223, 224, and 226; Ann Arbor 1967, nos. 18 and 19; Marshak 1972, pl. 14; and Harper 1978, no. 18, which includes references to publications on related pieces decorated with female cult images.
5. This series is discussed in Marshak 1972; and Melikian-Chirvani 1982, p. 25 and no. 1. See also Baer 1983, pp. 83–102, for a discussion of Islamic ewer types.
6. The dating and provenance of the Tiflis ewer are still being debated. A ninth-century date is proposed in Marshak 1972.
7. Melikian-Chirvani 1974d, fig. 7.
8. The decorated ewer, in the Hermitage, is published in Orbeli 1964–65, pl. 230B; the other example is published in Ann Arbor 1967, no. 15.

4. Bracelet

Gold: repoussé and chased;
  decorated with granulation and twisted wire

Syria, early 11th century

Height of clasp: 4.9 cm. (1$^{15}\!/_{16}$ in.);
  maximum diameter: 12.9 cm. (5$^{1}\!/_{16}$ in.);
  weight: 236.5 gm. (8.3 oz.)

48.25

Inscriptions (Arabic)

Bands on the shank (kufic):

detail of clasp

Victory, . . . increasing, . . . increasing,	النصر ال ✻ ال ... الصاعد ✻ ال ...
everlasting life, . . . triumphant victory,	الصاعد ✻ العمر الخالد الـ ... ✻ النصر الغالب
perpetuity, eternal glory, good fortune,	البقى ✻ العز الدائم اليمن الـ ... ✻ البركة
. . . perfect blessing, complete favor,	الكاملة ✻ النعمة الشاملة ✻ الشاملة الغبطة ✻
[interrupted by the hinge] *complete,*	النعمة السابغة ✻ الصاد
delight, abundant favor . . .	

The shank of the oval bracelet, or armlet, was fabricated from a single flat sheet, decorated with repoussé and chased designs, and then folded into a hollow tube with the seam on the inner side camouflaged by the decoration. Eleven bands of inscriptions, interspersed with beveled strips and separated by thin ribbons with strokes, diagonally encircle the piece and create a twisted effect. The kufic letters are raised and placed on a ground textured with round punches. There is a hinge on one side that allows the

✻ Rosettes indicate a break in the inscription panels by decorative elements.

bracelet to open. The clasp is attached to the tapering shank by three rows of granulation at either end. A band with a scale pattern appears on the inner side, covering the seam.

The elaborate circular clasp was made up of several parts that were soldered together. It employs a variety of techniques, including twisted ropes, granulation, and filigree. The clasp is in two sections held together by a draw pin. In the center of the upper side is a diamond-shaped unit, in which a gem was originally held in its core; on the four corners are small filigree domes (with gold grains at the pinnacles), interspersed with rosettes made up of granulations; a twisted rope forms the border. Around the diamond are four settings for gems, which also are lost; between them are filigree domes flanked by smaller domes, each topped by a grain with additional granulation around the edges. The underside of the clasp has concentric bands decorated with roundels and scrolls made of twisted wires. The sides of the clasp are decorated with vertical rows of granulations, which creates a fluted or ribbed effect.

The mate to this bracelet is owned by the National Museum in Damascus.[1] The Damascus example (fig. 25), found in Raqqa in 1939, also lacks its original five gems on the clasp. Its inscriptions, also in eleven bands, contain similar wordings. The dimensions are almost identical, the minor variations of millimeters owing to the warped and battered condition of some parts.[2]

25. Gold bracelet
Syria, early 11th century
(Damascus, National Museum, A 1056)

Both bracelets, exhibiting extremely refined filigree and granulation, exemplify the art of goldsmithing under Fatimid patronage. Since so few works have survived from this dynasty, these pieces are important for the study of the techniques and styles of luxury items. Also produced in this period were bracelets with diamond-shaped clasps, beaded necklaces, hair ornaments, crescent-shaped earrings, and various pendants employing similar filigree, granulation, and twisted-wire decoration.[3]

The meaning of the motifs have not yet been properly analyzed and understood. It is highly probable that the diamond-shaped unit with the missing gem in the center of the clasp was inspired by a square structure surmounted by a dome and flanked by four smaller domes (see also no. 2).

The production of a matching pair of bracelets suggests that these were worn on both wrists at the same time.[4] Since the inscriptions vary in terminology, one bracelet would bestow a series of good wishes that were continued on the other bracelet with a repetition of similar sentiments. On the Freer piece six of the panels are written in one direction; the remaining five panels are reversed, enabling the owner or beholder to read the inscriptions comfortably without twisting the wrist.

Technical Notes

The shank of the bracelet was basically formed by repoussé, with additional details added by chasing with a ring punch and tracers. The clasp was formed using sheet and the decoration was executed with twisted wire and granulation. The granules are very fine, with most of them having a diameter of 0.5 millimeters (0.02 inch) or less.

Besides the lost stones, the bracelet shows other damage as well. The ring is dented in many places and the hinge is broken. Some small globules of silver chloride corrosion are present on the surface. Traces of iron oxide can be found and are, presumably, the remnants of polishing compounds. Also, some clay or earth accretions can be found in the interstices of the design elements.

Five analyses of three areas on the shank give an average that shows the following high gold content:

Gold	Silver	Copper
98.5% (±0.5)	1.0% (±0.1)	0.5% (±0.4)

The clasp and its decoration were attached with hard solder, and the results of surface analyses thus show higher amounts of base metals, with 1–2% copper and 3–7% silver being present.

Provenance: Purchased from Mallon, New York, 1948.
Published: Atıl 1975, no. 14.
　　　　　　 Keene and Jenkins 1981, figs. 16a–b.

Notes:
1. Published in Damascus 1976, fig. 116; London 1976, no. 242; and Berlin 1982, no. 261.
2. Its maximum diameter is 13 centimeters (5⅛ inches); height of clasp: 4.4 centimeters (1¾ inches).
3. Keene and Jenkins 1981, figs. 15, 17a–b, and 18–22; Jenkins 1983, pls. 64 and 65. See also Jenkins and Keene 1983, nos. 37, 44, 45, and 47–51, for diverse eleventh- and twelfth-century objects from Egypt and Syria.
4. Another pair of matching gold Fatimid bracelets is published in Jenkins 1983, pl. 65. See also Jenkins and Keene 1983, no. 45; Berlin 1971, no. 157; and Paris 1977, no. 359, for other pairs attributed to Syria.

detail of clasp

5. Bracelet

Gold: repoussé and chased; decorated with
  granulation and twisted wire, and set with turquoise

Iran, first half 11th century

Height of clasp: 5.3 cm. (2¼ in.); maximum diameter: 10.6 cm.
  (4³⁄₁₆ in.); weight: 73.4 gm. (2.6 oz.)

58.6

Inscriptions (Arabic)

Four discs on the back (kufic):

Justice. There is no God but God the One. He has no partners. For al-Qadir Billah.	عدل ۞ لا لله الا ۞ الله و حده ۞ لا شريك له ۞ للقادر بالله

The most refined example of an almost microscopic granulation is found on this bracelet, which has a shank made of a hollow tube embellished with spirally applied twisted wire. The tube tapers toward the quatrefoil clasp and joins it with a band of grains flanked by twisted wire. At one side of the shank is a draw pin with a granulated head.

The clasp, produced separately, contains two large circular units on either side of the opening, which has two pins with granulated heads inserted into seven loops decorated with additional granulation and twisted wire. The circular units, embellished with large filigree domes surmounted by additional smaller domes and grains, are covered completely with granulation and twisted wire. Between them are two round and four oval hemispheres with the finest granulations. Two pairs of turquoise stones appear at the outer edge of the clasp, next to the tubular ring.

On the back of the four circular units are discs struck from a coin. They were made of thin gold plates pressed over the *dinar*, or gold coin, leaving the impression in relief. The Abbasid caliph, al-Qadir, whose name appears on these plates, was in office from 991 to 1031. The coin was of a Ghaznavid type minted in Nishapur between 1000 to 1028 during the reign of Sultan Mahmud (998–1030).[1] Seen behind the clasp is the central section of the obverse, which has a five-line inscription.

Unfortunately, the border has been obliterated by the mounting and is illegible; this portion would have included the date and the city where the original coin was minted. The original coin would have contained the name of the ruler on the reverse, which was not reproduced on the discs. The bracelet must have used contemporary coins and was produced, therefore, during the first half of the eleventh century. Its exact provenance is not easily determined, as Ghaznavid coins were circulated widely throughout eastern Iran, Afghanistan, and northern India. During Sultan Mahmud's reign the empire stretched to western Iran as well, controlling such centers as Rayy and Hamadan.[2] It would appear more likely, however, that the bracelet was produced in eastern Iran.

An identical bracelet (fig. 26), owned by the Metropolitan Museum of Art, New York, contains the four gold plates behind the clasp produced from the same coin.[3] In the Metropolitan example, the four stones at the edge of the clasp are missing.

The date and provenance provided by the Freer and Metropolitan bracelets are most useful for the study of the development of Islamic jewelry. Coins or fake coins were used in Byzantine jewelry and have continued to be employed in the Islamic world up to the present day. Similar to the previous bracelet (no. 4), the twisted tubular ring also dates from the late antique period.

The tradition of making a pair of identical pieces also links this bracelet with the Syrian example.[4] The bracelets must have been worn on both wrists, possibly over the cuffs of garments since they are quite wide. In the eleventh century the techniques of twisted wire, granulation, and filigree were greatly advanced, with the clasp forming the most elaborately decorated portion of the ornament. Among the characteristics of these Islamic bracelets are shanks that taper toward the clasp, which is generally quatrefoil in construction.[5]

26. Gold bracelet
Iran, first half 11th century
(New York, The Metropolitan Museum of Art, 57.88)

The bracelet is constructed basically of gold sheet, which has an average thickness of 0.2 millimeters (0.008 inch). The hollow tubular shank of the bracelet measures 12 millimeters (0.47 inch) in diameter. A seam runs along the inner side of the tube, and from X-radiographs it is apparent that the edges of the sheet used to form the tube overlap by 2 to 3 millimeters (0.08 to 0.12 inch). Twisted wire has been wrapped around the tube and set in grooves, which spiral from one end of the tubular section of the bracelet to the other. The grooves keep the twisted wire in place so that only a minimum of solder is necessary to secure the length of wire.

The granulation varies in size from the smallest, which are about 0.3 millimeters (0.012 inch) in diameter, to the largest grains, which circle the bases of the domes and measure approximately 0.9 millimeters (0.035 inch) in diameter. The overall execution of the granulation is accomplished.

When purchased by the Freer, only two turquoise stones were in place; the other two settings were empty. Matching turquoise stones were set at this time in order to complete the arrangement.

The condition of the bracelet is very good. Some dents and deformation have occurred to the tubular section and to one of the domes. Earthy accretions are also present in some of the recessed areas of the design.

Surface analyses of the shank by energy-dispersive X-ray fluorescence is complicated by the presence of the twisted wire and the solder used to secure it. The largest areas

Technical Notes

free of additions are the disks bearing the coin impressions. Analyses of three of the disks give the following average composition:

Gold	Silver	Copper
92.2% ($\pm$0.7)	6.1% ($\pm$1.0)	1.9% ($\pm$0.2)

As would be expected, areas where soldered decoration are present show higher percentages of copper and silver.

Provenance: Purchased from Safani Galleries, New York, 1958.
Published: Untracht 1968, p. 203.
Atıl 1971, no. 53.
Keene and Jenkins 1981, fig. 5a.

Notes:
1. Mitchiner 1977, pp. 148–49; Keene and Jenkins 1981, p. 253; and Jenkins and Keene 1983, p. 40.
2. It is interesting to speculate whose name the reverse of the coins would have contained. Sultan Mahmud is the most likely candidate, but in 1005 Nishapur was occupied by the Qarakhanids of Transoxiana and eastern Turkestan.
3. Keene and Jenkins 1981, fig. 5b; and Jenkins and Keene 1983, no. 16.
4. Other known matching pairs of gold bracelets from Iran are published in Paris 1977, nos. 361–62; and Jenkins and Keene 1983, no. 22. See also no. 8 in this catalogue.
5. See, for instance, Segall 1938, no. 225; and Jenkins and Keene 1983, nos. 17–18.

6. Belt Ornament

Gold: repoussé and chased
Iran, 11th–12th centuries
Height: 2.1 cm. (1³⁄₁₆ in.);
  length: 5.2 cm. (2¹⁄₁₆ in.);
  width: 3.8 cm. (1¹⁄₁₆ in.);
  weight: 32.7 gm. (1.2 oz.)
82.12

This hollow rectangular piece with an arch-shaped tip was meant to be used as a decorative sheath affixed to a leather belt. It was constructed in two pieces: the top half with a lion in high relief was formed by repoussé, its details chased and punched; the flat back was worked separately and soldered to the overhanging sides of the top with the short edge left open. The hollow inside has been filled with a bituminous material, which not only supported the high relief but also served as an adhesive to the leather strap inserted into the ornament. Two pins at the open edge held the strap in place.

The long sides and the arched tip are decorated with projecting trefoils; a pair of split-leaves or palmettes appear over the open edge. The lion, represented in a walking position with its head lifted high and its tail curved over the rump, is finely detailed: a series of curls decorate the long tail and the mane, which extends to the middle of the back; short strokes designate the fur on the body, and circular punches appear on the muzzle. The background is covered with overall ring matting.

Although gold belt fittings are rare, a number of bronze and silver examples have been published. Among the earliest is a group of tenth-century cast bronze pieces found in Nishapur.[1] Some of these have basically the same shape as the Freer piece, that is, a rectangle with an arch-shaped tip; several are gilded and decorated with palmettes or

27. Silver belt, gilt and nielloed
Iran, 11th–12th centuries
(London, The British Museum, OA 1939
3.13 20–38)

28. Gold pommel
Iran, 11th century
(Tehran, Archaeological Museum, 11625)

kufic inscriptions. A complete belt (fig. 27) composed of thirteen square and arch-shaped gilt and nielloed silver plaques was found at Nihavand in western Iran together with other silver and gold pieces.[2] This belt, dated to the eleventh to twelfth centuries, has two hanging or pendant straps, their tips encased in hollow arch-shaped sheaths supplied with a pair of studs for securing to the leather; each sheath has a ring, which was used to attach a sword or quiver.

An illustration from the *Materia Medica* dated 1224 shows a figure whose sword is attached with rings to a pair of pendant straps, suggesting that this was a common practice during the twelfth and thirteenth centuries.[3] Belts with double pendant straps bearing swords and quivers also are found in fourteenth- and fifteenth-century paintings.[4] Some fourteenth-century illustrations represent a different type of belt, which does not seem to buckle but wraps around the waist with its loose end adorned with a metal sheath.[5] This type appears on courtly figures, whereas the former with a pair of pendant straps was used by warriors and hunters. The Freer ornament most likely belongs to the second, or secular, type and must have been employed as the decorative sheath on the loose end of a belt that wrapped around the waist.

There also exist a number of detached metal ornaments that may be parts from similar belts. A group of arch-shaped silver pieces discovered in Central Asia are thought to date from the tenth or eleventh centuries.[6] Many are decorated with inscriptions, floral scrolls, and human or animal figures. One pair depicts a walking lion surrounded by foliage.[7] The animals are in low relief and shown in profile but are executed in a style that is far removed from the figure on the Freer ornament.

Rectangular belt plaques made of gilt bronze or silver also were produced in Turkey, Syria, and Iran during the twelfth and thirteenth centuries.[8] Dating from the same period and attributed to Turkey or Iran is a pair of gold palmette-shaped belt hooks or buckles decorated with hares and griffins.[9]

Lions, symbolizing imperial power and carrying astrological implications, were among the most popular themes in Iranian art, dating as far back as the first millenium B.C., as indicated by a gold cup with animal heads in relief.[10] In the Islamic period, particularly between the eleventh and thirteenth centuries, lions were fashioned into jewelry (see no. 7) and used as ornaments on architectural elements, furnishings, and standards, as well as on household pieces, such as incense burners and candlesticks (see no. 13). One of the rare examples is a gold sword pommel (fig. 28) found in Gilan, on the southeastern shore of the Caspian Sea.[11] Three winged lions with heads in high relief adorn this piece, which is attributed to the eleventh century. The lions—repoussé with chased details and set against a ring-punched ground—are depicted in the same posture as the one on the Freer ornament. This pommel appears to be the only known piece closely related in style and date.

The theme of a lion walking to the left with its tail curved over the body survived well into the fourteenth century and was used as a blazon during the Mamluk period.[12]

The two pieces making up the ornament measure 0.2 millimeters (0.008 inch) in thickness at the open edge. In contrast to the simple construction of the ornament is the execution of the decoration. A ring punch was used to give texture to the background surface, and many variously shaped punches and tracers were used to indicate the hair and facial features of the lion. The two pins driven through the ornament near the opening at one end distort the chased design in those areas.

Though the ornament bears some scratches and dents, it is in generally good condition. Some silver chloride and green copper corrosion is present on the surface, particularly along the edge where the two plates meet. The presence of the corrosion along this seam is probably caused by a corrosive attack upon the base metals of the solder used to join the front and back plates.

An average of the analyses of two areas, one on the front and one on the back, is as follows:

Gold	Silver	Copper
91.7% (±0.9)	5.8% (±0.9)	2.5% (±0.9)

Provenance: A gift of the Estate of Joseph M. Upton, Vermont, 1982; purchased in Tehran in 1944–45.

Unpublished

Notes:
1. Allan 1982b, pp. 28–30 and nos. 6–38; and Jenkins and Keene 1983, no. 14.
2. Gray 1938; and Tait 1976, no. 274.
3. Atıl 1975, no. 24.
4. See, for example, Atıl 1971, nos. 12–13 and 23–24; and Grabar and Blair 1980, nos. 49, 51, and 53.
5. These appear in the Demotte *Shahnama* illustrations. Grabar and Blair 1980, nos. 79, 81, 85, and 91.
6. Darkevich 1976, pls. 39 and 40.
7. Ibid., pls. 41/11–12.
8. One example in the British Museum is published in Erginsoy 1978, figs. 163a–c; Keene and Jenkins 1981, fig. 12; and İstanbul 1983, D127. For another type with circular and diamond-shaped plaques, attributed to Syria in the thirteenth century, see Keene and Jenkins 1981, fig. 23.
9. Harari 1964–65, p. 2499 and figs. 824a–b; and Berlin 1971, no. 373. For fifteenth- or sixteenth-century examples, see Sarre 1906, nos. 48–50.
10. Ettinghausen 1964, no. 21.
11. Ibid., no. 616.
12. It was the blazon of Sultans Baybars I (1260–77) and Baraka Khan (1277–79); see Atıl 1981, nos. 46 and 108.

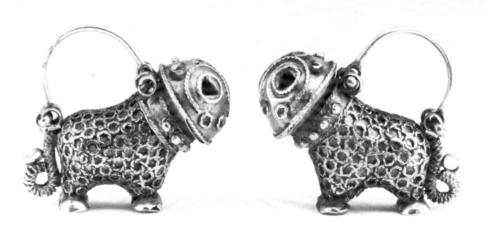

7. Pair of Earrings

Gold: hammered and chased; decorated with twisted wire.

Iran, 12th century

Height: 1.8 cm. (¾ in.); length: 2.0 cm. (¹³/₁₆ in.);
 width: 0.9 cm. (⅜ in.); weight 2.5 gm. (0.2 oz.)

80.200a–b

Each of the lion-shaped earrings is identical in size, weight, shape, and method of manufacture. The bodies, heads, ears, collars, feet, and tails were produced separately and joined together. Twisted wire fashioned into closely packed rings decorates the bodies; it also was used on the collars and tails, and to designate the facial features. Triangular and circular punches were employed for the eyes and mouth.

Objects and ornaments shaped as lions and other felines (see nos. 6 and 13) were popular in Iran during the Seljuk period. The lion was frequently fashioned into gold earrings, of which there exist a number of examples (such as figs. 29 and 30). The earrings share a similar size, fabrication, and configuration. The surface decorations, however, are slightly varied: some are adorned with open circles made of twisted wire, as in the case of the Freer pair; others are pierced or encrusted with gems.[1] With the exception of matching pairs in the Freer and in Berlin, and three pairs in the Birch Collection, all the other published examples are single earrings. Those in Berlin and in the Birch Collection are almost identical to the Freer set; these five pairs were most likely made in the same workshops.

Since none of the published examples comes from known excavations, the provenance of these pieces cannot be determined.[2] They appear to have been mass-produced once the goldsmith mastered the technique of working the parts from flat sheets, bending them to shape, adding the decorative twisted wires, and soldering them together.

The lion, an ancient symbol of imperial and divine power, seems to have revived during the Seljuk period. Providing a parallel between the king of the beasts and ruler of men, the lion represents majesty, strength, courage, and fortitude. It also personifies Leo, the fifth sign of the zodiac. It should be mentioned that the word for lion in Turkish, *aslan* or *arslan,* was used as a name by several eleventh-to-twelfth century Seljuk and Atabek rulers, including the renowned Alp Arslan (1063–72), in Iran, Iraq, Syria, and Turkey.

29. Gold earring
Iran, 12th century
(New York, The Metropolitan Museum of Art, 51.125.9)

30. Pair of gold earrings
Iran, 12th century
(Saint Thomas [U.S. Virgin Islands], Mr. and Mrs. Everett Birch Collection)

The bodies of the lions were formed in two symmetrical halves that were then joined. Seams run down the centers of the backs and the underside surfaces. The heads are hemispheres set on slightly concave circular pieces of sheet, which attach to the necks. The feet are small hemispheres set in pairs upon flat, oval-shaped pieces of sheet. All of the hemispherical parts, as well as the halves of the body, are regular in shape, with little or no variation between the parts of one lion and the parts of the other. This consistency in size and shape suggests that dapping punches and a dapping block were used to form the domed pieces. After forming, the various pieces were soldered together

Technical Notes

and the decoration was added. The major decorative element is twisted wire applied as small circles. Many of the details on the faces were executed in twisted wire as well. The eyes were formed by piercing the hemispheres with triangular-ended punches; the ears are small triangular pieces of sheet soldered to the tops of the heads. Collars composed of twisted wire and single rows of tiny beads circle the necks.

The earrings show some wear and abrasion but are generally in excellent condition. Only slight corrosion and accretions are apparent.

Because the earrings have a small size, the surface analyses give a combined reading for the body metal, the twisted wire, and the solder. The analyses for the two earrings are in close agreement. An average of six analyses, with three areas analyzed on each earring, is given below:

Gold	Silver	Copper	Cadmium
73.3% ($\pm$1.0)	20.3% ($\pm$0.7)	6.4% ($\pm$0.4)	trace

Provenance: Purchased from Axia, London, 1980.
Unpublished

Notes:

1. The Metropolitan Museum of Art (two single earrings or pendants, one published in Dimand 1944, fig. 77); Museum of Fine Arts, Boston (one single); Royal Ontario Museum, Toronto (one single); Museum für Islamische Kunst, Berlin (Berlin 1971, no. 389, one single and one pair); L. A. Mayer Memorial Institute of Islamic Art, Jerusalem (Harari 1964–65, pl. 1344A); Birch Collection, Saint Thomas, U.S. Virgin Islands, three pairs (Birch 1974, no. 125); and private collection, Japan (Egami 1961, p. 64, no. 4).

2. The piece in Japan was "found in Gurgan" according to the catalogue (Egami 1961, p. 64, no. 4), but this may be the dealer's attribution. Even if the earring was found in Gurgan, it was not necessarily produced there.

8. Bracelet with Eight Links

Gold: hammered and chased; decorated with niello
  and granulation

Iran, 12th century

Height: 1.0 cm. (6⅜ in.); length: 19.7 cm. (7¾ in.);
  width: 3.0 cm. (1³⁄₁₆ in.); weight: 33.4 gm. (1.2 oz.)

50.21

Inscriptions (Arabic)

1. Front (naskhi):

. . . glory and prosperity . . . power and happiness *. . . justice . . .* [repeated].	... العز و الاقبال ... الدولة و السعادة ... العدالة

2. Back (kufic):

. . . good fortune . . . [repeated].	... اليمن ...

front   *back*

Each of the eight links joined together to form this bracelet is made up of sheet gold decorated with chased designs set against a niello ground. The domical, or pyramidical, upper sides, which have settings for gems now missing, were produced separately and soldered to the flat backs. The links fall into three distinct types: three small and one large rectangle, two curving narrow strips, and two double circles. The upper sides of the rectangular pieces are shaped as a truncated pyramid with heavy claws to hold a gem. The claws of the larger piece have been broken off. Naskhi inscriptions on a niello ground are placed on the four slopes of each pyramid, with a row of granulation forming the border. The flat undersides of the small rectangles represent a winged and haloed sphinx and a winged griffin, both walking to the left; and a pair of birds, their heads turned back, flanking a stylized tree. Behind the animals and birds are floral scrolls. The large rectangle has a floral scroll evolving from a quatrefoil. Niello is applied to the sunken ground of all four pieces and a zigzag border encircles the outer edges.

The upper sides of the two curving narrow strips have a central square that repeats the truncated pyramidical form; here, however, the setting for the gem is a plain ring, and floral cartouches decorate the two outer edges. On either side of the square is a long, thin, and curved pyramidical band with naskhi inscriptions on a niello ground. Fine granulations frame the bands and the central unit. The underside of the square has a circle divided into four sections, each of which bears a heart-shaped leaf; flanking the circle are two kufic inscriptions.

77

Both the naskhi and kufic inscriptions are difficult to decipher and have been read only partially. The words, broken to accommodate the shape of the links, contain a number of extra letters, particularly *alifs*.

The remaining two links show a different program of decoration. The settings for stones on the domical upper sides have a collar framed by granulations; the flat backs show irregularly worked roundels with a scroll encircling a plain disc. These pieces also have loops on the outer edges and between the two domes, which suggest that they served another function. They are also the only links in the bracelet devoid of inscriptions. Their loops are formed by several wires, whereas those on the rectangular links are granulated and the ones on the curving strips are plain bands.

It appears that the Freer bracelet is composed of at least two separate groups of links. The first group, consisting of four rectangular and two curving narrow pieces, must have been produced in the same workshop and designed to be linked together, as indicated by the position of the loops. One of the smaller rectangles (its back showing a pair of birds) has a draw pin that slides through the entire piece, indicating that it served as some sort of a clasp. These six pieces, when reassembled, create a strip composed of a central unit made up of the large rectangle flanked by a pair of smaller rectangles; the two curving pieces fit the sides and the remaining small rectangle with the draw pin functions as the clasp at the back. Thus the bracelet becomes 17.0 centimeters (6¹¹⁄₁₆ inches) long with a diameter of 5.4 centimeters (2¼ inches), barely wide enough to fit a very slender wrist. It is possible that there were originally one large and one small rectangle at the back, next to the clasp.[1] The pair of double dome links do not fit into this scheme and must have belonged to another type of ornament.

An identical bracelet, embellished with recently applied turquoise, was formerly in the Museum of Fine Arts in Boston.[2] One of its rectangular units, also with a pair of

details of front and back of a link

birds on the back, has a similar draw pin at the side. There is no doubt that the Freer and Boston links were made at the same time in the same workshop and as a matching pair. The Boston bracelet was assembled in the same fashion as the reconstruction of the Freer piece, except that the pair of links with the double domes were used on either side of the large rectangle.

Elements shaped as truncated pyramids and heavy claws holding gems are found on several contemporary Iranian bracelets[3] and rings (see no. 9). The tradition of decorating the surface as well as the underside of an ornament or vessel is not uncommon in classical Islamic art. Inside the foot-ring of a number of ceramic and metal containers are intricate designs that can be seen only when the object is tilted in use (see no. 10). Jeweled pendants, earrings, and belt fittings also were designed with similar "surprises" known only to the wearer.

The ancient technique of applying niello to silver and gold vessels and ornaments appears to have continued well into the Islamic period. The technique produced a pleasant contrast between the dark and matte sunken ground and the bright and shiny raised surfaces.

The birds and fantastic creatures chosen to decorate the links are commonly found on other arts of the period, such as textiles, ceramics, metalwork, architectural decoration, and manuscript illumination. Confronting birds with the tree of life in the middle as well as walking sphinxes and griffins symbolized good wishes, well-being, and earthly and heavenly pleasures. They were among the ancient symbols of Iran that were used popularly during the eleventh and twelfth centuries.[4] Their theme is echoed in the inscriptions, which are now too faint and abraded in most areas to be read properly. Verbal messages reinforced by visual images frequently appear in Islamic art.

The eight adjoining links making up the bracelet are constructed of thin sheet; measurements of the thickness of the sheet along the edge average about 0.1 millimeter (0.004 inch). The rectangular links of the bracelet are essentially built up of two pieces of sheet, a truncated pyramidical piece attached to a flat rectilinear piece. Four additional pieces used at the corners form the claws that once secured the stones. The long, curving, narrow links entail four pieces of sheet for the basic shape and a fifth piece to circle and form the opening of the setting. The more elaborately shaped double-circle links were made up of a number of pieces. Various folds and seams in the metal suggest that the metalsmith had some difficulty achieving this form.

Each of the links is filled with what appears to be a bituminous substance. X-radiographs reveal the structure of the link that acts as a clasp; a split pin extends the length of the link, passing through a loop on the end of a post attached to the adjoining link.

Rows of granulation were used along the seams of all the links to serve as decoration and hide the joins. The grains on the rectangular and curving narrow links are regular in size, measuring about 0.5 millimeters (0.02 inch) in diameter. The grains on the

Technical Notes

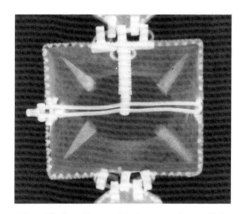

Magnified radiographic image of one link showing the hidden clasp. Actual size of the area illustrated: 30 x 30 mm. (1⅛ x 1⅛ in.)

double-circle links have greater variation in size, ranging from 0.4 to 0.7 millimeters (0.016 to 0.028 inch) in diameter.

The niello, applied in chased recesses, is the same material on all of the links. It is a complex mixture of sulfides of gold, silver, lead, and copper. The use of niello was determined by X-ray diffraction and X-ray fluorescence analyses.

Besides the missing stones and broken claws, there are other noticeable defects. Joining the links to one another are rings that appear to be modern repairs. Small losses and breaks also appear on a number of the links. Though somewhat abraded and worn, the links are relatively undistorted in shape.

The color of the metal of the various links differs. The gold of the double-circle links has a greenish tint whereas that of the rectangular and curving narrow links is reddish. Because of the difficulty in finding areas free of solder or niello, only a single analysis for each type of link is presented. Although different in color, the two links show similar analyses.

	Gold	Silver	Copper
Narrow link	84.9%	8.4%	6.8%
Double-circle link	86.3%	7.7%	6.0%

Provenance: Purchased from Heeramaneck Galleries, New York, 1950.
Published: Atıl 1971, no. 54.
Keene and Jenkins 1981, figs. 7a–b.

Notes:
1. This would make the bracelet 21.8 centimeters (8⁹⁄₁₆ inches) long, or 6.9 centimeters (2¹¹⁄₁₆ inches) in diameter, which is closer in size to other known examples.
2. This piece, acc. no. 65.247, was not published.
3. Jenkins and Keene 1983, nos. 25 and 30.
4. See Baer 1965.

9. Ring

Gold: hammered and engraved; decorated with niello, and set with turquoise and pearls

Iran, 12th century

Height: 3.7 cm. (1⁷⁄₁₆ in.); diameter: 2.0 cm. (1³⁄₁₆ in.); weight 8.0 gm. (0.3 oz.)

57.3

front

back

Inscriptions (Arabic)

1. Sides of the bezel (kufic):

Good fortune and blessing and blessing and joy and sovereignty.	اليمن ٭ و البركة ٭ و البر[كة] ٭ و اسر[ور] ٭ والمل[ك]

2. Front (kufic):

Sovereignty.	الملك

side

side

3. Back (kufic):

Blessing and good fortune and.	[البر]كة و ٭ اليمن و

This ring, fashioned from gold sheet, is hollow. Its bezel, or the upper portion, is shaped as a truncated pyramid with six heavy claws that hold a large turquoise stone. Kufic inscriptions rendered in niello appear on the two side panels and in the center panels of the front and back; triangular units filled with floral scrolls and set against a niello ground are placed in the remaining panels.

The lower portion reveals different designs. A bold kufic inscription reserved against a floral scroll with a niello ground appears on the front; the back has a small turquoise gem in the center, nielloed inscriptions above and below, and leaf-shaped nielloed units at the four corners. The two sides are identical; each has a large floral unit reserved against the same nielloed ground as used on the front. The four hollowed out corners contain pearls, one of which is a later addition, held by wire posts.

The shape of the bezel and the technique of decoration resemble those seen on the links from a Freer bracelet (no. 8). Precious metals fashioned into jewelry and inlaid with niello characterize eleventh- and twelfth-century metalwork. Similar techniques were applied to silver vessels, which were further enhanced by gilding (see no. 10).

Hollow silver or gold rings, fabricated from sheet and embellished with stones, were produced in the Roman, Byzantine, and Sasanian periods and continued to be made in the Islamic age. Among the earliest Islamic examples are those excavated in Nishapur, datable to the tenth century.[1] Some of the later Islamic examples are decorated with granulation and filigree but are devoid of gems[2]; others have gems, some of which bear inscriptions, and were used as seals or for talismanic and magical purposes.[3]

Technical Notes

The ring was formed with many small pieces of gold sheet. Seams can be found along the inside of the ring, around the bottom of the bezel of the small stone, along the claws that secure the top stone, and at the edge of the hollows in which the pearls sit. The various parts of the ring first were formed separately, presumably by hammering, and then all the parts were joined together. Radiographs show that the ring is hollow. At a few points, an edge view of the sheet is possible. Measurements taken at these points give an average thickness for the sheet of 0.3 millimeters (0.012 inch).

Incising or engraving, filled with niello, was used to execute the inscriptions and the floral designs. X-ray diffraction analysis of the niello shows that it is gold silver sulfide.

With the exception of a small dent and a corresponding split in the sheet along the bottom edge of the band, and some damage to the claws that hold the top stone in place, the ring is in excellent condition. Minute amounts of silver chloride and green copper corrosion can be found on the surface, particularly in the area of the niello. Also, some corrosion along the seams is apparent.

The average of two analyses made at different areas on the ring gives the following composition:

Gold	Silver	Copper
80.3% ($\pm$0.9)	13.1% ($\pm$1.8)	6.6% ($\pm$2.7)

Provenance: Purchased from Mallon, New York, 1957.
Published: Keene and Jenkins 1981, fig. 6.

Notes:
1. Keene and Jenkins 1981, figs. 4a–b; and Jenkins and Keene 1983, nos. 1c–e.
2. Harari 1964–65, pls. 1344D–E; Keene and Jenkins 1981, figs. 11a–b; and Jenkins and Keene 1983, no. 31, which includes references to other related pieces.
3. Birch 1974, nos. 109–10, 123, and 127; and Jenkins and Keene 1983, nos. 2 and 33–34.

10. Bottle with Cap

Silver: repoussé and chased; decorated with niello and gilding

Iran, early 12th century

Height: 24.9 cm. (9¹³/₁₆); diameter of body: 12.0 cm. (4¾ in.);
  weight: 385.4 gm. (13.6 oz.)

50.5

Inscriptions (Arabic)

1.   On the neck (kufic):

And blessing and good fortune and faith.	و بركة و يمن و دين

2.   On the shoulder (kufic):

Blessing and good fortune and joy and happiness and safety and honor and perpetuity to its owner.	بركة و يمن و سرور و سعادة و سلامة و كرا[مة] و بقا[ء] لصاحبه

The slender neck and bulbous body were hammered from thin sheets of silver and joined together above the shoulder. The six projecting rings on the neck and the disc inside the foot-ring were produced separately and soldered to the piece. The neck has been broken and repaired several times. Since bottles such as this were used to sprinkle rosewater and were held by the neck, the excessive handling and sprinkling action created a tremendous stress; the necks frequently snapped off at the joint, a weak point. Similar breaks can be seen at the bases of the long handles used on heavy incense burners (see nos. 2 and 12).

The entire surface of the Freer bottle is decorated with either gilding or niello; the raised areas have a fine floral scroll placed against a niello ground, and the sunken areas are covered with ring matting made by small circular punches.

Covering the mouth is a cap shaped as a ribbed dome with a loop and ring at the pinnacle. The neck is divided into two horizontal parts by the projecting rings decorated with leaves. The panel between the single ring at the top and the double ring below has a kufic inscription. The wider second panel, terminating with a triple ring, is decorated with intersecting bands that form two vertical rows of three alternating medallions. Long-tailed birds facing left appear in the medallions on the top row; harpies facing right are placed in those below. A band of overlapping leaves joins the neck to the shoulder. Below the band is another kufic inscription, framed on both sides by thin braided strips.

inscription on shoulder   *medallion in foot-ring*   *medallion with lion*

The widening portion of the body is divided into six medallions by intersecting bands that form tripartite loops at the interstices. The medallions represent single or double animals oriented toward the left. They depict a lion whose tail ends in a dragon's head; an eagle attacking a deer with long antlers that curve at the tips; a four-legged animal, possibly an ibex, with short, curved horns and a tail terminating in a dragon's head; a lion and a feline in combat; another ibex(?) with a bird perched on its rump; and a deer with fantastic antlers. All the creatures, excluding the last one, turn back their heads; with the exception of the lions, their faces are shown in profile. Beaded bands encircle their necks and shoulders, or the joint between the upper foreleg and body.

Just above the plain, splayed foot is another braided band, identical to the pair flanking the inscription on the shoulder. Under the foot, recessed into the foot-ring and repeating one of the compositions on the body, is a medallion representing an eagle attacking a deer or ibex with short, curved horns.

The images seem to have been chosen at random without a predetermined iconographic program. They represent the ancient symbols of royalty, victory, strength, and good wishes. The birds and harpies on the neck imply well-being, freedom of the soul, and happiness.[1] The message of the lion, the ubiquitous symbol of majesty, power, and royalty, is even more stressed when the animal is shown in combat; the eagle, another symbol of strength with divine implications (see no. 1), is shown overpowering a weaker, horned animal; the ibex and deer also reflect similar themes associated with royalty.

Mixed with the imperial themes are astrological symbols, such as the dragon-headed tail used on the lion and ibex. This motif appears frequently on the personifications of

medallion with stag

medallion with two lions

31. Silver bottle, partially gilt and nielloed
Iran, early 12th century
(Jerusalem, L. A. Mayer Memorial
Institute of Islamic Art, M 30–68)

32. Silver jug, partially gilt and nielloed
Iran, 12th century
(Berlin, Museum für Islamische Kunst,
I.2210)

the constellations and planets to symbolize the interaction of heavenly bodies with the moon's orbit and the solar and lunar eclipses.[2] If an attempt is made to identify the animals according to astrological symbols, the lion could represent Leo and the ibex could well be Capricorn.

The eclectic themes suggest that the artist relied upon different pictorial cycles and selected the images at random. These themes are based on pre-Islamic traditions and continued to be employed throughout the Islamic period.

A number of silver bottles, ewers, jugs, vases, bowls, and incense burners decorated with niello, and often gilding, are thought to have been made between the tenth and thirteenth centuries. Since none of these pieces is dated, a chronological development cannot be determined. The earlier examples reveal sparse decorations with bands of kufic inscriptions, several of which bear the name of Amir Abu'l-Abbas Valkin ibn Harun, thought to be a Daylamite prince of the tenth century.[3] This date is supported by both the style of writing and the decoration, which have parallels in contemporary epigraphic pottery. Later examples (see figs. 31 and 32) show gilding in addition to niello, and include floral motifs as well as animal figures.[4] Some render the motifs in relief, produced either by repoussé or by chasing and engraving.[5]

The Freer bottle must be among the last examples made in silver, which became a rare commodity after the turn of the twelfth century and was used mainly for inlays.[6] This object links the silver-vessel tradition with the new brass production, the first examples of which also relied on relief decoration but employed different techniques to create varied coloristic effects (see no. 13). The niello was replaced by bitumen or other black organic materials, and the gilded silver gave way to polished brass; the surface

85

became more colorful with the addition of silver, copper, and gold inlays.

The shape of the bottle has parallels in contemporary glass pieces, some of which are assigned to Gurgan, where this example was said to originate. The same shape appears in ceramic examples and continued well into the eighteenth century.

Technical Notes   Two main parts, the neck and the body, make up the essential form of the bottle; many additional pieces complete its structure. Both the neck and the body are extremely thin (0.2–0.3 millimeters or 0.008–0.012 inch). The neck can be seen on X-radiographs of the object to be slightly thinner than the body.

The body was raised from one piece of silver to form a spherical shape with a large opening inside the foot and a smaller one at the top. The neck was made from a thin sheet of silver, rolled into a cylinder and scarf-jointed with a wide joint along one side. The relief decoration was applied to both pieces before assembly.

Additional rings were probably cut from sheet, chased and finished, and soldered to the neck. A cylindrical collar of gilded silver was then applied below the lowest ring, and the undecorated metal of the neck that showed below the collar was cut into a series of tabs. The neck was then inserted into the body. The collar rested upon the lip of the upper hole, and the tabs protruded inside. The tabs were bent over and the whole assembly was soldered in place. The joint is barely visible from the outside. After the neck was fastened securely to the body, the craftsman soldered the bottom medallion into the foot to complete the bottle.

Securely fixed to the top of the neck by accretions is part of a cap for the bottle. The cap is a shallow dome decorated with chased details; a ring has been soldered to the top of the cap, and a loose ring passes through it for attachment of a safety cord to prevent loss of the cap.

The decoration on the bottle consists of raised inscriptions with animal forms and surrounding bands that stand above a ring-matted ground. On the neck, the decorative details were formed by chasing. For the body, the design seems to have been executed using repoussé as well, although chasing was used primarily. Except for the cap and those areas where wear or damage reveal the silver, gilding and niello entirely cover the surface.

A technical description of this bottle is made difficult because of the serious damage it has suffered and the numerous subsequent repairs it has undergone. The silver is extremely thin and brittle. In a metallographic section taken from one of the broken fragments, heavy corrosion and doubling of grain boundaries from the precipitation of copper can be seen; both contribute to the silver's extreme brittleness. Many breaks have occurred, but relatively few major losses appear, with the exception of the lower part of the neck and a portion of the bottom medallion.

X-ray fluorescence analysis strongly indicates the presence of mercury on the gilded surface; thus fire gilding most likely was used. The niello is the copper silver sulfide compound known as stromeyerite. Within the niello, thin scroll-shaped lines are present. Although now silver in appearance, these lines probably were once gilded.

Spectrographic analysis of a sample from the bottle carried out in 1956[7] gave the following results:

>10%	1–5%	0.1–1.0%	0.01–0.1%	0.001–0.01%
Silver	Copper	Gold	Iron	Zinc
	Lead	Bismuth	Silicon	Barium
		Tin	Magnesium	Nickel
			Aluminum	Vanadium
			Calcium	

Because decorative materials have been added to the outer surface and the solder from repairs covers much of the inner surface, it is difficult to obtain an accurate surface analysis of the alloy. A combination of the results from the spectrographic analysis and X-ray fluorescence analysis of one spot on the inner wall of the neck suggests a silver content of approximately 95%.

Provenance: Purchased from Kevorkian Foundation, New York, 1950.

Published: Gettens and Waring 1957, p. 88, no. 15.
Stewart 1967, p. 112.
Untracht 1968, p. 480.
Atıl 1971, no. 57.
Allan 1977b. p. 13.
Baer 1983, fig. 230.

Notes:
1. For the meanings associated with the harpy, see Baer 1965.
2. For a detailed study of the dragon, see Hartner 1938.
3. Harari 1964–65, p. 2500 and pls. 1345–46. Seven of the silver vessels in the Museum of the Gulistan Palace in Tehran bear this name. These objects have not been studied properly.
4. Ibid., pls. 1349–52.
5. Ibid., pl. 1353A; Berlin 1971, no. 367; and Baer 1983, fig. 105.
6. For a study of this problem see Allan 1977b.
7. Gettens and Waring 1957, p. 88

11. Bird-Shaped Vessel

Brass: cast; chased, engraved, inlaid with copper,
and set with blue-green glass

Iran, 12th century

Height: 16.0 cm. (6¼ in.); length: 14.0 cm. (5½ in.);
width: 7.0 cm. (2¾ in.); weight: 598.3 gm. (21.1 oz.)

73.4

The bird, resembling a plump partridge, stands upright on two feet. The hollow body and flat beak were cast separately; the latter, movable and attached with a pin, may be a modern replacement. The feet have three claws in the front; one claw on the left foot and the supporting single claw at the back of both feet have been broken off. There is a large opening in front on the lower chest; two other small holes under the tail and body appear to be casting flaws.

The body of the bird is decorated with linear designs. The wings are outlined and partitioned by vertical and horizontal broad bands inlaid with copper. Since chisel marks appear in some areas over the copper strips, the inlay must have been applied before the piece was engraved or chased. The round sockets of the eyes were originally set with glass beads; now only the right eye retains its dark blue-green glass bead.

Three medallions on the top of the head, upper back, and above the tail contain knotted motifs. A braided necklace, ending with a pendant below the neck, frames the head. The chest, divided into three horizontal bands, is decorated with overlapping feathers, simulated kufic letters, and floral scrolls. The wings, which cross at the back, are divided into three unequal parts: the semicircular shoulder has a series of double, overlapping feathers, followed by a band of scales; the wider back section is broken into five horizontal sections, alternately filled with feather and scale motifs.

This piece may have been designed as a drinking vessel, or aquamanile. Liquid would have been poured into the bird through the opening on the chest and released from the beak, held up like a rhyton. The opening must have had some sort of stopper or plug. It has also been suggested that such bird-shaped vessels held powdered incense.[1]

Animal-shaped vessels are not uncommon in the Seljuk period, and a number of partridgelike birds were used as either containers or incense burners.[2] Almost identical to the Freer piece is a bird (fig. 33) in the Cleveland Museum of Art that has the same round opening in the chest and movable beak.[3] Other similar objects, in the Keir Collection in Ham, Richmond, and in the David Collection in Copenhagen,[4] must have served the same purpose as the Cleveland and Freer examples. A bird standing upright on two feet was also used as an incense burner. These pieces, however, have a large doorlike opening in the chests, and the upper bodies are pierced.[5] A more functional incense burner in the shape of a bird is in two sections with a removable upper portion.[6] There also exist feline-shaped incense burners and more complex pieces composed of lions, birds, and other creatures.

The bird played a significant role in Islamic decorative vocabulary and was depicted frequently either alone or in groups on pottery and metalwork. Symbolizing the freedom of the spirit and soaring of the soul, it was always associated with heavenly delights and good fortune. The blue-green beads in the eyes could be interpreted as good luck charms to protect the owner from the evil eye and to ward off any misfortune.[7] This ancient talisman still is in use in the Islamic world.

This group of bird-shaped containers and incense burners is attributed to Iran and dated between the eleventh and thirteenth centuries. The inscriptions, when present, are generally a series of formulaic good wishes and do not contain names of owners and artists or dates. Their simple decorations and lack of silver and gold inlays suggest that they were produced for a domestic market and used as attractive household wares.

33. Bronze(?) bird-shaped vessel
Iran, 12th century
(Cleveland, The Cleveland Museum of Art, 48.458)

Technical Notes

The general shape and surface appearance of the bird suggest that it was cast, and this method of construction is confirmed by X-radiography. The radiographs clearly show the heterogeneous structure that results from casting, and the flow and distribution of lead globules. With the exception of the beak, the bird appears to have been cast in one piece. Although the junction between the legs and the body display some finishing marks, the legs show no sign of having been added to the body. Small rectangular holes, possibly remnants of chaplets, show in a number of seemingly random spots on the body. The shape and size of the holes are similar to those of the chaplets or chills on the pen box (no. 14). Another hole, caused by a shrinkage cavity formed because the metalsmith attempted to cast too thick a section, appears on the upper surface of the tail.

The top of the beak is an independent piece attached by a curved pin that acts as a hinge. The presence of paint on the ends of the pin and the different contours of the top of the beak and the head suggest that this movable part is a later replacement. A close examination reveals differences in the corrosion of the two parts. In the X-radiographs the beak is shown to be more dense and homogeneous than the body metal, which confirms that the beak is probably a replacement.

Chased and engraved lines were used to add detail to the body. The recessed lines appear white because of the presence of soil and wax. The straight, narrow lines of copper inlay are set into the wings and chest of the bird.

With the exception of the losses and a repair, the bird is in very good condition. A thick, even, green patina covers the surface.

One large repair can be seen as a white, radiopaque area on the X-radiographs at the upper front of the proper right wing. The repair appears to have been cast in at the time of manufacture, as the chased lines of the decoration run over it, and its patina is continuous and undisturbed. The deformation of the central hole in the chest and the area between it and the right wing are also covered with the same, continuous patina. An accident may have happened to this object during manufacture.

Because the condition of the surface is poor and there is a high percentage of lead in the alloy, the results of the analyses give only a rough approximation of the composition of the metal. A single measurement taken at the most corrosion-free area, and that which is considered most reliable, is given below.

Copper	Zinc	Lead	Tin
64%	13%	19%	4%

Provenance: Purchased from Safani Galleries, New York, 1973.

Published: Murray 1979, no. 89.

Notes:

1. Allan 1976, p. 299; see also Allan 1977b, no. 14 and p. 9, in which a similar piece is identified as an "incense-holder."
2. For a study of this group, see Baer 1983, pp. 57–60.
3. O. Grabar 1959, no. 57; and Melikian-Chirvani 1968c, fig. 3.
4. Fehérvári 1976b, no. 110; and Leth 1975, p. 65
5. See, for instance, Fehérvári 1976b, no. 109; Harari 1964–65, pl. 1298B; and O. Grabar 1959, no. 47.
6. Ettinghausen 1964, no. 621.
7. Turquoise appears in the eyes of a lion-shaped incense burner (Harari 1964–65, pl. 1297); all the bird-shaped drinking vessels and incense burners have settings for similar gems or glass beads, some of which are still intact.

12. Incense Burner

Brass: cast; pierced, chased, and inlaid with copper
  and black organic material

Iran(?), 12th century

Height: 22.8 cm. (9 in.); diameter: 9.8 cm. (3⅞ in.);
  weight: 745.6 gm. (26.3 oz.)

77.5

Inscriptions (Arabic)

Around the opening of the hood (kufic):

Good fortune and blessing and joy and happiness and safety.	اليمن و البركة و السرور و السعادة و السلامة

The incense burner with a cylindrical body resting on four feet, and partially covered by a semicircular hood, was cast in one piece. The rooster finial resting on the upper dome at the pinnacle was cast separately and soldered to the top; two loops on its crest and throat indicate that it served a different function on another piece. It was used most likely as a replacement when the original finial was lost, and may have been taken from a slightly earlier and possibly damaged piece. The long handle attached to the front of the body has been broken off and the opening has been filled in. Inside the body are three small metal pins set halfway down on the walls, and a fourth one is attached to the center of the base. These must have been used to support a grill, which held the incense above the fire.

The cylindrical body is divided into four panels by a pair of vertical, beveled grooves; the raised strips in between are decorated with strapwork or floral scrolls. In the center of each panel is a medallion framed by double lines; the medallions in the two front panels are filled with floral scrolls, but the pair in the back have geometric designs. A large medallion with geometric strapwork evolving from a six-pointed star appears under the base.

The hood, or half dome, covering one half of the body is divided into two by the same scheme as the panels on the body. Each quarter has a pierced, floral design; the central strip, decorated with a scroll, and the band of kufic inscriptions around the edge are not pierced. A series of open circles frames the arched opening. Copper inlays were used in the inner bands encircling the four medallions on the body, around the base of the finial, and around the two pierced triangular sections of the dome.

There are several other extant incense burners (see figs. 34 and 35) that have the same size and shape as the Freer example. Almost all of these pieces also have lost their long handles, which were structurally weak and frequently snapped off when the heavy containers were lifted. They are similarly decorated, with rooster or bird finials; some of the birds resemble peacocks with large tails, while others are more like ducks or partridges.[1] The majority of the published incense burners rest on three feet; the Freer incense burner is one of the few known examples to have four legs.[2] These legs with prominent paws or feet recall the more zoomorphic examples seen in earlier pieces (see no. 2) and point to the perseverance of this tradition.

The half dome on the cylindrical incense burners appears to have been replaced in the thirteenth century by a full dome.[3] The latter type, often lavishly inlaid with silver and gold, survived well into the fourteenth century and was produced in Syria and Egypt as well as in Iran.

The motifs and inscriptions of the Freer incense burner belong to a decorative vocabulary that was used commonly throughout the Islamic world during the twelfth and thirteenth centuries. Floral scrolls, geometric interlaces, and kufic inscriptions with traditional good wishes appear on all types of metalwork. Circular designs radiating from stars—symbolizing celestial light and fire—were employed on incense burners and candlesticks made in Iran, Syria, Iraq, Egypt, and Turkey. It is not possible, therefore, to assign the Freer incense burner to a particular region until further research has been conducted on these humble but nevertheless intriguing objects.

Since the later examples were generally hammered from sheet metal and inlaid with silver and even gold, a twelfth-century date is suggested for the Freer piece, which was cast and decorated only with copper.

34. Brass incense burner
Iran, 12th century
(Jerusalem, L. A. Mayer Memorial
Institute of Islamic Art, M 82–69)

35. Brass incense burner inlaid with
silver and gold
Made by Abu'l-Munif(?) b. Masud
Iran, 13th century
(Boston, Museum of Fine Arts, 46.1135)

Technical Notes

The incense burner is finely cast with even, thin walls. That the incense burner was cast in one piece, with the exception of the finial, is evident both visually and radiographically. X-radiographs show that there is no seam where the hood and legs meet the body. The integral casting of the legs is further demonstrated by the presence of mold flash running from the legs onto the bottom of the incense burner. X-radiographs also show the flow of small globules of lead throughout the piece.

The openwork on the back of the dome and the circular holes along the front skirt of the dome were not cast; rather, they were drilled and filed out as the artist worked from the outside to the inside surface. This is indicated by the sharp ridges, or burrs, which rim the inside edges of the openings.

The design areas contain recesses that often appear to have been cast, but tool marks indicating chasing are prevalent as well. A combined use of the two methods seems likely. Slight steps in the edge of the copper inlay also suggest the use of a punchwork groove for its application. The remains of a black organic material used as inlay can be seen in the recesses of the medallions.

The overall condition of the incense burner is good. The loss of the handle and finial have already been noted. The filled opening where the handle would have been attached is a roughly circular, jagged-edged hole measuring about 25 millimeters (1 inch) in diameter. No indication of how the handle was attached remains.

The incense burner has been cleaned and a bare metal surface can be seen in many areas. In contrast to these areas are the patches of green and red copper corrosion that can be found on the more protected areas of the surface.

In spite of what appeared to be a relatively clean surface, the results of X-ray fluorescence analysis of the surface were erratic. Thus, only a rough estimate of the composition of the metal can be given. The percentages given below are an average of three analyses made at different areas; the relatively large confidence-limit figures for the copper and lead should be noted. It would probably be safe to assume that more copper and less lead are present than the percentages indicate.

Copper	Zinc	Lead	Tin
56% ($\pm$32)	18% ($\pm$5)	22% ($\pm$27)	3.4% ($\pm$0.4)

Provenance: Purchased from Ahuan, London, 1977.
Published: Cranston 1977–78, fig. 41.
                   Murray 1979, no. 90.
Notes:
1. For a study of this type, see Baer 1983, pp. 50–54 and figs. 36–39, in which hooded incense burners are attributed to eastern Iran. For other related examples, see Harari 1964–65, pl. 1299; and Fehérvári 1976b, nos. 93–94.
2. Another rare four-legged piece, in the Victoria and Albert Museum, is published in Melikian-Chirvani 1982, no. 3, and attributed to Khorasan in the tenth century.
3. Aga-Oglu 1945.

13. Candlestick

Brass: hammered and chased; inlaid with copper, silver,
  and black organic material
Afghanistan, second half 12th century
Height: 40.3 cm. (15⅞ in); diameter: 47.7 cm. (18¾ in.);
  weight: 4,380.0 gm. (154.5 oz.)
51.17

Inscriptions (Arabic)

1. Band at the edge of the socket (foliated kufic):

With good fortune and blessing and power and safety and happiness and favor and health and mercy and comfort and beauty and increase and gratitude and thankfulness and [Prophet Muhammad's] intercession and perpetuity everlasting to its owner and to him.	باليمن و البركة و الدولة و السلامة و السعادة و النعمة و العافية و الرحمة و الراحة و الزينة و الزيادة و الشكرة و الشاكرة و الشفا[ع]ـة و البقا[ء] دائم لصاحبه و له

2. Thirty bosses on the base (naskhi):

Glory and prosperity and power and safety and happiness and abundance and favor and health and comfort and victoriousness and mercy and [Divine] support[?] and gratitude and religiosity[?] and comfort and sufficiency and honor and beauty[?] and [God's] care and mercy and comfort and thankfulness and ascending[?] and nobility and goodness and good omen and health[?] and beneficence and chasteness and honor and blessing and elevation and superiority and strength and potency, and perpetuity everlasting to its owner and [to him].	العز و الاقبا ٭ ل و الدولة ٭ و السلامة و ا ٭ لسعادة و التا ٭ مة و النعمة و ٭ [ا]لعافية و الـ ٭ [ر]احة و النا ٭ صرة و الرحمة ٭ و الـاباد و ا ٭ لشكر[ة] و الد ٭ ـاة و الرا ٭ حة و الكفاي[ـة] ٭ و الكرامة ٭ و الراعة و ٭ و العناية و ا ٭ لرحمة و الرا ٭ حة و الشا ٭ كرة و الصا[عد] ٭ و العلا[ء] ٭ ال ٭ لخيرة و الو ٭ ال و العا ٭ ف[ي]ـة و الانعام ٭ و الطاهرة و ا ٭ و ا الكرامة ا ٭ و البركة و ا ٭ و الرافعة ٭ و الرفعة و ا ٭ لقوة و القد ٭ رة و البقا دا ٭ ئم لصاحبه و ا

3. Band below the bosses on the base (kufic):

With good fortune and blessing and power and safety and happiness and favor and health and mercy and comfort and beauty and increase and religiosity and gratitude and thankfulness and abundance and strength and strength and power and superiority and elevation and sufficiency and honor and abundance and aid and victoriousness and unblemishedness and ascendancy and exaltedness and goodness and good omen and [God's] care and sufficiency and honor and first fruits and power and strength and generosity and victoriousness[?] and and [Divine] support and increase and sufficiency	باليمن و البركة و الدولة و السلامة و السعادة و النعمة و العافية و الرحمة و الراحة و الزينة و الزيادة و الديانة و الشكرة و الشاكرة و التامة و القوة و القادرة و الرفعة و الرافعة و الكفاية و الكرامة و التامة و النصرة و الناصرة و النزهان و الطالع و العالى و الخير و العال و العناية و الكفاية و الكرامة و البكر و السلطان و السدة و العطاية و الناجزة و التاييد و الزيادة و الكفاية و الكرامة و العلا و الثنا

and honor and nobility and commendation and charity and beneficence and perpetuity and victoriousness and aid and [God's] care and perpetuity everlasting to its owner and to him.

و الاحسان و الانعام و الدوامة و الناصر[ة] و النصر[ة] و العناية و البقا دائم لصاحبه و له

With the exception of a cylindrical piece set into the socket and neck, the overall shape of this extraordinary candlestick was constructed from a single sheet of brass that was hammered from the front and the back to create its shape. There are no seams in any of the parts, which attests to the remarkable technical ability of the metalsmith who was able to produce from a flat sheet the large, truncated, conical base, neck, and socket with elements in high relief.

detail of shoulder

The socket is composed of eight pyramids, with silver-inlaid strapwork decorating the four triangular sides of each unit. Below, on the widening edge, is a foliated kufic inscription, also inlaid with silver.

The sparsely decorated neck has a series of lancet leaves rising from a strapwork band, below which is a thin strip of copper. A scroll forming heart-shaped volutes, with trefoil leaves in each volute, joins the neck to the shoulder.

36. Brass candlestick inlaid with copper and silver
Afghanistan, second half 12th century
(Paris, Musée du Louvre, 6315)

The shoulder is composed of fifteen radiating and sunken scallops filled with floral scrolls. Copper is used on the triangular units between them, in a pair of leaves in the center of each scallop, and in the single leaf at the outer edge. Framing the shoulder is a floral scroll.

The high base is divided into five horizontal panels of varying widths. Each of the panels at the top and bottom contains a row of thirty lions seated on their haunches facing left, set against a floral background. The lions on the lower panel, which is wider, are more spread apart and raise their right paws. The animals are stylized with heads in high relief; they have bulging eyes, wide nostrils, and large mouths. The curls on the manes that fall on their backs are made by circular punches; crosshatching covers the bodies. Their long tails with widening and hatched tips swoop under the figures sitting behind. These two panels are devoid of any inlay.

A thin band of triangles alternately filled with copper and silver appears under the lions on the top panel. Below this is the widest portion of the candlestick, which has five rows of raised and alternately placed hexagonal units. Those on the upper and lower rows are cut in half and filled with floral scrolls inlaid with silver and framed by copper. The same scheme is used in the two rows of bosses adjacent to the half units; these are decorated with lobed medallions and floral scrolls. The bosses in the center have a rectangular inset outlined in copper with silver knots above and below. Naskhi inscriptions inlaid with silver and placed on a floral ground appear in the rectangles. Placed beneath the bosses is a kufic inscription on a floral ground, framed by copper strips.

The inscriptions that bestow a series of traditional good wishes to the anonymous owner are written in three different styles: foliated kufic appears on the socket, naskhi is placed on the thirty bosses, and plain kufic is used in the band on the base. Some of the words are embellished with extra *alifs* or are abbreviated; others are split into two adjacent zones, as in the case of those on the bosses.

The Freer example, with its large, truncated, conical base and a disproportionately squat socket and neck elaborately decorated with relief work and inlays, represents the earliest type of Islamic candlestick. Six other similar pieces are known to exist, each of which employs a series of bosses and rows of lions in the base with some modifications in the decorative layout. Three of them, in the Louvre (fig. 36),[1] the Museum of Islamic Art in Cairo (fig. 37),[2] and the al-Sabah Collection in Kuwait (fig. 38),[3] are almost identical to the Freer candlestick, except that they have a row of ducks standing on the shoulder and two bands of inscriptions flanking the bosses, which have been reduced to three rows. A fourth, now in the Hermitage, has lost its neck and socket; its top row of lions is replaced by a series of birds.[4] Another one, in the David Collection in Copenhagen, has four rows of bosses between the lion panels, but no inscriptions.[5] The sixth, in the Victoria and Albert Museum, also has lost its neck and socket; the base shows a series of birds at the top, confronted lions below, and three rows of bosses in the center, all of which recall the Hermitage candlestick.[6] The decoration of the bosses also varies: six-petaled roundels decorate the candlesticks in Paris, Cairo, London, Kuwait, and Leningrad; harpies, hares, and other animals with floral scrolls are used in the one in Copenhagen. A related eight-sided piece has lions and birds on the upper and lower portions of the base, while a predator attacking a prey is depicted on each side.[7]

Attributed to Khorasan during the late twelfth and early thirteenth centuries, these candlesticks reflect a perfected and sophisticated tradition, earlier examples of which appear to be missing. They also indicate the beginning of a new technique of metalworking in which brass became the most common material, and silver, copper, and gold were used sparingly and only for thin inlays.

Belonging to this group of inlaid brass objects with high-relief decoration is a series of ewers that frequently has similar lions decorating the spout.[8] The key piece in dating both ewers and the candlesticks is an ewer (fig. 6) in the Museum of the History of Georgia, Tiflis. The piece bears an inscription that states it was made by an artist named Mahmud ibn Muhammad ''of Herat'' in 1181/82.[9]

The history of Khorasan in the second half of the twelfth century is extremely turbulent because of the constant battles between the Ghaznavids, Seljuks, Ghurids, Khvarazmshahs, and Qarakhanids. A great amount of metalwork was presumably lost or melted down during these struggles. It is quite remarkable, therefore, that such an important series of candlesticks and ewers has survived.

37. Brass candlestick inlaid with copper and silver
Afghanistan, second half 12th century
(Cairo, Museum of Islamic Art, 15124)

38. Brass candlestick inlaid with copper and silver
Afghanistan, second half 12th century
(Kuwait, National Museum, Dar al-Athar al-Islamiya Collection, LNS 82 M)

Technical Notes

Radiographic image of an area along the base. The denser the material, the lighter it appears in the image. Thus, the silver inlay stands out as the sharply defined white areas. The mottled appearance of the body of the candlestick arises from the variations in density caused by blows of the hammer in the course of raising the piece. The hexagonal bosses, where the metal is stretched most thinly, appear darkest.

In forming the body, neck, and socket of the candlestick from one sheet, the metalsmith appears to have stretched the metal to its limit. A number of cracks and breaks are present. Most of these have occurred at those points where the metal has been raised the most, such as at the lions' heads or on the pyramidal forms of the neck.

A second piece of metal, cylindrical in shape, is set into the neck and serves to seat the candle. The top edge of this piece is crimped over the top edge of the socket and soldered in place.

The decoration of the candlestick includes silver and copper as well as what appears to be a black organic inlay. Very little black material is present and it is uncertain whether this is original inlay. The triangular pieces of silver and copper, which form a band below the lions, are set into relatively deep recesses. These recesses, formed by chasing and the use of punches, show no great concern for a regularity of outline, form, or depth. The pieces of silver used on the bosses exhibit a similar treatment, though the outlines are shaped with greater care.

The linear inlays of copper and silver are applied into deeply chased punch marks, which are usually aligned in two rows set to either side of a scribed guideline. A wide variety of punches was used for adding details to the lions and for recessing the background areas of the design.

Three holes are present in the neck near the rim; these are spaced equilaterally around the circumference of the neck. Seven holes are spaced equilaterally around the bottom edge of the candlestick. The placement of the three holes on the neck, their shape, and their integration with the design suggest that these holes are original. In contrast, the holes around the bottom edge are executed coarsely and disfigure the design; thus these holes seem likely to be later additions.

The holes, the cracks in the high-relief areas, and the areas of missing inlay are essentially the only defects on the candlestick. The area where the most inlay has been lost is on the band of triangles beneath the lions. The basic shape of the candlestick is undistorted. The outside surface is nearly free of corrosion, but the inside surface bears a thin layer of copper corrosion products.

The average of six analyses of different areas gives the following results:

Copper	Zinc	Lead	Tin
76.6% (± 0.9)	23.3% (± 1.1)	trace	not detected

Provenance: Purchased from Minassian, New York, 1951.

Published: Atıl 1971, no. 60.

               Allan 1977a, p. 163.

               Allan 1977b, fig. 45.

               Baer 1983, fig. 21.

Notes:

1. Paris 1971, no. 131; and Paris 1977, no. 320.
2. Harari 1964–65, pl. 1321.
3. Jenkins 1983, pl. 71.
4. Sarre and Martin 1912, pl. 144, no. 3044.
5. Leth 1975, p. 71.
6. Erginsoy 1978, fig. 112; and Melikian-Chirvani 1982, no. 43.
7. This example is in Kuwait; Jenkins 1983, no. 70.
8. See, for example, Sarre and Martin 1912, pls. 141–43; Dimand 1944, fig. 81; Harari 1964–65, pls. 1322–28; Baer 1965, figs. 24 and 25; Scerrato 1966, pls. 24–25; Paris 1971, no. 130; Fehérvári 1976b, no. 53; London 1976, no. 188; Allan 1982a, no. 5; and Melikian-Chirvani 1982, no. 45.
9. Giuzalian 1938; and Mayer 1959, p. 59.

14. Pen Box

Brass: cast; engraved, chased, and inlaid with copper,
   silver, and black organic material

Made by Shazi for Majd al-Mulk al-Muzaffar

Iran or Afghanistan, dated 607 A.H. (1210/11 A.D.)

Height: 5.0 cm. (2 in.); length: 31.4 cm. (12⅝ in.);
  width: 6.4 cm. (2⁹⁄₁₆ in.); weight: 1,555.0 gm. (54.8 oz.)

36.7

Inscriptions (Arabic)

1. Top of the lid (naskhi):

The most illustrious excellency, the great, the wise, the just, the supported [by God], *the triumphant, the victorious, Majd al-Mulk, the honor of state and religion, the luminous star of Islam and Muslims, the chosen among kings and sultans, the light of the nation, the splendor of the community, the example of the great and the perfect, the pillar of dignity, the lord of the viziers, the king of lieutenants, the possessor of good fortune, the minister of Iran, the grand vizier of Khorasan, al-Muzaffar, son of the deceased vizier, Majd al-Mulk, may God multiply* [increase] *his power.*	الصدر الاجل الكبير العالم العادل المؤيد المظفر المنصور مجد الملك شرف الدولة و الدين شهاب الاسلام و المسلمين اختيار الملوك و السلاطين ضياء الملة بهأ الامة قدوة الاكابر و الاماثل عمدة المعالى سيد الوزرأ ملك النواب ذو السعادات دستور ايران صدر و نظام خراسان المظفر بن الصدر الشهيد مجد الملك ضاعف الله قدره

2. Side of the lid (animated kufic):

The work of Shazi, the engraver [or designer], عمل شاذى النقاش * فى شهور سنة سبعة
in the months of the year seven and six hundred وستماية
[607 A.H. or June 25, 1210–July 14, 1211 A.D.].

3. Sides of the base (animated naskhi):

Glory and prosperity and power and safety العز و الاقبال و الدولة و السلامة و العافية و
and health and [God's] care and satisfaction العناية و القناعة و الشفاعة و النصرة و الناصرة
and [Prophet Muhammad's] intercession و الزيادة و الشاكرة و الشكرة و النعمة و
and aid and victoriousness and increase الرياضة و الراحة و الرحمة و الزيادة و التامة
[vision of God] and thankfulness and و التائيد و الديانة و الدوامة و الكفاية و البقاء
gratitude and favor and tranquillity and دائم لصاحبه
comfort and mercy and increase [vision of
God] and abundancy and divine support and
religiosity and duration and sufficiency
and perpetuity everlasting to its owner.

This rectangular pen box with rounded corners was acquired in Bukhara; it is among the most important pieces of Islamic metalwork produced before the Mongol conquest. The inscriptions, which give the names of the patron and artist and the year in which the object was made, help to establish the provenance and date of a number of other related examples.

front

The lid and the base were cast separately, and originally joined by a clasp in the front and two hinges at the back. The top of the lid has a continuous naskhi inscription framed by copper strips and placed against a scrolling vine with large leaves. The central panel is composed of a floral scroll with fourteen pairs of volutes enclosing animal heads. A pair of hares appears at each end of the panel, and ducks are placed between

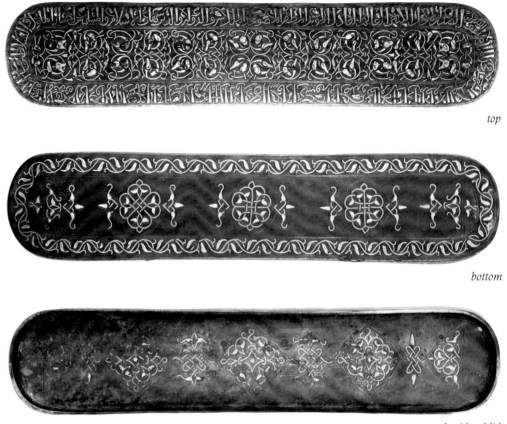

top

bottom

underside of lid

the volutes; each volute contains the heads of two different species of animals, which are repeated in mirror image in the adjacent unit. The animals are either long-eared (hares, foxes, and wolves) or horned (bulls and goats), and are occasionally interspersed with lions.

The sides of the lid are decorated with two long panels—each with ten four-legged winged animals—placed between the clasp and the hinges. The creatures, depicted in mirror image, have their backs to the hinges and walk toward the clasp, lifting up one front paw. Beginning from the clasp, they represent in each panel a sphinx with a halo, a griffin, a wolf(?), a fox(?), two hares (one replaced by a fox in the left panel), a lion, two bulls, and another fox. Some turn their heads to the back, while others are in profile. A floral scroll fills the background. Between the hinges at the back is a third panel, which contains an inscription rendered in kufic with vertical letters terminating in leaves or duck heads. The inscription, divided into two equal halves by a knot, is placed on a scroll devoid of inlay.

The underside of the lid reveals three complete and two half-lobed medallions joined by knots. These units are outlined in copper and filled with floral scrolls.

The lower half, or base, of the pen box contains a braid on the recessed edge that enables the lid to sit securely. Encircling the sides is a panel of naskhi inscription, outlined in copper, interrupted by the clasp and the hinges. Human heads appear at the top of the vertical letters, and behind the inscription is a scroll with animal heads similar to those on the top of the lid. The interior is empty and the inkwell is missing. It appears that the inkwell was inserted on the left and the remaining area was reserved for pens.

Placed around the edge of the bottom is a scroll. In the center is the same composition used on the underside of the lid: three full and two half-lobed medallions with finials filled with scrolls. Copper strips appear around the edge and the medallions. Tiny circular punch marks, producing an overall ring matting, are applied to the background of all the inlaid sections.

The owner of this pen box, Majd al-Mulk al-Muzaffar, was the grand vizier of the last Khwarizmshahs, Ala al-Din Muhammad, and founded a library in Merv, where he died in 1221 during the Mongol invasion of that city.[1] This official must have been a statesman with scholarly interests, which is indicated by his commission of the pen box. The pen box was a symbol of the learned class in the Islamic administrative system and became the blazon of such dignitaries in the Mamluk period.[2] Some of these containers are rectangular whereas others have rounded corners, such as the one (fig. 39) made in 1281 by Mahmud ibn Sunqur.[3] The latter shape appears to have survived well into the fourteenth century.[4]

39. Brass pen box inlaid with silver and gold
Made by Mahmud b. Sunqur
Egypt(?), dated 1281
(London, The British Museum, 91 6–23 5)

The maker of the Freer pen box, Shazi, has signed himself *al-naqqash*, usually translated as the designer or decorator, a term used more commonly by manuscript illuminators, although there have been cases in which it was employed by metalworkers.[5] The artist has chosen to be remembered for his expertise in design and refined workmanship, and obviously was proud of the way he has rendered the decoration like an illuminator would. His name appears on two other undated examples: a portable penholder (fig. 40) and a flask shaped like a bird (fig. 41), both of which were found in Herat.[6] The latter is signed *amal Shazi al-naqqash al-Haravi*, which suggests that the artist was either trained in Herat or originated from that city. The wedge-shaped portable penholder, meant to be suspended by a loop attached to the top, has the same animated inscriptions and scrolls as the Freer pen box. It has, additionally, the same style of writing in rendering the signature. Although the penholder found in Herat bears no dedication, it is possible that both it and the Freer piece were made for the same patron.

Herat was a major center for inlaid metalwork in the late twelfth and early thirteenth centuries. One of the key pieces for the study of Islamic metalwork is a bucket (fig. 1) in the Hermitage, popularly called the Bobrinsky Kettle.[7] The inscriptions state that it was made in 1163 by Masud ibn Ahmad *al-naqqash* of Herat and inlaid by Muhammad ibn Abd al-Vahed.[8] This bucket is the earliest dated object employing animated inscriptions.

There are several other contemporary examples made by artists who use the *nisba* (word referring to a city) al-Haravi, including a second bucket in the Hermitage, made by Muhammad ibn Nasir ibn Muhammad[9]; and the ewer (fig. 6) in Tiflis made in 1181/82 by Mahmud ibn Muhammad al-Haravi.[10] The *nisbas* used on Islamic objects, however, can be misleading and do not necessarily indicate where the artists were working. For

40. Brass penholder inlaid with silver
Made by Shazi
Afghanistan, early 13th century
(Herat, The Naqshibandi Foundation)

41. Brass bird-shaped flask inlaid with silver
Made by Shazi al-Haravi
Afghanistan, early 13th century

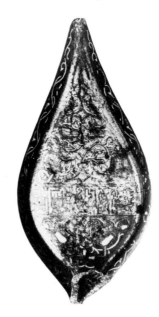

example, metalworkers with the *nisba* al-Mawsili, meaning "of Mosul," are known to have worked in Mosul as well as in Damascus and Cairo. It is possible that Shazi al-Haravi was working in Herat, one of the major centers in Khorasan, which was governed by his patron, Majd al-Mulk al-Muzaffar. On the other hand, he may have set up shop in Merv, where the grand vizier had his court, or in Bukhara, where the piece was acquired.

The general appearance of the pen box might lead one to assume that the box was made from metal sheet. Yet an examination of the pen box surprisingly reveals a cast structure. No seams or solder are apparent where the horizontal surfaces meet the verticals on either the box or the lid. Nor are there any seams or joining marks where the indented lip on the box meets the walls of the body. A cast structure is shown most clearly by X-radiography. The radiographs reveal the heterogeneity of the metal. Under magnification, dendritic structures can be discerned. More obvious is what appears to be gas porosity. Also discerned on the radiographs are what appear to be small fills, or chaplets, which are present in both the box and lid. These "chaplets" are rectangular in shape and measure about 2.8 by 1.0 millimeters (0.11 by 0.04 inch); fifteen were counted on the box and lid. The shape of the pen box does not suggest that chaplets would have been needed for casting. An alternative is that the rectangular pieces are not chaplets but rather chills, serving as points to initiate the crystallization of the molten metal during casting. A successful casting of the thin walls of the pen box may have required chills. On the radiographs the edges of the rectangular pieces appear soft and blurred, which suggests that the rectangular inserts were in place at the time of casting and that the cast molten metal heated and fused into the metal of the inserts. In addition, the metal of the pen box generally has the rather turbid appearance that one often sees in cast structures, but this turbidity is not present in the areas immediately surrounding the rectangular inserts. A rapid solidification in the area of the chills would result in local rejection of lead and a small grain size in the metal, which gives a homogeneous radiographic appearance. The metal solidifying farther away from the chills would develop larger grains, which give the turbid appearance. On the surface these inserts are usually covered with silver inlay, but in the few places where the inserts are visible, they appear to be pure copper, similar in color to the copper inlay.

The silver inlay is set into depressions measuring 0.2 to 0.3 millimeters (0.008 to 0.012 inch) in depth. In areas where the inlay has been lost, one can see tool marks, which indicate that the depression was cut or chiseled out; the depression is slightly undercut at the edges so that the inlay may be fit in securely. The linear silver inlay was applied into double rows of punch marks made with a square-ended punch. The

Technical Notes

Radiographic image showing gas porosity as dark spots; chills as small dark rectangles; and a turbid and dense overall appearance indicating a cast structure with a high lead content.

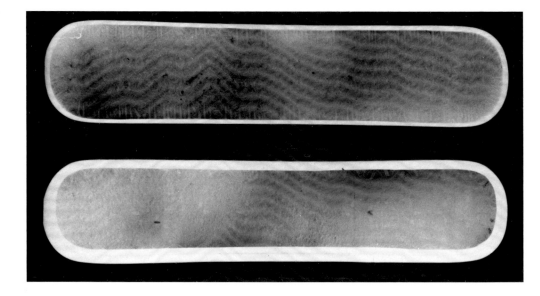

Magnified image of a radiograph. The fine, white curving lines are silver inlay. The dark rectangular area is a "chill," a piece of metal used in the casting of the pen box to initiate solidification of the molten metal. The dark spots are areas of porosity, and the very small white dots are lead. The homogeneous area around the chill indicates a rapid cooling of the molten metal when cast, resulting in a fine grain size. Farther away from the chill, the metal solidified more slowly and larger grains formed, thus creating a more mottled and grainy radiographic image. Actual size of the area illustrated: 30 x 20 mm. (1⅛ x ¹³⁄₁₆ in.)

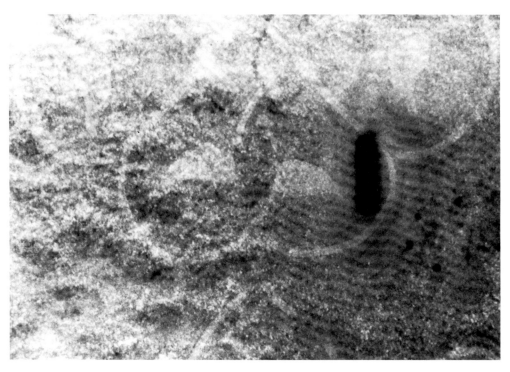

inlaid copper lines were applied in slight depressions, which were formed by engraving three parallel grooves; the ridges resulting from the cutting of the grooves act to secure the copper inlay once it is applied into the depression. Fine parallel scratches extend over many separate sections of inlay, suggesting that after being applied, the inlay was

Photomicrograph showing the stepped contour of the inlaid silver lines. Actual size of the area illustrated: 10 x 7 mm. (⅜ x ⁹⁄₃₂ in.)

Magnified image of an inlaid section. In the area on the left, the inlay is missing, revealing the deep depression used to seat the inlay. Actual size of the area illustrated: 16 x 13 mm. (⅝ x ½ in.)

made flush with the surrounding surface in the course of the finishing process. Details have been added to the inlay by chasing. The success of this inlay method is exemplified by the fact that so little of the inlay has been lost.

Chased and engraved lines and ring matting executed with circular punches appear on the body metal in the areas lying between the inlay. In some cases this work was done after the inlay was applied, as lines can be seen that cut across the silver inlay, apparently accidentally.

The condition of the pen box is generally good. Some losses have occurred; most noticeably missing are the latch and hinges, which had been attached with rivets. The inlay, however, is remarkably intact. For the most part, the pen box has a thin, dark, brown patina. Green corrosion products are present in some areas.

Four analyses of areas on the lid and bottom of the pen box indicate that the two parts are composed of the same alloy. An average of the four analyses is given below.

Copper	Zinc	Lead	Tin
69.6% ($\pm$3.0)	13.3% ($\pm$4.0)	15.2% ($\pm$5.5)	1.4% ($\pm$0.3)

Provenance: Purchased from Kevorkian Foundation, New York, 1936.
Published (Selected):

Répertoire, vol. 10, no. 3671.
Herzfeld 1936.
Pijoán 1949, fig. 241.
Rice 1954, fig. 8.
Rice 1955b, fig. 26.
Mayer 1959, p. 82.
Harari 1964–65, p. 2521 and figs. 841a–b.
Scerrato 1966, pl. 23.
Atıl 1971, no. 58.
Melikian-Chirvani 1974a, fig. 8.
Erginsoy 1978, fig. 126.
Melikian-Chirvani 1979b.
Baer 1983, fig. 178.

Notes:
1. For a detailed account of this official, see Herzfeld 1936.
2. See Atıl 1981, nos. 13, 20, 21, and 23.
3. Atıl 1981, no. 13; see also Baer 1981 and Baer 1983, pp. 66–71, for a discussion of pen boxes.
4. See, for example, Allan 1982a, no. 16.
5. This term appears on several works signed by al-Mawsili artists. Atıl 1981, no. 10.
6. Melikian-Chirvani 1979b, figs. 2–5 and 8; and Melikian-Chirvani 1982, figs. 40 and 41.
7. Ettinghausen 1943a; Mayer 1959, pp. 61–62, which includes a full bibliography; and London 1976, no. 180.
8. See Melikian-Chirvani 1982, pp. 82–83, notes 61–62, for the inscriptions.
9. Mayer 1959, p. 71 and pl. X; and Giuzalian 1978.
10. Giuzalian 1938; and Mayer 1959, p. 59; see also Allan 1982a, no. 5.

15. Candlestick

Brass: cast; engraved and inlaid with silver and black organic material

Iran, 13th century

Height: 16.3 cm. (6⁷⁄₁₆ in.); diameter: 18.0 cm. (7¹⁄₁₆ in.);
  weight: 1,029.0 gm. (36.3 oz.)

54.128

Inscriptions (Arabic)

1. On the shoulder (naskhi):
   Not deciphered

2. On the base (kufic):

With piety [once], *with good fortune* [repeated]. بالبر باليمن

The base, neck, and socket of this piece were cast together, and two separate pieces to hold the candle were soldered into the neck. The shape, with a projecting scalloped shoulder and faceted concave socket and base, is quite unusual. The proportions, however, are characteristic of thirteenth- and fourteenth-century candlesticks, with the base about two and one half times the height of the socket and in the same general form.

The socket with nine concave facets is decorated with a scroll that has a pair of human-faced leaves in each unit. The neck is divided into two panels with a large floral scroll above a series of lancet leaves.

A braid joins the neck to the shoulder, which is encircled by a band with naskhi inscriptions that repeat the vertical *alifs* and *lams* joined by horizontal letters. A floral scroll appears on the projecting edge of the shoulder with nine scallops; the tip of each scallop is accentuated by a raised leaf or teardrop motif.

The base is composed of three horizontal panels: lancet leaves decorate the upper panel and kufic inscriptions are placed in the lower panel; the wide middle section is divided into nine concave units, each with a lobed medallion surrounded by floral scrolls. The medallions represent haloed figures seated on cushions or benches that are depicted as elongated double leaves with additional foliage around them. Three of the figures are shown frontally; they wear conical hats and hold in each hand a dragon-headed staff. Flanking them are musicians with various instruments. A tambourine player and a lyre player face one of these figures, while a second tambourine player and a flutist face the second. The orientation of the musicians flanking the third figure shows a variation: one is depicted frontally and holds clappers or cymbals; the other faces away from the central figure and has a long-necked bottle with what looks like a cup.

The scenes in the medallions are symbolic of both astrological themes and good wishes. The figures holding dragon-headed staffs represent the overpowering of the evil Jawzahr, the dragon associated with solar darkness and the eclipse.[1] The musicians, showing the joyfulness and festiveness of the occasion, must be partaking in the celebration of this victory. These sentiments are echoed in the kufic inscriptions, which repeat the words "with joy." The conquest of darkness becomes a most meaningful theme on a candlestick, which has the function of providing light. The symbol of the victory of good over evil or light over darkness also is seen in the lancet leaves (representing sun rays) that encircle the upper base and lower neck.

There seems to be no apparent reason why the candlestick was designed with nine facets. Divisions into seven (for the planets) or twelve (for the signs of the zodiac, as in no. 19) would have made far better sense. It is conceivable that the artist wanted to adhere to units with a decorative program of threes, which was employed on the horizontal divisions of the socket neck, shoulder, and base.

The use of fairly large pieces of coarsely inlaid silver and the style of writing indicate

42. Brass candlestick inlaid with silver
Iran, mid-13th century
(Paris, Musée du Louvre, 6034)

43. Brass candlestick inlaid with copper
and silver
Iran, ca. 1220–50
(London, Victoria and Albert Museum,
571–1878)

44. Brass candlestick inlaid with silver
and gold
Iran(?), second half 13th century
(Copenhagen, The C. L. David Collection,
27/1972)

that the candlestick belongs to a group of objects made in the thirteenth century, attributed to western Iran. Most of the candlesticks in this group have round bases[2] and a few show faceting.[3] Only three published examples (figs. 42–44), in the Louvre, the Victoria and Albert Museum, and the David Collection, contain nine-faceted bases.[4] It should be mentioned that this type of faceted candlestick served as a model for a rare group of Ming dynasty blue-and-white porcelain examples with octagonal bases (see fig. 45).[5]

Technical Notes

The construction of this candlestick has some rather anomalous features, one of which is seen in the three pieces that make up the candlestick. These pieces are: a) the body, neck, and socket of the candlestick, b) an inset piece at the top of the socket, and c) another inset piece set inside the neck, the top of which is at the same level as the bottom of the socket. The inset pieces apparently were meant to seat the candle and are soldered in place with soft solder. Because the lower inset piece serves no function, it appears that the top inset piece was added over the lower piece at some later date to raise the point at which the candle would sit.

With the exception of the two insets, the candlestick appears to be cast as one piece, although the shape of the candlestick would suggest a multipiece construction. The cast structure is verified by stereo X-radiographs, which show a fine porosity in the metal in those few areas where toolwork has not removed such features, and an absence of any seams or joins. Visual inspection also fails to reveal any seams, and the use of solder is not evident anywhere on the outside surface of the body.

Tool marks on the inner surface of the base indicate that, after casting, the walls of the candlestick were thinned down by scraping. The walls, at some points, were thinned to such a degree that the punchwork on the outer surface broke through the inner wall. The reason for reducing the wall thickness to such a great extent, given the effort required to scrape down the surfaces, is unclear.

The candlestick bears much of its original silver inlay. Inlaid line decorations simply consist of thin strips of silver driven into double rows of punch marks. For wider areas of inlay, an outline of the area to be inlaid was chased onto the surface of the candlestick with small punch marks. The silver, cut to shape, was then hammered in, with the edges of the inlay becoming joined mechanically at the punch marks. In these wider areas of inlay the background has not been cut away; thus the inlay stands slightly above the surface of the candlestick, except at the edges of the inlay, which are pressed into the punch marks and are flush with the body. Details were added to the inlay by engraving; in some places the engraving tool cut entirely through the inlay.

Engraving also was used for the line decorations in the areas surrounding the inlay.

45. Blue-and-white ceramic candlestick
China, 15th century
(Shanghai, Shanghai Museum)

Also present on the body metal are recessed areas, which bear short parallel striations. A similar treatment of the body metal can be found on other Islamic vessels; it seems to be a surface prepared for the application of black inlay consisting of an organic material. A black material is found on the candlestick in some of the recesses, but it is unclear whether this material is original and was applied intentionally.

Although the candlestick shows some abrasion and loss of inlay, it is in generally good condition. The silver is free of tarnish and the base metal has a deep-brown patina.

The average of four analyses of different areas on the surface gives the following results:

Copper	Zinc	Lead	Tin
73.6% ($\pm$5.0)	5.8% ($\pm$0.8)	16.2% ($\pm$4.6)	4.1% ($\pm$0.5)

Provenance: Purchased from Minassian, New York, 304; formerly in the Homberg Collection.

Published: Homberg 1908, no. 336.

Ettinghausen 1960, pl. 2.

Untracht 1968, p. 151.

Atıl 1971, no. 59.

Melikian-Chirvani 1973, p. 51.

Allan 1977a, p. 164 and pl. VIIb.

Erginsoy 1978, fig. 130.

Baer 1983, fig. 26.

Notes:

1. This theme is discussed in Hartner 1973–74; Allan 1982a, nos. 2–3 and 5–6; and Baer 1982.

2. See, for instance, the examples published in Melikian-Chirvani 1982, nos. 76 and 76a.

3. Harari 1964–65, pl. 1316; Melikian-Chirvani 1973, pp. 64–69; and Allan 1977a, p. 163 and fig. 7 (B/1).

4. Melikian-Chirvani 1973, pp. 62–63; Melikian-Chirvani 1982, no. 77; and Leth 1975, pl. 78, respectively. See also Baer 1983, pp. 30–32 and figs. 24 and 25.

5. Mayuyama 1973, pl. 206; and Tokyo 1984, pl. 77.

16. Ewer

Brass: hammered and spun; handle cast; chased and
  inlaid with silver, copper, and black organic material
Made by Qasim ibn Ali for Amir Shihab al-Din
Syria, dated Ramadan 629 A.H. (June–July 1232 A.D.)
Height: 36.7 cm. (14⁷⁄₁₆ in.); diameter 21.3 cm. (8³⁄₈ in.);
  weight: 2,670.0 gm. (94.1 oz.)
55.22

Inscriptions (Arabic)

1. Band on the lower neck (naskhi):

Glory and prosperity to our master, the illustrious amir, the great, the pious, the devout, the godfearing, the gun-bearer Shihab al-Dunya w'al-Din, [the officer] of al-Malik al-Aziz.	العز و الاقبال لمولانا الامير الاجل الكبير الزاهد العابد الورع المندقدار [sic] شهاب الدنيا و الدين الملكى العزيزى

2. Ten lobes on the shoulder (naskhi):

The work of Qasim ibn Ali, the apprentice of Ibrahim ibn Mawaliya al-Mawsili. This [was made] in Ramadan of the year twenty-nine and six hundred [629 A.H. or June–July 1232 A.D.].	عمل قاسم ٭ بن علي ٭ غلام ابر ٭ اهيم ابن ٭ مواليا ٭ الموصلى ٭ وذلك فى ٭ رمضان ٭ سنة تسع ٭ عشرين وستمائة

3. Band on the foot (naskhi):

Eternal glory and secure life and complete brilliance and prosperity . . . . . . and increasing good luck and . . . . . . and . . . and power, permanence [and] victory [and] long life to its owner.	العز الدائم و العمر السالم ٭ و الزهر الشامل و الاقبال ... ٭ ... و الجد الصاعد و ... ٭ ... و ... و الدولة ٭ الباقى [و] النصر [و] البقا[ء] لصاحبه

The ewer consists of several parts that were made separately and soldered together: the ovoid body that tapers toward the foot, the splayed foot, the tall neck flaring at the mouth, the hinged flap covering the mouth, the straight spout, and the curved handle. The spout is not original but belongs to a contemporary or slightly earlier piece. Spouts and handles of ewers often broke off and were replaced. This has been observed on a number of similar pieces dating from the thirteenth and fourteenth centuries.

The decoration of the Freer ewer is highly unusual in that it employs only floral motifs and inscriptions. It is entirely devoid of figural representation, which was the most characteristic decorative feature of the period (as seen in nos. 17 and 18). A series of ogival units, outlined by thin bands and split-leaves and joined by crescents, covers the neck and body. Each unit encloses an individually composed floral design densely filled with curving branches bearing stylized leaves and buds and placed over a tightly wound scroll. Two horizontal rows with five ogees appear on the neck, while the body reveals four registers of ten. The units are placed alternately and increase or decrease in size to fit the contour of the piece.

The everted mouth is covered by a hinged, semicircular flap decorated with floral scrolls and encircled by a braided band. Another floral scroll appears on the neck, above

detail of shoulder

detail of lid

the section with the ogival units; this latter section is bordered by two thick rings bearing pearl bands. The dedicatory naskhi inscription on the lower neck, set against a tightly wound scroll, is outlined by thin, pearl bands. A row of lancet leaves or sun rays appears above, and ten raised scallops, bearing in naskhi the name of the maker and the date, are below. Pearl bands also encircle the underside of the lip, the shoulder, the lower body, and the inscription around the foot. A projecting ring with a braided pattern separates the body from the foot, which has a thick and rounded edge. The naskhi inscription on the foot, placed on a tightly wound scroll, is broken into five panels by crescents; the script is quite worn, and several words are too abraded to be read. The underside of the foot is decorated with fourteen recessed scallops radiating from a central boss.

The faceted handle has a distinctive globular thumb-rest, decorated with sun-ray motifs. The sides of the handle and the ball in the middle bear braids; the upper surface has floral scrolls, but the underside is plain. The handle is affixed to the neck and shoulder by heart-shaped units.

A similar unit connects the straight spout, which employs a different composition and design. The upper and lower panels have kufic inscriptions; the wide central section is filled with geometric interlaces; and below the plain ring, next to the body, is another kufic inscription. Copper inlays that appear on the bands separating the panels are not found on other parts of the ewer. The inscriptions are worn and seem to contain the

119

usual repertoire of good wishes.

According to the inscriptions on the neck, the ewer was made for a gun-bearer, or *bunduqdar* (which appears to be misspelled), named Shihab al-Din, who was in the service of a ruler with the titles al-Malik al-Aziz. The patron is identified as Shihab al-Din Tughrul, the Turkish regent of the Ayyubid sultan al-Malik al-Aziz Ghiyath al-Din, who ruled Aleppo between 1216 and 1237. The sultan was enthroned when he was a child, and his regent was in charge of the city until he came of age in 1232. Shihab al-Din, renowned for his loyalty and piety, founded the Atabekiya Madrasa in Aleppo, where he was buried in 1233. The Freer ewer was made the same year the sultan was enthroned, shortly before the death of Shihab al-Din.

The maker, Qasim ibn Ali, states that he was the *ghulam*, or apprentice, of Ibrahim ibn Mawaliya al-Mawsili, whose name appears on an ewer in the Louvre.[1] Although the Louvre ewer (fig. 46) has been poorly restored and lacks its original neck, handle, spout, and foot, its shape was the prototype for the one made by Qasim. Both pieces have ovoid bodies tapering toward the foot, and a scalloped collar around the neck. The same features appear on other contemporary ewers, some of which are faceted, including those in Cleveland (fig. 47), dated 1223; the Metropolitan Museum of Art (fig. 48), dated 1226; the Keir Collection in London, dated 1242; and the Louvre (fig. 49), dated 1258.[2] The same master also trained, in addition to Qasim, a metalworker named Ismail ibn Ward, who made a small box in 1220, now in the Benaki Museum in Athens.[3] Although Ibrahim ibn Mawaliya and his two apprentices are known only through single pieces of metalwork, their signed pieces help to establish an atelier that was active during the first half of the thirteenth century. The master and Ismail ibn Ward use the *nisba* al-Mawsili after their names, which indicates that they were at one time connected with the city of Mosul. Whether or not their workshop was in Iraq is speculative, but it is more likely that Qasim ibn Ali worked in Syria, since his patron, Shihab al-Din Tughrul, was residing in Aleppo.

Another atelier, headed by Ahmad ibn Umar al-Dhaki al-Mawsili, was active in the same region and at the same time as Ibrahim ibn Mawaliya and his apprentices. Five pieces of inlaid metalwork are known to have been made by this second workshop.[4] Artists using the *nisba* al-Mawsili continued working well into the fourteenth century in Egypt and Syria under the patronage of the Mamluks. They constitute an elite corps of metalworkers who specialized in intricate compositions and a rich repertoire of figural decoration. Having been trained by one of its earliest masters, Qasim ibn Ali must have belonged to this group, although he did not use the *nisba* in his only extant work. It is interesting to speculate whether he also represented figural compositions in his other works and added al-Mawsili after his name.

This type of Islamic ewer, often made with a matching basin similar in shape to catalogue number 18, was a luxurious personal item used in Muslim ablution rites. It was popularly produced in the Ayyubid and Mamluk periods.[5]

46. Brass ewer inlaid with copper and silver
Made by Ibrahim b. Mawaliya al-Mawsili
Iraq(?), early 13th century
(Paris, Musée du Louvre, K 3435)

47. Brass ewer inlaid with silver
Made by Ahmad b. Umar al-Dhaki al- Mawsili
Syria(?), dated 1223
(Cleveland, The Cleveland Museum of
Art, 56.11)

48. Brass ewer inlaid with silver
Made by Umar b. Hajji Jaldak
Syria(?), dated 1226
(New York, The Metropolitan Museum of
Art, 91.1.586)

49. Brass ewer inlaid with silver
Made for Sultan Salah al-Din Yusuf
Made by Husayn b. Muhammad al-
Mawsili in Damascus
Syria, dated 1258
(Paris, Musée du Louvre, 7428)

Technical Notes

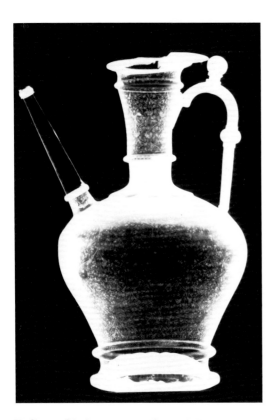

Radiographic image. Note the variations in density (as indicated by the various shades of the image) between the spout added as a repair, the body, and the cast solid handle.

Different methods were used to shape the various parts of the ewer. The body of the vessel appears to have been formed mainly by spinning. Concentric lines, which can indicate spinning, can be seen near the base in areas uncovered by the loss of inlay. The radiographic appearance of the vessel further suggests spinning by its general homogeneous density interrupted only by slight variations that follow concentric paths around the vessel. In addition, there is a centering mark on the bottom of the ewer, but owing to repairs in this area, this bit of evidence for spinning is not as supportive as it normally would be. The raised petals circling the base of the neck, however, would have to have been formed after spinning by hammering.

The neck of the vessel has a radiographic appearance similar to that of the body. No seam can be discerned running along the vertical length of the neck. The inside surface of the neck, as well as the lid, appears to be tinned.

The handle is cast and the hinges used to attach the lid may be cast as well. Alternatively, the hinges may be made from sheet metal, as the lid appears to be. Metal pins were used to join the hinges to the two parts of the lid.

All the parts extending from the main body of the ewer have been soldered in place. The neck of the ewer fits onto the body with the barely visible join occurring just below the lower collar on the neck. The neck narrows into a sleeve that extends down into the opening of the body. This join appears original in contrast to those that attach most of the other parts. The obvious use of soft solder suggests that the other joins are later repairs.

While there is an abundant and disfiguring use of soft solder to attach the base of the spout, the handle, and the lid, these parts appear to be original. The composition, decoration, and fit of the parts do not suggest that they are later additions. A thick ring of solder joins the bottom of the vessel to the body and obscures any vestige of the original contour of the lower edge of the foot. Although the originality of the inside bottom of the vessel is questionable, X-ray fluorescence analysis shows that it has the same composition (within experimental error) as the body.

In addition to the visual differences, X-radiography and elemental analysis suggest that the spout is not original. Radiographs show that the spout is made from much thinner sheet than that used for the other parts of the vessel. The angle of intersection between the two pieces and the fit of the spout into the body further suggest that this join is a repair.

The silver inlay is set into punched and chiseled recesses. The larger pieces of inlay stand slightly above the surface, as the underlying metal has been only lightly removed from the central areas of the recesses. The thin lines of silver inlay were hammered into double rows of punch marks. Chasing was used to decorate the surrounding areas of the body metal.

With the exception of the central section of the spout, where some copper inlay is present, only silver inlay is found. The use of a black compound for an inlay is not clear, although a black material resembling inlay is present in the woven decorations on the top of the ewer and near the foot.

Aside from the repairs to the ewer, the condition of the vessel is fair. Although many of the large, cresent-shaped pieces of silver have been lost, the other areas of inlay are mostly intact. The metal surfaces, being free of corrosion, exhibit their natural color.

Analyses of the body, neck, and base of the ewer agree to within plus or minus one percent, so it would appear that the same metal was used for these parts. The analysis of the spout differs from that of the body in that the presence of tin as well as a much higher percentage of zinc are indicated. The cast handle contains a higher percentage of alloying elements than the body; particularly evident is lead, which was added presumably to improve the flow of the molten metal and lower the casting temperature. One analysis of the handle, one of the spout, and the average of two analyses taken on the body are given below.

	Copper	Zinc	Lead	Tin
Body	83.2% ($\pm$0.7)	14.4% ($\pm$0.2)	2.1% ($\pm$0.1)	not detected
Handle	76.1%	17.0%	4.5%	1.9%
Spout	79.2%	18.9%	1.2%	0.3%

Provenance: Purchased from Kevorkian Foundation, New York, 1955; formerly in the Brimo de la Roussilhe Collection, Paris.

Published (Selected):

Wiet 1932, p. 19, no. 15; p. 23, no. 20; and p. 171, no. 42.

Kühnel 1939, fig. 9.

Répertoire 1939, vol. 10, no. 3977.

Ettinghausen 1943b, no. 46.

Rice 1953b, pp. 66–69 and pls. X–XI.

Rice 1957a, pp. 286 and 325–26.

Mayer 1959, pp. 78–79.

Ettinghausen 1960, pl. 3.

Schneider 1973, pl. 7.

Atıl 1975, no. 26.

Erginsoy 1978, fig. 139.

Baer 1983, fig. 76.

Notes:

1. Rice 1953b, pp. 69–79 and pls. XII–XXII. This ewer is decorated with naskhi and kufic inscriptions, and inlaid with silver and copper. It is possible that the spout on the Freer ewer comes from a similar example, which employed both kufic and copper.

2. Rice 1957a, pls. 1–2, 10–11, 13c, and 14a.

3. Rice 1953b, pp. 61–66 and pl. IX.

4. Rice 1957a.

5. Although there are a fairly large number of single ewers and basins, few matching sets have survived. For two extant sets made in the 1270s, see note 8 in no. 18 in this catalogue.

17. Canteen

Brass: hammered and worked on lathe; chased and inlaid
  with silver and black organic material

Syria(?), mid-13th century

Diameter: 36.9 cm. (14½ in.); height of neck and spout: 9.0 cm. (3½ in.);
  depth: 21.5 cm. (8½ in.); weight: 5,069.0 gm. (178.8 oz.)

41.10

Inscriptions (Arabic)

1. Around the central medallion (kufic):

Eternal glory and secure life and increasing good luck and enduring power and overwhelming safety and perpetuity to the owner.

الجد الصاعد ا * و العمر السالم و العز الدائم و
و الدولة الباقى * و السلامة الغالبية و البقا[ء]
لصا[حبه]

2. On the shoulder (kufic):

Eternal glory and secure life and complete prosperity and increasing good luck and good fortune and pledges and everlasting favor and affluent living and abundant good fortune and lofty victory and enduring power, overwhelming safety, everlasting favor and perfect honor to the owner.

العز الدائم و العمر السالم و الاقبال الشاملة
و الجد الصاعد و اليمن * المواعد و النعمة
الخالدة و العيش الرغد و الخير الوافر و النصر
العالى و * الدولة الباقية السلامة الغالبية النعمة
الخالدة و الكرامة الكاملة لصا[حبه]

3. On the shoulder (animated naskhi):

Eternal glory and perfect prosperity, increasing good luck, the chief, the commander, the most illustrious, the honest, the sublime, the pious, the leader, the soldier, the warrior of the frontiers.

العز الدائم و الاقبال الكامل الجد الزائد *
العميد الضابط الامجد الصالح الرفيع * الودع
الهادى المحارب المرابط

4. On the neck (naskhi):

. . . the noblest . . . health [well-being].

... الاكرم ... العافية

124

This unique canteen, the shape of which can be traced to pilgrim flasks produced during the Roman and Parthian periods, is the largest known example made in brass. It was made in several sections and soldered together. The spherical top with a flattened central medallion and the flat back with a central socket are joined at the shoulder, which has three bands separated by thick rings. The cylindrical neck and the spout with two slender handles are off-center and affixed to the side. Produced in two main sections, the top extends to the second band on the shoulder and was soldered to the third band that curves up from the back; the seam is hidden by the projecting ring. The neck with the spout and the handles were made separately, as was the conical socket on the back, which consists of two parts: a flat cap and a cone 10.1 centimeters (4 inches) in diameter and 18.7 centimeters (7⅜ inches) deep. The canteen must have been designed to hang on a post inserted into the socket and turned by the handles until the contents, filtered through the strainer, were poured out.

The design is based on units of threes, which are repeated on the front, back, and shoulder. The spherical front has three concentric zones, with the middle and outer ones divided into three panels. The medallion in the center represents the Madonna and Child Enthroned, attended by two patriarchs or saints. Two pairs of angels appear to carry the throne, which is an elaborate structure with drapery covering the legs, a large cushion on the seat, and two posts flanking the high back. The saint on the left wears a turban and uses the gesture of praying or adoration with open palms; the other is a bare-headed and bearded man who holds a boxlike object. A meander band frames the medallion.

The inscription panel in the next zone is interrupted by three roundels bearing geometric strapwork. A meander band also encloses this panel and loops around the large medallions separating the three scenes in the outer zone. The medallions are filled with animated floral scrolls composed of a variety of birds and ducks, and the torsos of such winged creatures as lions, harpies, griffins, and hares.

The three panels in the outer zone represent specific episodes from the Life of Christ: the Nativity, the Presentation in the Temple, and the Entry into Jerusalem. The first is divided into two horizontal registers showing the Manger Scene above and the Washing of the Christ Child below. In the center of the upper register is the grotto in which Mary is seen reclining next to the crib bearing the Christ Child while three animals (two oxen and a donkey) peer in. On the left, riding toward the grotto, are three magi, the foremost wearing a high, furry hat resembling the *sharbush* of the Turkish amirs. Opposite are three angels, with a fourth one flying over Mary. In the center of the lower register is the infant Christ in a deep, crescent-shaped bowl with a high foot or stand, flanked by a seated man and a standing figure pouring water from a large jar. On the left is a shepherd with three horned animals and on the right is another seated figure, with two others standing behind him. One of these figures points up toward the grotto, his gesture linking the two registers.

Moving counterclockwise, following the direction of the script as well as the orientation of the canteen when it is turned by the handles for pouring, is the second panel, which shows the Presentation in the Temple. The scene takes place in a tripartite structure with three domes, each embellished with a cross. On the lintel of the central part are three fish and a bird, used either as general symbols for water and sky or as specific symbols related to Christian iconography. The fish was associated with Christ and with the Baptism, whereas various birds had different attributes. For instance, the dove meant purity and peace, the eagle symbolized resurrection, and the partridge referred to the Church and to truth. Under this lintel is Christ seated on a pedestal, flanked by Simeon and Mary. A figure holding a box or basket, most likely portraying Joseph, appears in the left wing; opposite, holding a scarflike scroll, is another figure, who must be Anna. Above are two birds and four angels flying toward the central dome.

The third panel, representing the Entry into Jerusalem, shows Christ in the center,

front

riding sidesaddle on a donkey while three children spread garments on the ground before them. Two other children have climbed the trees flanking the central figure. On the upper left is a personage with a cross on the chest of his garment; opposite is a domed building with two men, one of whom carries a child on his shoulders. Above are two angels flying toward the center.

The three zones on the shoulder of the canteen are defined by thick rings with chevron designs; rings with one-half chevrons, or diagonal strokes, separate the shoulder from the top and the back. The first two panels face the top and the third one faces the back, indicating that the two halves were worked separately and then joined together.

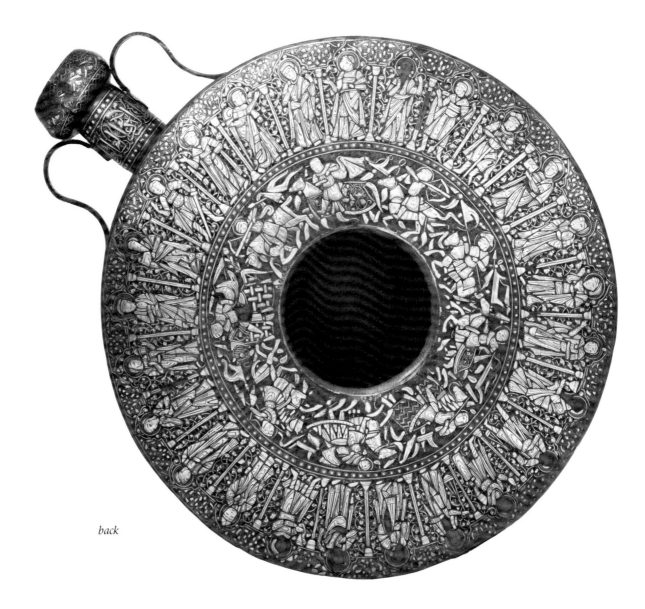

back

The zone closest to the top has an inscription divided by three roundels with geometric designs. The middle zone also contains an inscription, which is divided into three; here, the inscription is animated and the roundels contain a seated figure holding up a crescent. The animated inscription employs diverse real and fantastic creatures, including birds, harpies, dragons, felines, unicorns, griffins, winged lions and horses, horned animals, and various quadrupeds; in addition, human figures who ride horses (and even camels) bear bows and arrows, shields, swords, and lances, or wear animal masks. The figures, whose legs, arms, and torsos make up the strokes of the letters, are shown in combat, with both the humans and animals attacking one another.

128

The last zone on the shoulder has thirty roundels with a hawk attacking a bird inserted between every two units, which contain seated figures facing one another. The figures represent either musicians playing a lyre, zither, lute, flute, tambourine, or drum, or drinking personages holding beakers. Surrounding them are additional beakers, tall-necked bottles, or high-footed bowls filled with rounded fruit. The scheme of pairs of musicians and drinkers facing one another is abandoned in several cases; one musician and drinker are portrayed frontally; in two instances, a pair of musicians and a pair of drinkers face one another; in another roundel a dancer substitutes for a musician; and flanking the spout is a drinker and a tambourine player, both of whom turn toward the roundels with the birds next to them.

The back, or the flat side, of the canteen has the conical socket in the center with two concentric zones around it. The outermost zone has twenty-five figures standing under a series of ogival arches separated by columns. The figures in seventeen of the arches portray saints with long flowing robes and stoles; they carry books, censers, footed bowls, or caskets. In six of the arches the figures depict warriors wearing short tunics, boots, and long scarves draped over their shoulders; they hold swords, shields, beakers, lances, censers, and books. The only pair that can be identified properly seem to represent the Annunciation with Gabriel and Mary: a figure with wings gestures toward another who withdraws slightly. The majority of the figures appear to be men; some saints have beards; and most—except a warrior who bears a turban and a saint who has a tall hat—wear small caps. With the exception of Gabriel, who turns right to face Mary, and three or four figures who are depicted frontally, most of the personages are oriented counterclockwise.

This orientation is far more pronounced in the next zone, which is separated by a beaded band and depicts nine horsemen participating in a tournament. The galloping riders carry lances with banners and horsetails. They are attired in tunics and have scarves draped over their torsos and flowing at the back; one wears a turban and two (one of whom turns back while shooting) carry crossbows. The horses are equipped with decorated blankets, some of which cover only the hind quarters while others extend all the way down to their ankles. The lively movement created by the riders contrasts with the static positioning of the figures in the previous zone.

The neck bears a nashki inscription placed between two pearl bands, and the spout has a floral scroll enclosed by two braids. Similar braids appear on the lower half of the handles; chevron designs are on the upper half. One of the handles lacks any silver inlay and may have been added during a later restoration.

The background of the panels employs two different types of scrolls that are used alternately. A loose scroll with leaves and buds appears behind three areas: the naskhi inscription on the neck, the kufic inscriptions encircling the central medallion on the front and shoulder, and the panel with standing figures on the back. In the latter area, the spandrels of the arches are inlaid in reserve, that is, the background is covered with

detail of front

silver, whereas in the areas around the figures the leaves and branches of the same
scroll are inlaid with silver, with the interstices (or background) filled with finely hatched
lines. The second type, composed of a tightly wound scroll with a single leaf in each
volute, is found in the three scenes from the Life of Christ on the top, the animated
inscription and the thirty medallions on the shoulder, and panel with nine riders on
the back.

The Freer canteen employs an extraordinarily varied repertoire of both pictorial and
decorative themes, and represents the epitome of the art of metalwork. The models

detail of back

used by the maker include contemporary metalwork as well as manuscript illustration, an indication that a rich repository of themes and motifs was available to the artists. The scenes from the Life of Christ depicted on the front were influenced by contemporary Christian manuscripts made in Syria,[1] and the saintly figures standing between arches on the back follow a peculiar convention found in a number of inlaid brasses produced during the first half of the thirteenth century.[2] Other decorative themes common to the metalwork of the age include: two types of scrolls and fine hatching used in the background; inscriptions rendered in both kufic and naskhi; and solar, lunar, and royal themes used in the roundels on the shoulder, symbolized by geometric interlaces, figures holding crescents,[3] and hawks attacking birds.

Even such outstanding features as the animated naskhi inscriptions and scrolls with fantastic creatures can be seen on several other pieces of contemporary metalwork. The closest examples to the fully animated inscription employed on the Freer canteen appear on the famous Wade Cup (fig. 7) in Cleveland; on an ewer (fig. 8) dated 1232, made by Shuja ibn Mana, in the British Museum; on an incense burner (fig. 10) made for the Ayyubid ruler of Egypt and Syria, Sultan al-Adil II (1238–40), in the Keir Collection, Ham, Richmond; and on a basin (fig. 9) made in 1252/53 by Davud ibn Salama al-Mawsili, now in the Musée des Arts Décoratifs in Paris.[4] The Wade Cup is thought to have been made in northwestern Iran in the 1230s; the inscriptions on the 1232 ewer state that it was made in Mosul; and the remaining pieces were produced either in Egypt or Syria during the middle of the thirteenth century.

It appears that the tradition of using animated inscriptions on metalwork, which began in Iran during the twelfth century (see no. 14), moved westward and was perfected by the Ayyubid artists. It continued to be employed in the early Mamluk period, as observed in the candlestick made for Kitbugha (fig. 12) around 1290 and the Fano Cup (fig. 11) in the Bibliothèque Nationale in Paris.[5] The scroll with fantastic creatures seen in the three medallions on the top also was perfected in the Ayyubid period (see also no. 18) and continued to be popular under the Mamluks.

The interest in representing Christian themes on inlaid metalwork, unique to the Ayyubid period, reflects the multifaceted society of the age, and the interaction between the Muslim and Christian communities. The patrons of the pieces representing Christian themes are anonymous; the exceptions are a tray (fig. 53) in the Louvre[6] and a basin in the Freer Gallery (no. 18), both made for the last Ayyubid sultan, Najm al-Din. Only two artists have signed and dated their works: in 1242/43 Ahmad al-Dhaki al-Mawsili made an ewer, now in the Keir Collection; and in 1248/49 Davud ibn Salama made a candlestick owned by the Musée des Arts Décoratifs.[7]

The most unusual scene in the Freer canteen is the panel with nine horsemen participating in a tournament, or *furusiyya* exercises, which were popular in the Ayyubid and Mamluk periods. This form of exercise enabled the young warriors to practice the art of horsemanship and warfare while providing entertainment for the spectators. There are no extant illustrated *furusiyya* manuals dating from the thirteenth century, although this subject was frequently depicted in the Mamluk period.[8] It is not possible to determine whether the metalworker created the imagery for this scene himself or relied on the manuscript illustrations or sketchbooks made available to him.

Among the intriguing aspects of the Freer canteen are the identification of its patron and the determination of its purpose. One can hypothesize that the patron was a Christian interested in *furusiyya* exercises; he was particularly familiar with the cities of Bethlehem and Jerusalem, as suggested by the themes chosen for the three scenes on

50. Blue-and-white ceramic canteen
China, ca. 1400–1430
(Washington, D.C., Freer Gallery of Art,
58.2)

the top; he was also a connoisseur of metalwork who commissioned a highly competent artist to make his canteen; and he was possibly a foreigner, maybe a Crusader, who wanted the largest and most spectacular "pilgrim flask" to take home with him as a souvenir of his stay in Palestine.

The history of the canteen from the time it was made to the nineteenth century is not known, but in 1845 it was in the collection of Prince Filippo Andrea Doria.[9] Its almost pristine condition—it has only a few repairs and lost silver inlays—suggests that the canteen was cherished in European aristocratic circles (see also no. 18). Why the name of the patron was not included in the inscriptions is difficult to explain; only a few Ayyubid pieces, however, contain dedications, and these almost always refer to reigning sultans. It is possible that it was customary to include only the names of royal patrons and to omit references to other clientele. It should also be mentioned that this unique and spectacular canteen became the model of an equally rare Ming dynasty blue-and-white porcelain example (fig. 50).[10]

Technical Notes

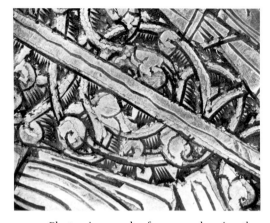

Photomicrograph of an area showing the hatching, or striated recesses, used in the background. Actual size of the area illustrated: 27 x 21 mm. (1¹⁄₁₆ x ¹³⁄₁₆ in.)

Seven pieces make up the canteen. These pieces are the spherical top and flat back of the body, the two handles, the neck and its spout, and the socket with its inner cone and flat cap. In forming the canteen, raising was apparently used. But the regularity of the rounded forms and the consistent density of the walls as revealed by X-radiographs are traits that suggest additional working with a lathe.

The tubular neck and cone were shaped by bending flat sheet into a cylinder, tapering the mating faces for a scarf joint, and soldering together the edges. Additional shaping was necessary to create the spout. This was done by raising the end of the neck, as indicated by the irregular surface present on the inside of the spout. The handles could easily have been formed by either hammering or casting, but their radiographic appearance does not reveal a cast structure. The strainer within the base of the neck was made simply by drilling holes into the body of the canteen. All of the various parts of the canteen were joined together with soft solder.

The decoration is composed chiefly of silver inlay. The broad areas of inlay are seated in recesses made with punches and chisels. The recesses are deep enough in most cases to allow the inlay to sit flush with the surface. The body metal and the inlay are further decorated with chased lines. The inlaid silver lines are seated in double rows of punch marks. There is also an extensive use of a black organic compound as an inlay. Close inspection reveals that two different types of punches were used in preparing the surface for the inlaid silver lines, one type having a rectangular cross section and the other an oval cross section. The resulting lines have either a stepped or an undulating profile. This difference is barely visible without magnification and does not seem to play a decorative role.

The condition of the canteen is very good. As has been noted, little inlay has been lost. The metal is cracked in some areas, such as along the edge of the spout and, in the worst case, along the edge of the flat side of the body. Also, there are many fine concentric ridges on the inner wall of the central socket, which may have resulted from use of the canteen.

Two samples of the body metal have been previously removed and analyzed by wet chemical methods. The results of these analyses have already been published[11] but are repeated below. The difference between the two results is greater than the experimental error of the procedure, and probably reflects an actual difference in the compositions of the two sheets.

Sample Site	Copper	Zinc	Lead	Tin	Iron	Total
Exterior of body	81.7%	15.2%	1.4%	not detected	1.2%	99.5%
Interior of socket	84.0%	12.8%	1.4%	not detected	0.7%	98.9%

The analytical figures derived by wet chemical methods for the exterior of the body compare well with the results obtained by X-ray fluorescence surface analysis. An average of three analyses on separate areas on the flat side of the canteen yielded the following results:

Copper	Zinc	Lead	Tin
80.9% ($\pm$1.6)	16.2% ($\pm$0.8)	2.2% ($\pm$0.5)	trace

Provenance: Purchased from Kevorkian Foundation, New York, 1941; formerly in the collections of Prince Filippo Andrea Doria, Pamphili(?), and George Eumorfopoulos, London.

Published (Selected):

Lanci 1845, vol. 2, pp. 141–45; vol. 3, pls. XLV–XLVI.
Devonshire 1927, figs. III–IV.
Dimand 1934.
San Francisco 1937, no. 191.
Eumorfopoulos 1940, p. 43.
Sotheby's 1940, no. 72.
Pijoán 1949, figs. 258–61.
Ettinghausen 1950, pl. 3.
A. Grabar 1959, fig. 2.
Pope 1959, pls. IB and IIB.
Ettinghausen 1965, pl. X.
Untracht 1968, p. 151.
Pope 1972, pl. 7b.
Schneider 1973.
Leroy 1974–75, fig. 4.
Atıl 1975, no. 28.
Erginsoy 1978, figs. 162a–f.
Nicolle 1979, fig. 181.
Nicolle 1981, pl. 10.
Ghulam 1982, pp. 340–79.
Baer 1983, fig. 198.
Katzenstein and Lowry 1983, pls. 6–7.

Notes:

1. Schneider 1973 discusses the sources of these themes.
2. For a study of this group of metalwork, see Katzenstein and Lowry 1983, in which fifteen objects are listed. The socket of a candlestick in Montreal should be added to this list; Salam-Liebich 1983, no. 50.
3. For a discussion of this theme see Ettinghausen 1971.
4. The Wade Cup is published in Rice 1955b and Ettinghausen 1957. For the 1232 ewer see Barrett 1949, no. 12; and Harari 1964–65, pls. 1329–30. The incense burner mentioned in

Rice 1955b, p. 32, is published in Fehérvári 1968 and 1976b, no. 129. For the basin of Davud ibn Salama see Paris 1971, no. 157, and Paris 1977, no. 156.

5. The base of the candlestick is in the Walters Art Gallery, Baltimore, and the neck and socket are in the Museum of Islamic Art, Cairo; see Atıl 1981, no. 15. The Fano Cup has been published in a number of sources, including Rice 1955b, pl. XV; Paris 1971, no. 171; and Paris 1977, no. 321.

6. Paris 1971, no. 153.

7. The ewer is published in Fehérvári 1976b, no. 131. For the candlestick see Paris 1971, no. 156.

8. Atıl 1981, no. IV.

9. Lanci 1845, vol. 2, pp. 141–45; and vol. 3, pls. XLV–XLVI.

10. Pope 1959. See also Taiwan 1963, pls. 3 and 3a–b, for a similar example.

11. W. T. Chase, ''Technical Notes'' in Schneider 1973, pp. 155–56.

18. Basin

Brass: hammered and turned; chased and inlaid with silver
  and black organic material
Made for Sultan Najm al-Din Ayyub
Egypt or Syria, ca. 1240s
Height: 23.3 cm. (9⅛ in.); diameter (rim): 50.0 cm. (19¹¹⁄₁₆ in.);
  weight: 5,201.0 gm. (183.4 oz.)
55.10

Inscriptions (Arabic)

1. Band on the exterior (plaited kufic):

عز لمولانا السلطان الملك * الصالح السيد
الاجل العالم * العامل المجاهد المرابط *
المؤيد المنصور نجم الدين * ايوب ابو [sic]
محمد ابن ابى بكر ابن ايوب

Glory to our master, the sultan, al-Malik al-Salih, the lord, the illustrious, the learned, the efficient, the defender [of the faith], *the warrior* [of the frontiers], *the supported* [by God], *the victor, Najm al-Din Ayyub Abu Muhammad ibn Abu Bakr ibn Ayyub.*

2. Band on the interior (thuluth):

عز لمولانا السلطان الملك الصالح السيد *
الاجل العالم العامل المجاهد المرابط المؤيد
* المظفر المنصور نجم الدنيا و الدين ملك
الاسلام و * المسلمين ابى الفتح ايوب ابن
الملك الكامل ناصر الدنيا * و الدين محمد
ابن ابى بكر ابن ايوب خليل امير المؤمنين
عز نصره

Glory to our master, the sultan, al-Malik al-Salih, the lord, the illustrious, the learned, the efficient, the defender [of the faith], *the warrior* [of the frontiers], *the supported* [by God], *the conqueror, the victor, Najm al-Dunya w'al-Din, the lord of Islam and Muslims, Abu'l-Fath Ayyub, ibn al-Malik al-Kamil Nasir al-Dunya w'al-Din Muhammad ibn Abu Bakr ibn Ayyub, the beloved of the Commander of the Faithful* [that is, the caliph], [may his] *victory be glorious.*

Representing the epitome of the technical and aesthetic achievements of Ayyubid metalwork, this imperial basin is divided into horizontal registers of varied widths, each intersected by five medallions or roundels; on both the outside and inside it is decorated richly with figural compositions, animals, inscriptions, and floral scrolls. Uniting different components of the design is a continuous band that encircles the panels, and loops around the medallions and roundels.

The thick and widening rim bears a floral scroll on the outside and a braided band underneath. Below the rim is another thin floral scroll. The wide panel on the upper portion of the exterior contains a plaited kufic inscription giving the name of the patron, with an animated scroll in the background. This scroll includes heads of humans as well as lions, hares, long- and short-eared animals, and horned creatures. Scenes from the Life of Christ appear in the five lobed medallions inserted between the text. The medallions, moving counterclockwise, represent the Annunciation (Gabriel approaching Mary, who sits on a bench); the Adoration (Mary holding the Christ Child while seated on a low bench, attended by two angels); the Raising of Lazarus (Christ, joined by another man, performs the miracle as Lazarus rises from his tomb); the Entry into Jerusalem (Christ on a donkey, flanked by two figures); and three figures, the central one holding a bowl, thought to represent the Last Supper.

The next panel depicts a lively polo game, with units of four riders separated by five lobed medallions bearing scrolls composed of the same animal and human heads seen above. Here, some human heads are embellished with pointed caps while others are hatless. The polo players, accompanied by an occasional dog or hare, ride amidst branches bearing lotus blossoms and buds. Although the game seems to progress toward the left, one or two players ride in the opposite direction; the horses of those on the far right of each unit, as well as a few others in each group, are shown with twisted necks and heads, looking back. The riders carry polo sticks and wear small caps, textured tunics, and boots. They are depicted in lively and naturalistic poses, contrasting with the rigidity of the scenes and inscriptions above.

The following register is considerably narrower and contains twenty-five real and fantastic animals walking to the left. The creatures are divided into five groups by lobed roundels representing musicians playing a flute, tambourine, lute, lyre, and a smaller lutelike string instrument that may represent a *rabab*. The animals include such quadrupeds as bears, hares, lions, donkeys, deer(?), wolves(?), and cheetahs(?) together with winged unicorns, griffins, and sphinxes. A floral scroll with split-leaves and blossoms appears on the lowest exterior zone.

The inner rim of the basin has two thin bands, the first bearing a floral scroll and the second showing thirty-nine quadrupeds and a bird. The animals, which run counter-

interior

139

detail of exterior

clockwise, represent the same species of real and winged creatures found on the exterior. Below is a wide panel with thuluth inscriptions, divided into five sections by lobed medallions containing scrolls that have tendrils ending in human and animal heads, similar to those filling the medallions on the exterior. The next register has a row of thirty-nine saints standing between columns bearing ogival arches decorated with geometric interlaces. The figures, facing each other in pairs with the exception of one, are bareheaded, and wear long and loosely draped robes. A floral band fills the lowest register.

detail of interior

The bottom of the basin is badly worn; all the inlay is gone and parts of the design are obliterated. The bottom contains two concentric zones placed around a central medallion, which has an animated floral scroll radiating from twelve human or beast heads. The inner zone has five groups of three figures portraying drinkers with beakers and musicians playing flutes, drums, tambourines, lutes, and zithers; they are seated amidst beakers, long-necked bottles, and high-footed bowls holding rounded fruit. Between the groups are lobed medallions with floral scrolls. The outer zone contains a continuous animated scroll with a border of lancet leaves or sun-ray motifs extending toward the inner walls.

base

The exterior of the base has a medallion with a European coat of arms that was added in the eighteenth century, as suggested by the stylistic features of the engraving. In the center is a shield with a rampant bull, a chevron, and two roses; flanking it are two unicorns with a knight's helmet and another bull above. Enclosing these elements are floral decorations and ribbons inscribed in Latin with the motto *Depulsis hostibus anglis rosae, non fert iste iugum de Lucae stemmate Taurus, solum dulce iugum Chri[s]ti.* Written in the Latin dactylic hexameter, with the word *rosae* inserted in an odd nonmetrical manner, the phrase can be translated as: "Now that the English enemy is beaten, the bull from the lineage of Saint Luke does not bear the yoke of the [English] rose; [he] only [bears] the sweet yoke of Christ."[1]

The shield has been identified as that used by a cadet branch of the Counts of Borniol of France.[2] It seems that this branch, once ruled by the English, was able to overthrow the enemy and celebrated this victory by inserting the commemorative design on the base of the basin.

The patron of the basin, al-Malik al-Salih Najm al-Din Ayyub, was the last Ayyubid sultan. He ruled over Diyarbakır (1232–39), Damascus (1239 and 1245–49), and Egypt (1240–49), and lost his life while fighting against the Crusade of Saint Louis in 1249, after which date his empire fell into the hands of the Mamluks. Three other pieces of metalwork bear his name: an oversized bowl (fig. 51) in the University of Michigan[3]; a basin (fig. 52) in the Museum of Islamic Art in Cairo, which has the same shape as the Freer example[4]; and a tray (fig. 53) in the Louvre, also decorated with Christian figures.[5] The inscriptions on these objects do not contain dates or the names of the artists or of the cities in which they were made.

Among the titles of the sultan on the Freer basin is *khalil amir al-mu'minin* (beloved of the Commander of the Faithful), which must have been used by Najm al-Din after he received the caliphal investiture in 1247. Although this title was at times employed by Ayyubid rulers without the official investiture, it would be safe to date the basin toward the end of Najm al-Din's reign.

51. Brass bowl inlaid with silver
Made for Sultan Najm al-Din Ayyub
Egypt or Syria, ca. 1240s
(Ann Arbor, University of Michigan,
Kelsey Museum of Archaeology, 28801)

52. Brass basin inlaid with silver
Made for Sultan Najm al-Din Ayyub
Egypt or Syria, ca. 1240s
(Cairo, Museum of Islamic Art, 15043)

53. Brass tray inlaid with silver
Made for Sultan Najm al-Din Ayyub
Egypt or Syria, ca. 1240s
(Paris, Musée du Louvre, MAO 360)

The shape of the Freer basin, with its rounded base and flaring rim, was characteristic of Ayyubid metalwork and continued to be popularly employed by Mamluk artists, surviving into the seventeenth century.[6] Among the Ayyubid examples is the basin (fig. 54) made by Ahmad ibn Umar al-Dhaki for Sultan al-Adil II (1238–40), the brother and predecessor of Najm al-Din.[7] In the Mamluk period, some of these basins were made with matching ewers, a practice that might have existed earlier although no such sets dating from the Ayyubid era have come to light.[8]

The extraordinarily rich repertoire of themes found on the Freer basin suggests that it was not made as a mere functional object for washing or ritual ablution. The pictorial scenes were carefully selected and reflect the owner's taste and activities. Decorative features, such as animated scrolls, bands with running animals, different styles of scripts used in the inscriptions, seated musicians and drinkers, as well as the fill-ins in the background that alternate the tightly wound spirals with the looser split-leaf scroll, were common to the metalwork vocabulary of the age. The panels with polo players, on the other hand, relate to one of the sultan's personal interests. Najm al-Din was renowned for his fondness of this game and built a polo ground in Cairo and a bridge over the Nile to give easy access to it.[9]

The inclusion of Christian themes, although found on other contemporary metalwork (see no. 17), appears highly unusual for an object made for a valiant defender of Islam who lost his life fighting the Crusaders. Although this was a period of continual war between the Muslims and the Crusaders, there were periods of peace and diplomatic exchanges, however brief. Both parties were involved with internal problems that necessitated alliances among the adversaries. One such instance occurred in 1240 when Najm al-Din, faced with family rivalries, made a treaty with Theobald of Champagne, King of Navarre.[10] One wonders whether such diplomatic negotiations also included the exchange of gifts. A most befitting gift from the sultan would be an object exquisitely decorated with the donor's titles and epitaphs as well as his favorite activities. The inclusion of Christian themes would reflect his universality and ecumenism and also honor his new ally. If indeed this was the case, the basin was then taken to France and passed into the hands of the Borniol family during the eighteenth century.

The identification of the centers of metalworking under the Ayyubids is far from being determined. Syria is generally thought to have been the source for objects decorated with Christian scenes, owing to the large Christian communities residing there. On the other hand, Egypt, particularly Cairo, also had a substantial Christian population and was the capital of the empire. With the exception of two ewers, inlaid pieces dating from this period do not bear inscriptions stating where they were executed. The exceptions are one ewer (fig. 8) made by Shuja ibn Mana in 1232 in Mosul[11]; and the other by Husayn ibn Muhammad in 1258 in Damascus for al-Malik al-Nasir Yusuf, the last Ayyubid ruler of that city.[12] In contrast, several objects produced during the early Mamluk period have inscriptions stating that they were made in Cairo,[13] which must have been producing metalwork under the Ayyubids as well.

54. Brass basin inlaid with silver
Made for Sultan al-Adil II
Made by Ahmad b. Umar al-Dhaki
Egypt or Syria, ca. 1238–40
(Paris, Musée du Louvre, 5991)

145

It is not possible, therefore, to determine where the Freer basin was made, since there is no documentation supporting either Egypt or Syria. Metalwork ateliers must have existed in both countries, and decorative themes were shared by a number of artists working in different regions. The distinction between Egyptian and Syrian ateliers cannot yet be established for Ayyubid or Mamluk metalwork.

Technical Notes

The basin was formed from one sheet of metal by what appears to be a combination of raising and turning. No seams or joins are to be found on the vessel. Raising is indicated by the radiographic appearance of the walls, which shows irregular variations in density. The particular evidence that suggests turning are the slight concentric ridges apparent on the bottom of the basin, several concentric striations on the sides, and a centering mark on the outside surface of the bottom. Polishing methods using a lathe might leave concentric striations as well, but would probably not leave ridges such as those found on the bottom surface. Also, the walls are quite regular in their thickness, measuring 1.0 to 1.5 millimeters (0.04 to 0.06 inch). The exceptions are the somewhat thinner corner where the sides meet the bottom and the rim that is appreciably thicker.

The broad areas of silver inlay are set into recesses formed with punches to create the outline and with chisels to remove the central area. The depth of the recesses leaves the inlay lying flush with the surrounding surface. The inlaid lines of silver are set into double rows of punch marks. Chasing was used to add detail to the inlay and to decorate the body metal. It is interesting to note the difference in technique between the original chased decorations and the later addition of the engraved crest on the bottom of the basin.

Chasing, together with hatching, was also used to prepare some of the recessed areas of the design for the application of an organic black inlay material. The composition of this black material is undetermined.

Much of the inlay on the basin has been lost. Besides the complete loss of the inlay on the inside bottom surface, the inner walls are also missing numerous areas of inlay. The outside surface has fared much better, but many of the larger pieces of inlay used for the bodies of the figures have also been lost. Some cracks are present at the corner, and one area was repaired at some time with soft solder. The silver inlay and the body metal are, for the most part, free of corrosion.

The average of five analyses of three different areas on the surface of the basin is given below.

Copper	Zinc	Lead	Tin
78.9 ($\pm$0.5)	19.0% ($\pm$0.3)	1.4% ($\pm$0.2)	0.5% ($\pm$0.1)

Provenance: Purchased from Stora, New York, 1955; formerly in the Duc d'Arenberg Collection, Brussels.

Published (Selected):

Migeon 1903, pls. 11–12.

Sarre and Martin 1912, pl. 147.

Répertoire, vol. 11, no. 4302.

Rice 1952, pl. 9b.

Schneider 1973, figs. 19 and 21.

Sourdel-Thomine and Spuler 1973, pl. XXXVIII.

Atıl 1975, no. 27.

Erginsoy 1978, figs. 156a–c.

Ghulam 1982, pp. 186–99.

Baer 1983, figs. 100 and 126.

Katzenstein and Lowry 1983, pls. 3–4.

Notes:

1. The reading and translation were supplied by Robert A. Brooks, the late undersecretary of the Smithsonian Institution.

2. This identification was provided by Helmut Nickel, curator of arms and armor at the Metropolitan Museum of Art, New York. In Rietstap 1965, vol. 2, p. 1207, it is stated that the Borniol Counts of Dauphiné, Nivernais, Normandie, and Provence used the following colors: a blue shield with a gold chevron, two golden roses, and a silver bull. According to the code of hatching used on the Freer basin, the colors depicted here are a white shield with a blue chevron, two red roses, and a red bull. It was suggested by Dr. Nickel that this coat of arms belonged to a branch of the Borniol family. The Société Française d'Héraldique et de Sigillographie of France did not offer further assistance.

3. O. Grabar 1961.

4. Izzi 1965.

5. Paris 1971, no. 153.

6. Wiet 1932, pp. 65–69, lists over seventy such basins. For another Ayyubid example see Allan 1982a, no. 12. Mamluk pieces are discussed in Atıl 1981, p. 51 and nos. 18, 21, and 26–27.

7. Rice 1957a, pls. 6–9; and Paris 1971, no. 150.

8. Two sets with matching basins and ewers are known to have been made in the 1270s: one set was signed by Ali ibn Abdallah (Kühnel 1939); the other was made by Ali ibn Hamud (Mayer 1959, pp. 33–34; and Harari 1964–65, pls. 1341–42).

9. Rice 1952, p. 572, note 5.

10. Humphreys 1977, pp. 268–69.

11. Barrett 1949, no. 12; and Harari 1964–65, pls. 1329–30.

12. Rice 1957a, pls. 13c–d; and Paris 1971, no. 152.

13. Rice 1957a, pp. 325–26, nos. 17–28; and Atıl 1981, no. 10.

19. Candlestick

Brass: cast and turned; chased and inlaid with silver
and black organic material

Turkey, late 13th century

Height: 20.0 cm. (7⅞ in.); diameter: 19.7 cm. (7¾ in.);
weight: 1,764.0 gm. (62.2 oz.)

81.27

Inscriptions (Arabic)

1. On the socket (animated naskhi):

Eternal glory, complete and perpetual prosperity, command, prosperity.	العز الدائم الاقبال الشـ ٭ ـامل و الالباقى المر الافبا[ل]

2. On the neck (naskhi):

Eternal glory, complete and perpetual prosperity.	العز الدائم الاقبال ا ٭ لشامل و الباقى ا

3. Inner band on the shoulder (kufic):
   Alifs and *lams* joined by *ains, dals,* and *kafs*.

4. Outer band on the shoulder (naskhi):
   Too abraded to be read properly.

5. Upper band on the base (kufic):
   Same as inner band on shoulder.

6. Lower band on the base (kufic):
   Same as inner band on shoulder.

Among the most popular metalwork produced during the thirteenth and fourteenth centuries is this type of candlestick, which has a concave socket and base and a short cylindrical neck. The Freer piece is decorated with inscriptions, running animals, medallions with astrological symbols, and floral and geometric motifs.

The socket, framed by thin strips with braids or strokes, has an animated naskhi inscription broken into two by roundels bearing birds. The neck, framed by broad braided bands, has a plain naskhi inscription intersected by the same two roundels.

The shoulder, greatly abraded from years of use and handling, contains two concentric bands. The inner band, broken into four units by eight-petaled rosettes, reveals a kufic

detail of medallions representing May–August

inscription. The outer band, interrupted by four geometric roundels, alternates a panel of naskhi inscriptions with that of three four-legged animals running to the left. Although these inscriptions are difficult to read, the wording appears to follow the phrases found on the socket and neck.

The base is divided into six horizontal zones of unequal widths. The upper zone has a kufic inscription, followed by a thin floral scroll. The widest portion of the base contains twelve medallions with astrological symbols; it is placed over a frieze of fifteen running quadrupeds, which are interrupted by five six-petaled rosettes. Below is another kufic inscription broken by five geometric roundels. The flaring foot has a series of diagonal lines.

The backgrounds reveal two different types of scrolls that are used alternately: a loose vine with large leaves and a tightly wound hooked scroll. The interstices of the medallions employ either a third type of scroll having split-leaves, or a geometric motif.

The medallions appear at first to represent either the signs of the zodiac or the personifications of the planets. Upon comparison with various symbols used to identify the months of the year, it becomes clear that what is depicted here is a twelve-month calendar. The months and their respective zodiac signs are depicted in the following manner:

1. January (Aquarius): a standing figure pulls a bucket from a well.
2. February (Pisces): a seated figure is shown with two fish.
3. March (Mars): a seated figure is shown with a sword and shield.
4. April (Venus): a seated figure is shown with a lute.
5. May (Mercury): a standing figure sows.
6. June (Cancer): a disc (moon?) is enclosed by the claws of a crab.
7. July (the sun): a disc is shown with radiating rays.

detail of medallions representing September–December

8. August (Mercury): a seated figure is shown with a writing tablet.
9. September (Libra): a seated figure is shown with a balance.
10. October (Scorpio): a standing figure is shown with scorpions(?).
11. November (Sagittarius): a standing figure is shown with a bow and sheaf.
12. December (Saturn): a seated figure is shown with a pickaxe(?).

It appears that the artist has chosen to represent the twelve-month calendar not with the labor associated with each month but with the corresponding astrological symbols. There exist at least seven contemporary candlesticks that depict the labors (see fig. 55), based on Byzantine and Georgian cycles.[1] Although the shape, size, surface division, decorative motifs, and inscriptions of the Freer candlestick conform with those used in the examples showing the labors of the months, its iconography is highly innovative.[2] These seven candlesticks represent the cycle of labors associated with the twelve-month Gregorian calendar, which is based on the seasons. In the Islamic world, where the lunar calendar is used, the first month (that is, Muharram) is not always in winter. Hence it makes far better sense to avoid references to activities representing the months according to the seasons and to replace them with the proper astrological symbols that remain the same, regardless of the season into which a particular month falls throughout the course of the year.

This candlestick belongs to a series of at least sixty examples that appear to have been mass-produced with identical shapes and sizes.[3] Their shapes can be related to a group dated to the second half of the thirteenth century and assigned to the Fars region in Iran.[4] Their decorative vocabulary utilizes a wide range of princely themes, astrological symbols, inscriptions, and floral and geometric motifs that are found in contemporary Syrian and Iranian metalwork. The inscriptions do not indicate where or when they were produced. Only one example bears the name of the maker, Shirin ibn Avhad al-

151

Quvayi[5]; another unique piece gives the name of the patron, Muhammad ibn Sadr al-Din Yusuf ibn Salah al-Din, both of whom are otherwise unrecorded.[6]

In the past the entire group was attributed to Tabriz or to western Iran. These pieces were recently assigned to Turkey, more specifically to Konya, the capital of the Seljuks of Anatolia,[7] or to Siirt, a city in the southeast governed by the Artukids until the fifteenth century.[8] Whether or not they were all made in one location or were produced in a wider region encompassing southeastern Turkey, northern Iraq and Syria, and northwestern Iran cannot yet be determined.

55. Brass candlestick inlaid with silver and gold
Turkey, late 13th century
(Ann Arbor, The University of Michigan Museum of Art, 1965/1.182)

The candlestick is extremely regular and symmetrical in shape, with a wall thickness that averages approximatey 3 millimeters (⅛ inch). The shaping of the candlestick would seem to be the result of the combined processes of casting and turning. Radiographs of the candlestick reveal its fine porosity and inhomogeneity, as well as voids in the metal, which suggest a cast structure. A lack of apparent joins also suggests that the candlestick was cast in one piece. Concentric ridges and striations, which indicate turning on a lathe, are present on both the outside and inside surfaces of the base. On the outer surface the striations can be found in areas once covered with inlay, and thus seem to be the result of a shaping process rather than of polishing.

A plate forms the shoulder of the candlestick and divides the neck from the base. Passing through the center of the plate, in line with the vertical axis of the candlestick, is a circular hole that measures 8 millimeters (⁵⁄₁₆ inch) in diameter. This hole could well serve to secure the candlestick during a spinning or turning process, and possibly allow for a support for the interior mold pieces of the neck and base during a casting process. The exact purpose of the hole remains unclear.

The inlaid silver lines and the broader areas of inlay were applied in basically the same manner. The silver lines are set into double rows of roughly circular punch marks. The broader areas of inlay also were applied with single or double rows of punch marks to affix the outer edge of the inlay. The body metal lying under the broader areas of inlay was only slightly recessed, particularly along the edges, thus leaving the center of the inlay standing above the surrounding surface. Linear and textural toolwork on the body metal surrounding the inlay is present, but the surface condition is such that it is difficult to tell whether it is the result of chasing or engraving, although the shapes suggest a chasing technique using punches. There also appear to be some remains of a black organic inlay material.

The loss of surface detail and much of the inlay is the major detriment to the candlestick. The shape is still intact and little corrosion is present.

Three areas on the surface were analyzed. An average of the results is given below.

Copper	Zinc	Lead	Tin
78.4% (±1.9)	11.0% (±0.7)	5.2% (±0.4)	4.7% (±1.7)

Provenance: Purchased from Ahuan, London, 1981.
Unpublished

Notes:
1. Six of these have been published in Rice 1954; Atıl 1972; and Soucek 1978, no. 70. For the seventh see Sotheby's 1983, no. 304.
2. There appears to be in Bursa another contemporary candlestick that represents the same cycle (İstanbul 1983, D147). A careful study of the pieces with twelve medallions depicting astrological symbols may reveal other similar examples.
3. In addition to some fifty examples in Rice 1954 and Atıl 1972, at least a dozen more have been studied, including those in Fehérvári 1976b, nos. 134–36; Allan 1982a, nos. 7–9; Melikian-Chirvani 1982, nos. 168–72; and İstanbul 1983, nos. D143–48.
4. For this group see Harari 1964–65, pls. 1333 and 1364; Melikian-Chirvani 1969d, figs. 1–5; and Melikian-Chirvani 1973, pp. 56–58.
5. This candlestick is in the Museo Civico, Bologna. Rice 1954, pp. 18–19 and pls. 11–12.
6. In the Es-Said Collection, London. The patron is thought to be an Ayyubid prince. Allan 1982a, no. 9.
7. Soucek 1978, nos. 69–70.
8. Allan 1978, and 1982a, nos. 7–10.

20. Bowl

Brass: hammered and turned; chased and inlaid with
silver, gold, and black organic material

Iran, early 14th century

Height: 7.2 cm. (2⅞ in.); diameter: 16.6 cm. (6¹³⁄₁₆ in.);
weight: 366.8 gm. (12.9 oz.)

49.11

Inscriptions (Arabic)

1. Upper band on the body (naskhi):

Glory and victory and prosperity and favor and generosity and eminence and excellence and liberality and graciousness and knowledge and liberality and.	العز و النصر و الاقبال [و] النعم وا ٭ لجود [و] المجد والافضال [و] الك ٭ ر[م] والحلم والعلم والكرم وا

2. Medallions on the body (thuluth):

Glory to our master, the greatest sultan, lord of the necks of the nations, the sultan of sultans of the Arabs and non-Arabs, the wise, the just, the defender [of the faith], the warrior [of the frontiers], the supported [by God], the victorious, the triumphant over enemies, the inheritor of the kingdom of Solomon, the most just . . .	عز لمولانا ا[ل]سلطان الا ٭ عظم مالك رقاب الامم سلطان ٭ سلاطين العرب و العجم العا ٭ الم العادل المجاهد المرا ٭ بط المؤيد المظفر المنصور على ال ٭ عدا وارث ملك سليمان اعدل ا

This small bowl is among the earliest examples of metalwork produced in Iran after the Mongol conquest. Its design utilizes a six-part division, which in some cases is either subdivided into two units of threes or multiplied by two, creating a twelve-part composition. The flattened rim, broken into equal parts by six geometric roundels, is decorated with a braided pattern that alternates with a scroll. A beaded band encircles the outer edge. Below is a frieze broken into equal parts by six geometric roundels and filled with two alternating designs placed on a floral ground: naskhi inscriptions and a group of three quadrupeds shown running to the right. The quadrupeds include a predator (wolves or lions) chasing two prey (ibexes, foxes, or hares); the one in the middle turns back its head toward the aggressor. A band intersected with six geometric roundels and filled either with a braided strapwork or a floral scroll appears in the next zone.

The widest portion of the swelling sides has six oval medallions with bold thuluth inscriptions; these are interrupted by six medallions, each of which represents a horseman riding to the left. Floral scrolls appear behind the inscriptions and the riders; geometric motifs fill the interstices. The riders have haloes and wear caps; with the exception of one figure who is emptyhanded, they hold a mace in their right or left hands.

The lower portion of the walls is densely covered with intersecting circles and floral motifs, radiating from lancet-shaped leaves or sun rays placed around the edge of the

interior

base. At the center of the base is a medallion composed of six intersecting lobed semicircles filled with floral motifs. Surrounding this is a six-pointed star, also filled with florals; knotted cartouches appear between the points of the star.

The interior of the bowl repeats the solar theme seen on the outer base. Here, radiating from a central disc is a twelve-pointed star with additional rays in the interstices. Four rows of fish, each row shown swimming in the opposite direction, create a concentric whirling movement around the star.[1] In a fifth row, fish swim vertically down the inner walls with their heads pointed toward the swirling creatures in the center.

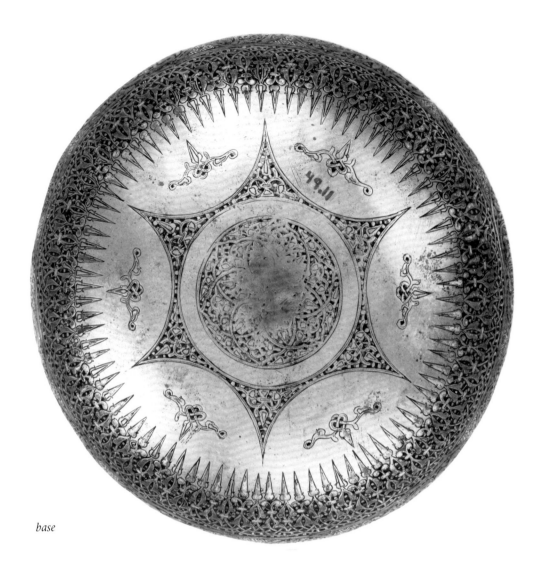

base

The piece is lavishly inlaid with silver; gold appears only on the tripartite inscription on the upper portion of the walls and in the small geometric roundels.

The bowl not only is designed and executed with great care but also reveals a sophisticated use of symbols, particularly in the placement of the solar themes on both the exterior and interior of the base. On the exterior the sun radiates from a central core and explodes into a star encircled by rays, which in turn surround the edge of the bowl and move up into the outer walls, symbolizing the divine light in the heavens or in the sky. On the interior the sun and its radiating rays are engulfed by fish swimming clockwise and counterclockwise, representing the solar body's manifestation in the water.

The placement of the symbols is intentional: when liquid is poured into the bowl, the celestial light in the water becomes visually evident; when the bowl is tilted during use, the image of sun in the heavens is fully exposed to the observers.

The revolving geometric motifs in the small roundels on the rim, on the upper two bands of the body, and in the interstices of the medallions and oval units also reflect the theme of celestial light. The roundels are inlaid with gold, which further accentuates the concept of the brilliant and omnipotent light of the heavens.

The Freer bowl belongs to a series of fourteenth-century brasses inlaid with silver and/or gold assigned to the province of Fars in southern Iran. Many of these objects employ the phrase "inheritor of the kingdom of Solomon," a title used by the rulers of Fars who controlled Persepolis and Pasargadae, sites thought to be associated with the patriarch Solomon.[2] The attribution of the entire series to Fars is further stressed by the inscriptions found on several of the pieces. The name of one of the last Inju rulers of the area, Jamal al-Din Abu Ishaq (1341–53), is inscribed on a bowl (fig. 56) in Brussels decorated in a manner almost identical to the Freer example; and on a bucket in the Hermitage, made in 1332/33 by Muhammad Shah al-Shirazi.[3] The *nisba* al-Shirazi also appears on a bowl (fig. 13) made in 1305 by Abd al-Qadir ibn Ahmad al-Khaliq, now in Galleria Estense in Modena.[4]

The majority of the objects in this series are bowls that have fairly consistent proportions and shapes. Their decorative repertoire is limited to such princely themes as entertainment scenes, hunters, riders, and enthroned personages (fig. 57; see also no. 21). The earliest dated example is the 1305 bowl in Modena.[5] Other dated bowls were made in 1338 by Said (fig. 59); in 1347 by an unknown artist; and in 1351/52 by Turanshah (fig. 58) for Muhammad ibn Muhammad ibn Abdullah al-Jurjani, an unknown patron.[6]

Although the decorative themes found on the Freer bowl are very close to those employed on the one made for Abu Ishaq in the middle of the fourteenth century, the refined execution of the motifs and the minute scale of the parts suggest that it was produced around the same date as the 1305 example made by Abd al-Qadir.

56. Brass bowl inlaid with silver and gold
Made for Jamal al-Din Abu Ishaq
Iran, ca. 1340s
(Brussels, Musées Royaux d'Art et d'Histoire, E.O. 1492)

57. Brass bowl inlaid with silver and gold
Iran, early 14th century
(Kuwait, National Museum, Dar al-Athar al-Islamiya Collection, LNS 116 M)

58. Brass bowl inlaid with silver and gold
Made for Muhammad b. Muhammad b. Abdullah al-Jurjani
Made by Turanshah
Iran, dated 1351/52
(London, Victoria and Albert Museum, 760–1889)

Technical Notes

The bowl appears to have been shaped basically by raising. Radiographic images of the bowl show variations in the density of the metal that makes up the bottom and walls of the vessel, although no difference in thickness can be discerned. Moreover, the bowl is slightly asymmetrical, which it would not be if the bowl were produced by spinning, unless the irregularity were caused by subsequent working or damage.

A centering mark and concentric striations on the inside of the bowl, however, suggest that some turning or polishing with a lathe was employed. As the striations occur mostly near the rim, the marks may be the result of the shaping or finishing process used to produce the relatively thick lip of the bowl.

The decoration of the bowl shows a variety of materials and techniques. Silver inlay was predominantly used, but also present are some small areas of gold and black inlay. Again, the technique used employed the application of silver sheet onto a punch-marked surface. The linear silver and gold inlay was applied to the punch marks that follow, and are placed to either side of, a scribed line. A similar use of a scribed line to denote the course of the inlay was employed for the decoration of the other bowl in this catalogue with a similar attribution (no. 21), although other differences in technique are apparent.

Wider areas of inlay were applied into a punch-marked outline and there was no indentation of the underlying metal. In one area it was possible to lift up a loose edge of inlay to examine the surface it covered. A thin layer of resinous material was present, which suggests that adhesive was employed in the application of the inlay. The adherence of the inlay would seem, nonetheless, to be mainly mechanical. One could also see the slight undercutting of the body metal along the outline under which the edge of the inlay fit.

The bowl was further decorated by chasing to add details to the silver inlay. In addition, black inlay, an organic compound containing minute amounts of calcite and quartz, was applied to hatched recesses on the body metal. The black material is sometimes found in the punched outline of lost inlay and thus may be a later addition or, if original, displaced from its correct location.

As with many of the other inlaid brass vessels, the bowl has suffered the loss of much of its inlay. On the inside of the bowl, only one small piece of silver inlay remains. The outside surface has fared much better, but a number of the larger pieces of inlay are now missing. Also, some dents slightly distort the shape of the bowl. Otherwise the bowl is in good condition.

Two areas on the surface were analyzed with the following results:

Copper	Zinc	Lead	Tin
75.9% ($\pm$1.4)	21.5% ($\pm$0.7)	1.5% ($\pm$1.4)	trace

Provenance: Purchased from Stora, New York, 1949.

Published: Ettinghausen 1957, fig. 40.

Atıl 1971, no. 61.

Campbell 1973, pls. 21 and 22.

Melikian-Chirvani 1982, note 60, pp. 155–56.

Notes:

1. For a detailed study of this "fish-pond" concept see Baer 1968. The most complicated and elaborate design based on this theme was employed inside the famous Louvre basin produced at the turn of the fourteenth century during the Mamluk period. Atıl 1981, no. 21.

2. Melikian-Chirvani 1971b.

3. The Brussels bowl, however, is considerably larger than the Freer example; Montgomery-Wyaux 1978, figs. 18 and 19. For the Hermitage bucket see Harari 1964–65, pl. 1363B; and Allan 1982a, p. 106, for the corrected reading of the date.

4. Scerrato 1966, pl. 47; Baer 1968, pls. I–VI and figs. 1–8; and Baer 1983, fig. 169.

5. A second bowl, formerly owned by the Mr. and Mrs. Jack A. Josephson Collection, New York, now in the al-Sabah Collection in Kuwait (Jenkins 1983, pl. 93), was published erroneously as being dated 1305 (Katonah 1980, no. 43). This example is almost identical to the Freer bowl, except that the quadrupeds on the uppermost band run counterclockwise whereas in the Freer example they run clockwise. Inside is a radiating star enclosed by an intricate fish-pond theme; musicians, mermaids, turtles, eels, and other sea creatures recall the design in the Louvre basin.

6. The 1338 bowl is published in Melikian-Chirvani 1969c, pls. II–IIIa; and Paris 1971, no. 138. The 1347 example, in Lyon, appears in Baer 1968, pl. VIII; and Melikian-Chirvani 1969b, figs. 1–12. For the one made by Turanshah, see Melikian-Chirvani 1982, no. 104. The latter has an unusual decoration and represents episodes from the *Shahnama*.

21. Bowl

Brass: hammered and turned; chased, and inlaid with silver,
gold, and black organic material

Iran, mid-14th century

Height: 12.0 cm. (4¾ in.); diameter: 23.0 cm. (9 in.);
weight: 999.2 gr. (35.2 oz.)

80.25

Inscriptions (Arabic)

1. On the body (thuluth):

Glory to our master, the greatest sultan, lord of the necks of the nations, the sultan of sultans of the Arabs and non-Arabs, the wise king[?].	لعز لمولانا السلطان ا ٭ لاعظم مالك رقاب الامم ٭ السلطان السلاطين العرب [و] ٭ العجم العالم المل[ك]

2. Between the vertical letters of the above (kufic):

Perfect [repeated], *favor.*

الكاملة   النعمة

This bowl, larger and deeper than the previous example (no. 20), was produced in the same manner. Its shape is slightly different: the rim band is higher and the swelling of the walls is not as pronounced. Its composition employs a different program and is based on four-part divisions. The rim has a scroll with intersecting circles and the walls contain a wide inscription panel interrupted by four medallions. The base shows a radiating design composed of sixteen cartouches, each filled with a blossom that resembles either a lotus or a peony. Floral scrolls appear in the background of the inscription panels, medallions, and cartouches. The interior of the bowl is undecorated.

The medallions on the walls represent a central figure seated on a benchlike throne, flanked by two standing attendants who hold maces. Blossoms are placed beneath the thrones in three of the medallions; a duck appears in the fourth. The figures wear small caps and their heads are encircled by haloes. Gold inlays have been applied to the faces, hats, and maces as well as to the garments of the enthroned personages.

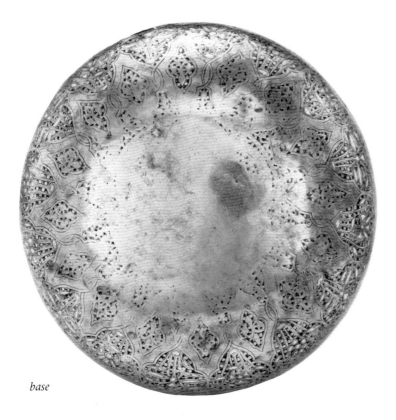

base

59. Brass bowl inlaid with silver and gold
Made by Said
Iran, dated 1338
(Paris, Musée du Louvre, 7880–118)

The inscriptions in the panels between the medallions are characteristic of a group of bowls (see fig. 59 and no. 20) made during the fourteenth century in the province of Fars in southern Iran, which was ruled by the Inju and Muzaffarid sultans.[1] Identical phrases appear on three other bowls similarly decorated with medallions representing enthroned figures flanked by two attendants: two are in Lyon; the third is in the Victoria and Albert Museum.[2] Two of these also have kufic letters interspersed with the vertical shafts of the thuluth inscriptions.[3]

A number of other fourteenth-century examples employ the theme of an enthroned personage with standing attendants.[4] The figures on the pieces wear conical caps and the majority of the attendants hold maces or clubs. It has been suggested that the attendants represent dervishes or mystics paying tribute to their shaykh who is seated in the center.[5] The lack of crowns on the enthroned figures and the use of conical caps, which recall Sufi headdresses, tend to support this attribution. Also associated with symbols of Sufism are certain decorative motifs on the Freer bowl, such as interlacing circles on the rim, lotus blossoms on the base, and the solitary duck beneath one of the thrones, which are thought to represent celestial light as well as immortality and resurrection.

Even though the scenes in the medallions and motifs with solar symbols imply a Sufi patronage, the titles used in the inscriptions are imperial and refer to a sultan, however anonymous. The combination of royal and mystic themes makes the identity of the owner of the Freer bowl difficult to establish. Bowls with a similar mixture of themes

164

were not uncommon for the period and reflect a ruling class that was profoundly involved with Islamic mysticism.

The bowl, formed from relatively thin sheet, appears to have been shaped by hammering, although turning may have been used as well. The walls of the bowl become progressively thicker as they rise toward the lip, which is triangular in cross section and quite thick in comparison to the walls. Many irregular scratches circle the inner surface of the bowl, beginning where the diameter starts to decrease and extending up to the lip.

Thin sheets of gold and silver inlay compose the figures and the characters of the inscription. Punches were used to raise the lip and undercut an outline of the area to be filled with inlay. The lip was then hammered down over the edge of the inlay. In some cases the lip was raised to such an extent that when it was hammered down to secure the inlay, the edge of the inlay became buckled and creases were formed in the body metal adjacent to the inlaid area. The linear silver inlay is much thicker than the broad areas of silver inlay. Wire was probably used for these lines and the silver was set into rows of triangular-shaped punch marks that follow scribed lines.

A black compound has been used extensively as inlay on the bowl. This material was applied in slight depressions chased with hatched lines. X-ray diffraction analysis of the inlay shows the presence of quartz and calcite, two minerals that have been found commonly in previous analyses of bitumen from the area of Iran.[6]

Although the bowl shows a number of signs of wear, its overall condition is good. Some inlay has been lost and the decoration on the bottom of the bowl has been worn away. A crack in the rim bears an old repair consisting of a metal patch attached with soft solder. Little corrosion is present.

The average of three analyses of various areas on the surface is as follows:

Copper	Zinc	Lead	Tin
79.0% ($\pm$0.9)	19.0% ($\pm$0.5)	0.9% ($\pm$0.2)	1.0% ($\pm$0.4)

Provenance: Purchased from Axia, London, 1980.
Unpublished

Notes:

1. For published examples of this group of objects, see Ettinghausen 1935; Harari 1964–65, pls. 1363A, 1367–70, and 1372; Baer 1968; Melikian-Chirvani 1969b–d and 1973, pp. 70–73, 79, and 86–89; Campbell 1973; Leth 1975, p. 83; Allan 1982a, no. 24; Melikian-Chirvani 1982, nos. 91–92, 95–98, 102, 104, 108; and Jenkins 1983, pl. 93. See also notes, 3, 4, and 6 for catalogue no. 20 in this publication for objects inscribed with dates and names of patrons and artists.

2. Melikian-Chirvani 1969b, figs. 18–22; and Melikian-Chirvani 1982, no. 98.

3. Kufic inscriptions placed over the thuluth script appear on two other contemporary bowls: one formerly in the Harari Collection (Ettinghausen 1935; and Harari 1964–65, pls. 1366 and 1367A); and the second, dated 1338, illustrated here in fig. 59. They are also used on a fourteenth-century candlestick in the British Museum (Barrett 1949, pl. 35).

4. Those that show a seated figure flanked by two standing attendants are in the British Museum (Barrett 1949 pl. 36; and Harari 1964–65, pl. 1370); Louvre (Melikian-Chirvani 1969c, pls. IXa and X); Victoria and Albert Museum (Melikian-Chirvani 1973, pp. 86–87; and Melikian-Chirvani 1982, no. 97); and in the David Collection, Copenhagen (Leth 1975, p. 83). Four attendants flanking the central figure are represented on a bowl formerly in the Cartier Collection, now in the Es-Said Collection, London (Harari 1964–65, pl. 1372; and Allan 1982a, no. 24); and on a second example in the Musée des Arts Décoratifs, Paris (Melikian-Chirvani 1973, p. 79).

5. Allan 1982a, pp. 107–8.

6. Marschner and Wright 1978, pp. 150–71.

22. Plate with Central Boss

Brass: hammered and turned; chased and inlaid with silver and gold

Made for an amir of Sultan al-Malik al-Nasir

Egypt, mid-14th century

Height: 3.2 cm. (1¼ in); diameter: 28.9 cm. (11⅜ in.);
  weight: 1,024.0 gm. (36.1 oz.)

53.89

Inscriptions (Arabic)

1. Central medallion (thuluth):

His exalted excellency, the lord, the high, the just, [the officer] *of al-Malik al-Nasir.*	المقر العالى المالكى العالى العادلى الملكى الناصرى

2. Band around the cavetto (thuluth):

His exalted excellency, the lord, the learned, the efficient, the just, the vanquisher, the defender [of the faith], *the warrior* [of the frontiers], *the warden of the marches, the viceroy, the lord,* [the officer] *of al-Malik al-Nasir.*	المقر العالى المالكى العالمى * العاملى العادلى الغازى المجاهد[ى] * المرابطى المشاغر[ى] الكفيلى * المالكى الملكى الناصرى

The shape of this plate, with its raised central medallion, curved cavetto, and flattened rim, is highly unusual for Mamluk metalwork. On the other hand, the thuluth inscriptions, pairs of flying ducks, and lotus blossoms that decorate the piece are among the most characteristic features of fourteenth-century inlaid brasses produced in Egypt and Syria.

The raised central medallion, or boss, surrounded by a radiating inscription, has a six-petaled rosette in the core. Around it is a band divided into eight units, alternately filled with large lotuses flanked by five-petaled blossoms and two pairs of ducks flying around a branch with flowers. A thin ribbon outlines the band and loops around the units with the lotuses and ducks. The sloping edge of the boss is decorated with chevrons.

Encircling the boss is a wide band of inscriptions broken into four panels by ogival medallions alternately bearing large lotuses with smaller blossoms and three pairs of addorsed and confronted flying ducks. Pendants extending from the medallions, interspersed with cartouches filled with floral scrolls, appear in the sparsely decorated cavetto and in the zone between the boss and the inscription panel.

The rim bears a pearl band and a frieze of fourteen quadrupeds separated by flying ducks. The animals, which run counterclockwise, represent real and fantastic creatures, including deer, tigers, wolves, cheetahs, gazelles, foxes(?), hares, lions, and elephants as well as a winged griffin, sphinx, and unicorn.

The plate has lost almost all of its gold inlay and parts of the silver. The execution of the inlay was fairly crude and neither the silver nor gold were carefully affixed into chased areas and lines. Gold was used in the circular inscription on the central boss, in the five-petaled blossoms flanking the large lotuses, in the branches between the flying ducks, and in the center of the lotuses.

The inscriptions state that the owner was an officer in the service of Sultan al-Malik al-Nasir, a title used by several Mamluk rulers. The stylistic features suggest that this sultan may have been Hasan (1347–51 and 1354–61), a renowned patron of the arts who commissioned the famous complex in Cairo and a number of glass and metal objects.[1] The motifs used on the Freer plate can be found on a rosewater sprinkler made for Sultan Hasan.[2]

Only one other plate with the same shape (fig. 60) has been published.[3] This example, in the Keir Collection in Ham, Richmond, is divided into identical zones but employs only birds in the central boss and only lotus blossoms in the four medallions intersecting the wide inscription band. The inscription, read as "al-Maliki al-Salihi,"[4] most likely refers to Sultan Salih (1351–54), who ruled between the first and second reigns of Sultan Hasan.

During the fourteenth century a large number of inlaid brasses were made for the Mamluk amirs who were identified only by the titles of their masters. These objects were mass-produced and available to a number of officers who served the same sultan. The relatively poor quality of workmanship indicates that ateliers supplied both imperial pieces for the rulers as well as objects of lesser value for members of the lower ranks. The decoration employed stock-in-trade features, such as bold thuluth inscriptions, often written in a circular format with the vertical shafts of the letters radiating from the core; rosettes with swirling petals and large lotus blossoms; and ducks flying in pairs, either addorsed or confronted. Circular inscriptions, rosettes, lotuses, and ducks are associated with solar symbolism. These motifs may have had astrological meanings and were used as charms for their magical or protective values.

60. Brass plate inlaid with silver
Egypt, mid-14th century
(Ham, Richmond [England], The Keir
Collection)

Technical Notes

Photomicrograph illustrating the inlay technique. Along the bottom of the photograph, double rows of punch marks indicate areas where lost silver inlay was replaced and subsequently lost again. Actual size of the area illustrated: 27 x 21 mm. (1¹/₁₆ x ¹³/₁₆ in.)

The plate appears to have been formed by hammering, with some final shaping and finishing executed by turning and polishing on a lathe. Radiographs of the plate have a mottled appearance, which describes the variations in density that are the result of hammering. Moreover, the prominent presence of concentric striations and centering marks on both sides of the plate confirm the use of a lathe. Slight undulations in the surface, which follow a concentric path around the plate, tend to suggest turning or the use of the lathe for polishing.

The silver inlay was applied between rows of punch marks. The metal underlying the inlay has been recessed in some cases. Chasing or cutting away the metal, the metalsmith worked from the center of the area to be inlaid toward each edge. This left the inlay standing above the surrounding surface along its center and flush along the edges. For some of the inlay, the underlying metal was not recessed. Chasing was used to add further details to the inlay. Narrow lines of silver inlay were executed by the typical method of hammering silver strips or wire into a double row of closely spaced, small punch marks.

In a number of areas, one finds two double rows of punch marks. The double rows exhibit the use of different punches in a dissimilar manner and the rows often meander across each other. These marks appear to indicate areas of repair where lost inlay was replaced, and often lost again.

Besides the silver inlay, there are a few very small fragments of gold inlay. The gold inlay is found in lines applied to single rows of punch marks. Between the inlaid areas, the background has been finished with fine, chased hatching.

The plate has a deep green-brown patina against which the bright silver inlay stands out sharply. With the exception of the lost inlay and a few nicks and other signs of wear, the plate is in fine condition.

An average of the analyses of two areas on the surface yields the results given below.

Copper	Zinc	Lead	Tin
82% (±11)	15% (±12)	0.9% (±0)	1.6% (±1.1)

Provenance: Purchased from de Lorey, Paris, 1953.
Published: Grousset 1931, fig. 165.
San Francisco 1937, no. 193.
Atıl 1975, no. 78.

Notes:
1. For references to his glass and metal objects see Atıl 1981, nos. 31 and 52.
2. Ibid., no. 31.
3. Fehérvári 1976b, no. 154.
4. This reading was given in Rogers 1977, pp. 238–39.

23. Globe

> Brass: spun and turned; pierced, chased, and inlaid with
> silver and black organic material
> Egypt or Syria, mid-14th century
> Diameter: 12.5 cm. (4¹⁵⁄₁₆ in.); weight: 543.0 gm. (19.2 oz.)
> 39.58

This globe, which may have been designed to be used as both a hand warmer and an incense burner, is constructed of two hemispheres that lock together by two pins fitted into grooves. Inside one of the hemispheres is a cup-shaped fire pot attached to gimbals

61. Pierced silver globe
China, 7th–9th centuries

made up of three circular discs connected by pivots. The gimbals allow the fire pot to remain upright, regardless of the way the globe is turned.

The exterior of each hemisphere has four concentric zones separated by thin strips and is pierced with circular holes. On the top is a medallion containing geometric strapwork with braids and knots, followed by a band of scrolling vines bearing trefoil leaves. The next zone is the widest and has a geometric design; the motifs around the edges are made to resemble plaited kufic inscriptions, with the vertical shafts of the letters forming elaborate knots. The trefoil scroll seen at the top also appears around the edge. Floral scrolls fill the background of all zones.

The shape and construction of the globe predates the Mamluk period. Similar pieces (see fig. 61), made in silver, were produced in China as early as the T'ang period.[1] The Chinese examples are smaller and were meant to be incense burners suspended by chains from ceilings. Pierced globes with gimbals also were produced in Europe in the thirteenth and fourteenth centuries; since most of these do not have hooks for suspension, they must have been used as hand warmers.[2]

The majority of the known Islamic pierced globes date from the Mamluk period. One of the earliest examples (fig. 62), in the British Museum, was made around 1270 for Badr al-Din Baysari, a Syrian amir.[3] With a diameter of 18.4 centimeters (7¼ inches), it is probably the largest in the series. Other Mamluk globes are about the same size as the Freer piece, and some have loops at the top for suspension.[4]

Mamluk pierced globes, thought to have been made for export to European cities with colder climates, were imitated by Venetian artists in the sixteenth century.[5] The Venetian pieces are remarkably similar in technique and decoration to the Mamluk globes, and are often embellished with overall scrolls (see no. 24). Some were made by Muslim artists—including Zayn al-Din and Mahmud ibn al-Kurdi[6]—who emigrated to Venice around 1500.

The decoration of the Freer globe, with its geometric designs simulating plaited kufic inscriptions and scrolls bearing trefoil leaves, suggests that it was produced during the fourteenth century, either in Egypt or Syria. Plaited kufic was used on early Mamluk metalwork, including two candlesticks, one dated 1269 and the other made around 1290.[7] Designs based on this type of script appear slightly later, as observed on the glass mosque lamps made for Sultan Hasan around 1360.[8] Scrolls with trefoil leaves became popular after the middle of the fourteenth century and were frequently employed on inlaid brasses.

62. Pierced brass globe inlaid with silver
Made for Badr al-Din Baysari
Syria, ca. 1270
(London, The British Museum,
78 12–30 682)

Technical Notes

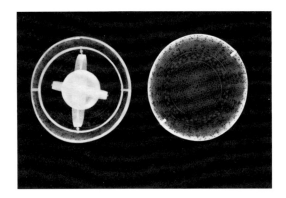

Radiographic image of the two halves. The image of the left half shows the structure of the gimbals with its three bands suspending a bowl in the center.

The halves of the globe were shaped basically by spinning. The centering marks and concentric lines on the outer surface of the globe, as well as the identical shape of the two halves, attest to this method of forming. Turning also appears to have been used to reduce the thickness of the walls, which measure about 0.8 millimeters (0.031 inch) in depth. Concentric striations on the inner surfaces of the walls are evident, and in some cases the striations extend across the slight lips that rim the edges of the drilled holes. The tool marks and the smooth, regular interior surfaces of the narrow walls of the globe—undeformed by the chased design on the exterior surface—suggest that the walls were turned down on the inside following the drilling and chasing of the exterior surface. On one half of the globe a lip was added at the rim. The lip acts to seat and lock the other half.

The rings of the Cardan suspension, or gimbals, were formed from flat strips bent into circular forms. The ends of the strips were then hammered firmly together. The bowl, with walls 2.5 to 3.0 millimeters (0.10 to 0.12 inch) thick, is roughly formed. Although it may be cast, the crude shape, irregularly thick walls, and deep file marks may indicate that the bowl was hammered and filed into shape from a metal blank.

The silver inlay is applied between rows of circular punch marks; the punch marks are placed slightly apart from one another and so do not form a continuous lip. The applied inlay thus has a scalloped edge. The metal that lies underneath the silver has been either very slightly recessed or not recessed at all. In a few cases additional punch marks were added on top of the inlay to secure it more firmly.

The piercing of the globe is made simply of drilled holes of identical size. Further embellishment of the globe consists of chased lines, all of which, it would appear, once held a dark inlay consisting of an organic compound.

The techniques of manufacture and decoration of the globe are almost identical to those of the Freer's Veneto-Islamic bucket (no. 24). On both objects the use of spinning is apparent. In addition, the inlay technique is extremely similar on these two works and quite different from that seen on the other inlaid brasses. Finally, the organic material used as inlay is different from that found on the other brasses. The inlay of both the globe and bucket is more brown than black and exhibits some solubility in organic solvents. The organic compound used as inlay on the other brasses is quite black and generally unaffected by organic solvents.

The general condition of the globe is good. The shape of the two halves and the condition of the gimbals mechanism are nearly perfect. In a number of areas, however, inlay has been lost, particularly along the thin bands that circle the rims where the two halves join. Nevertheless, the overall impression given by the inlay has been little diminished.

Analyses of the top and bottom halves of the globe agree with one another and indicate that the same metal was used for both. The metals used for the bowl and inner rings appear similar, but the latter has a greater amount of copper present; between the various rings and the bowl, the analyses vary by only plus or minus 2 percent. The average of four analyses for the halves of the globe and the analysis of one of the rings is given below.

	Copper	Zinc	Lead	Tin
Globe	72.8% ($\pm$2.4)	25.7% ($\pm$2.0)	1.7% ($\pm$0.6)	not detected
Center Ring	77.8%	21.2%	1.2%	not detected

Provenance: Purchased from Stora, New York, 1939.

Published: Ettinghausen 1960, pl. 4.

Masuda 1961, p. 23.

Atıl 1975, no. 80.

Notes:

1. Two such examples are published in Gyllensvärd 1971, nos. 44a–b.
2. Beard 1940; and Masuda 1961, p. 24.
3. Atıl 1981, no. 11.
4. Two Mamluk examples from the Medici Collection are published in Bargello 1981, nos. 1–2. One of them (no. 2) has the same pseudokufic decoration as the Freer globe.
5. See, for example, the pieces illustrated in Scerrato 1967, nos. 31–32; and Paris 1971, no. 173.
6. Zayn al-Din's hand warmer is now in the Walters Art Gallery, Baltimore (Mayer 1959, p. 91; and Ettinghausen 1966, fig. 13). The one made by Mahmud ibn al-Kurdi is in Museo Civico, Bologna (Mayer 1959, p. 58).
7. The first, made by Muhammad ibn Hasan al-Mawsili, is in the Museum of Islamic Art, Cairo. The second, bearing a dedication to Zayn al-Din Kitbugha, who later became sultan, is broken; the neck and socket are in the Museum of Islamic Art and the base is in the Walters Art Gallery. Atıl 1981, nos. 10 and 15.
8. See, for instance, the Freer example acc. no. 57.19 published in Atıl 1975, no. 76.

24. Bucket with Handle

Brass: spun; chased and inlaid with silver and black organic material; inside gilded

Venice, mid-16th century

Height (without handle): 16.9 cm. ($6^{11}/_{16}$ in); diameter: 30.2 cm. ($11^{7}/_{8}$ in.); weight: 2,661.0 gm. (93.9 oz.)

45.14

The shape of this bucket, with its rounded bottom, straight walls, and bail handle swinging in brackets, dates back to the early Islamic period. There exist eighth-century Umayyad examples as well as a number of ninth- and tenth-century pieces made in Egypt and Iran.[1] A related shape with a more rounded body and at times a high splayed foot was fashionable in Iran during the twelfth and thirteenth centuries.[2] The earliest dated example of the latter type is the celebrated Bobrinsky Kettle (fig. 1) in the Hermitage, made in 1163 by Masud ibn Ahmad of Herat.[3]

The straight-walled type, used as a basin without a handle, reappeared in the late Mamluk period, with fifteenth- and sixteenth-century examples produced in Egypt and Syria.[4] It was popular in Iran about the same time and was depicted in several manuscript illustrations representing bath scenes.

base

177

63. Bronze(?) tray inlaid with silver
Made by Nicolo Rugina
Italy, dated 1550
(Vienna, Österreichisches Museum für
Angewandte Kunst, G0.81)

The Freer bucket belongs to a distinct type of metalwork produced in Venice both by western Asian artists who emigrated there and by local craftsmen who imitated Islamic techniques. About thirty of these pieces bear the names of Muslim artists, including Muhammad, Muhammad Badr, Qasim, Umar, and Zayn al-Din.[5] The most prolific was Mahmud ibn al-Kurdi, whose name appears on some twenty trays, bowls, boxes, ewers, buckets, and hand warmers.[6] The only dated piece is a vase made in 1505 by Ali al-Din and Shams al-Din Muhammad al-Birjandi, in the Museum für Islamische Kunst in Berlin.[7] The undated examples are generally assigned to the first half of the sixteenth century.

Venetian metalworkers who were working in the Islamic tradition called themselves al-Azzimina, after the Arabic word *al-ajam,* meaning non-Arab.[8] By the middle of the sixteenth century, the Venetians could duplicate the technical virtuosity of their teachers, as indicated by the tray (fig. 63) made in 1550 by Nicolo Rugina of Corfu.[9]

The origin of the Veneto-Islamic style has been the subject of ongoing debate. Some scholars feel that it was initiated by Timurid artists who emigrated to Venice at the end of the fifteenth century; others point to the Mamluk tradition of Egypt and Syria as its source. Specific motifs seen on Veneto-Islamic pieces are related more closely to late Mamluk metalwork, and several bear the same Arabic inscriptions.[10]

The decoration of the Freer bucket with two superimposed scrolls, one creating well-defined units and the other forming the background, is characteristic of early Veneto-Islamic work. The projecting rim has a meander pattern on the upper surface and a floral scroll at the edge. The exterior is divided into three registers defined by thin lines, and two narrow bands encircle a wide central portion. A silver inlaid scroll bearing split-leaves forms a mesh covering the surface, its interlacing branches creating elaborate knots and cartouches of diverse shapes. In the background is a finely executed floral scroll with minute trefoils and split-leaves. An identical decoration appears on the rounded base; here, the silver-inlaid scroll evolves from a central medallion containing a ten-pointed star bearing a roundel in its core.

The interior of the bucket is gilded; the edge contains a silver-inlaid scroll with split-leaves, placed against a hatched ground. The bottom contains a lobed medallion enclosing a scroll with large leaves that evolves from an eight-pointed star; inside the star is an eight-petaled rosette with a central roundel. The medallion is not inlaid but employs both hatched and cross-hatched backgrounds.

The surfaces of the handle are also decorated: a series of diamonds appears on the inner side; braids flanking a scroll with silver inlaid diamonds and quatrefoils embellish the upper side.

In addition to the Freer example, at least six other Veneto-Islamic buckets are known to exist. One of these is signed by Zayn al-Din[11]; two others bear the name of Mahmud ibn al-Kurdi[12]; and the remaining are not inscribed.[13] The decoration of the Freer bucket with two superimposed scrolls is found on a number of pieces made in Venice by the Muslim artists, such as a bowl and covered box signed by Zayn al-Din[14]; and another covered box and plate made by Mahmud ibn al-Kurdi.[15] It is highly possible that the Freer bucket was also made by one of these Muslim artists working in Venice.

Technical Notes

Concentric striations, centering marks, and the general radiographic appearance of the bucket indicate that the piece was formed by spinning. On the X-radiographs, one can see the regular thinness of the metal along the corner where the walls and the bottom meet. Small cracks are present in some areas; they seem to have resulted from the stress induced by the spinning process. The walls have a regular thickness that gradually increases as the walls rise and that measures from approximately 1.2 to 2.0 millimeters (0.05 to 0.08 inch). A band has been added around the rim and attached with soft solder. The rim band, together with the handle, has been shaped from strips of metal measuring 5 to 6 millimeters (0.20 to 0.24 inch) thick. The ends of the handle were cut, filed, and bent into their present shape. The rough treatment of the semicircular pieces where the handle attaches to the bucket and the ends of the handle suggest that the handle once had terminals, which are now lost.

Photomicrograph illustrating the inlay technique. Actual size of the area illustrated: 30 x 20 mm. (1⅛ x ¹³⁄₁₆ in.)

Silver inlay, gilding, and chased designs make up the decoration of the bucket. The inlay is applied on outlines of punch marks. The punch marks are grouped loosely and do not form a sharp outline. The metal underlying the inlay was not recessed. For the wider areas of inlay, random punch marks were applied to the underlying body metal, apparently to provide a better hold on the inlay. Mercury gilding was used to gild the interior of the bucket and the inner surface of the handle; gold and mercury were detected by X-ray fluorescence.

The chased recesses of the body metal show a stepped topography, or hatching, which appears to be a ground prepared for the application of black inlay. A blackish material is now present in some of these recesses, but whether or not it is inlay is unclear. It does not fill the recesses as one would expect but rather lies thinly on the surface.

With the exception of the lost terminals for the handle, and some abrasion of the bottom surface, the bucket is in excellent condition.

An average of the analyses of three areas on the surface gave the following results:

Copper	Zinc	Lead	Tin
82.2% (±0.8)	15.3% (±3.5)	1.6% (±2.2)	0.7% (±2.1)

Provenance: Purchased from Brummer Gallery, New York, 1945.

Published: Atıl 1971, no. 62.

Atıl 1975, no. 79.

Notes:

1. See, for example, Ettinghausen 1943a, figs. 2, 5, and 6; and Fehérvári 1976b, nos. 24–26.
2. For this type see Barrett 1949, no. 10: Pinder-Wilson 1962; Harari 1964–65, pls. 1291–92 and 1306A–8; London 1976, no. 179; Fehérvári 1976b, nos. 89–92; and Giuzalian 1978.
3. Ettinghausen 1943a; Mayer 1959, pp. 61–62; and London 1976, no. 180.
4. Atıl 1981, no. 38.
5. Mayer 1959, pp. 63, 67, 78, 87, and 91; pls. XI and XV.
6. Ibid., pp. 56–58; Robinson 1967, fig. 91; and Paris 1971, no. 174.
7. Mayer 1959, pp. 31–32; and Berlin 1971, no. 339.
8. This word was also used to refer to outsiders and Iranians.
9. Migeon 1927, vol. 2, fig. 271.
10. Melikian-Chirvani 1974c.
11. This is in the Victoria and Albert Museum. Mayer 1959, p. 91.
12. The one is in Lázaro Galdiano Museum, Madrid; the whereabouts of the other is unknown. Ibid., p. 58.
13. One of the buckets is in the Gambier-Parry Collection, Courtauld Institute Galleries, London (Robinson 1967, fig. 90). According to files in the Freer Gallery, there was an example mounted on top of a thirteenth-or fourteenth-century candlestick, in the Lázaro Collection, New York; and another in the Stora Collection, New York.
14. Mayer 1959, pl. XV; and Bargello 1981, no. 4.
15. Robinson 1967, fig. 91; and Paris 1971, no. 174.

25. Vase

Brass: cast and turned; engraved and inlaid with gold

Afghanistan, ca. 1500

Height: 12.8 cm. (5 in.); diameter: 13.3 cm. (5¼ in.);
  weight: 656.0 gm. (23.1 oz.)

77.4

Inscriptions

1. On the neck:
   Scraped.

2. On neck, neck ring, and body (Persian, naskhi):
   Not deciphered.

3. Inside the foot-ring:

The humble Hafiz Ali, in the year 930 [1523 A.D.].	الفقير حفيظ على سنة ٩٣٠

The vase is decorated with rectangular panels containing inscriptions, which are loosely linked to diversely shaped cartouches filled with floral motifs. On the neck are six rectangular panels alternating with quatrefoils, framed by two trefoil bands. The ring at the base of the neck also has six rectangular panels. The body repeats the same scheme of horizontal registers divided into six units. The central register in the wider portion contains an enlarged version of the decoration applied to the neck. Above and below are single cartouches alternating with double cartouches. Surface abrasions on the rim and body suggest that the piece was at one time supplied with a handle and used as a jug. The handle was applied over the decorated surface with no provisions made in the design to accommodate it.

The piece is quite worn and obviously has changed hands several times. The inscriptions on the neck have been scraped, and those on the neck ring and body are too abraded to be read properly. The incised inscription placed inside the foot-ring must refer to a later owner.

The Freer vase belongs to a group of some thirty vessels that have the same shape: a high cylindrical neck and bulbous body. Inlaid with silver or gold, or both, they are decorated only with floral motifs and inscriptions and do not reveal any figural compositions. The floral motifs range from fairly naturalistic blossoms to stylized scrolls and leaves; the design is organized either in well-defined horizontal registers with panels and cartouches, or in overall patterns without divisions. The inscriptions, rendered both in Arabic and Persian, contain benedictions, verses from classical poetry, Shiite evocations, and phrases reflecting Sufi mysticism.

Dated examples indicate that the height of production was between the 1460s and 1510s, thus covering the late Timurid and early Safavid periods. The earliest in the series is the example (fig. 64) made in 1461/62 by Habib Allah ibn Ali Baharjani and the latest appears to be the jug (fig. 65) dated 1511.[1] The *nisbas* of the artists who have signed several of the pieces refer to cities or sites in Khorasan. One of the vessels, in the British Museum, was made in 1497 for Sultan Husayn Bayqara, the Timurid ruler of Herat and a renowned patron of the arts.[2] It is conceivable, therefore, that Herat was the center of production in the second half of the fifteenth century and continued to be active during the early decades of the sixteenth century.

Some of the vessels have a single dragon-shaped handle; others are supplied with domical lids. The type with the handle was most likely based on Timurid jades, such as the one dedicated to Ulugh Beg (1417–49), owned by the Gulbenkian Foundation in Lisbon.[3] It should be mentioned that the handles on most of the pieces are identical; they were cast and applied to the body over the decoration. They follow the type used in Ulugh Beg's jug, that is, the head of the dragon is on the rim; its curved tail terminating in a palmette is attached to the body. It appears that these handles were added at a later date in the same center.[4]

The Freer vase has a considerable amount of undecorated areas forming the background, which is unusual and not found on other examples in the series.[5] It is possible that the panels on the neck contained a dedication that was erased when the piece changed hands. In 1523 it came into the possession of Hafiz Ali, who is otherwise unknown.

The Freer vase belongs to a series of late Timurid metalwork that in technique, shape, and style of decoration survived well into the Safavid period.[6] Although Herat fell to the Safavids in 1510, the new regime did not drastically change the artistic traditions as observed in the production of metalwork and illustrated manuscripts. It was in the middle of the sixteenth century that Herat began to be overshadowed by the Safavid capitals of Tabriz and Qazvin. It is interesting to note that the Timurid tradition was also influential in the development of Ottoman art, and the same type of vessel was produced in the İstanbul court.[7]

64. Brass jug inlaid with silver
Made by Habib Allah b. Ali Baharjani
Afghanistan, dated 1461/62
(London, Victoria and Albert Museum,
943–1886)

65. Brass jug inlaid with silver and gold
Afghanistan, dated 1511
(London, The British Museum,
1878 12–30 732)

Technical Notes   Although a number of techniques were employed in forming the vase, the basic shape was cast. X-radiographs of the vase reveal porosity in the metal and an inhomogeneous structure indicative of casting. Further shaping and thinning of the walls was executed by turning. The walls of the neck of the vase in particular are quite thin, too thin to have been simply cast. With concentric striations on the inner surface of the neck and a centering mark on the bottom of the vessel, the use of a turning process seems most likely. Also, gas pores resulting from the casting process can be seen on the metal surface; the pores were presumably revealed as the metal that once covered them was cut away in the course of turning.

A rivet is present just below the rim on one side of the vase. Beneath the rivet are two areas, one on the neck and one on the body, that appear worn or damaged. It seems that this area was once the point of attachment for a handle.

The wear the vase has suffered obscures what remains of the decoration, but the general materials and methods employed are still apparent. The only obvious inlay material on the vase is gold; no silver was found. A black material also is present in some of the interstices of the design but seems to be randomly present on the surface of the vase and thus is not clearly inlay. The gold inlay is applied to double rows of small, narrow punch marks. With the exception of these punch marks, no other chasing is evident. The raised areas of the design are set off by incised or engraved lines. The recessed areas are the result of cross-hatching from incising or engraving.

At the junction of the neck and the body, a crack runs more than a third of the distance around the neck. Globules of what appear to be soft solder are present on the interior surface in the area of the crack; they may be the remains of an attempt to repair the defect. Solder is distinctly present on the bottom of the vase in an area inside the foot. On the inside of the vase, opposite the solder, one can see the irregularly shaped hole, which the solder repair covers; the hole resembles a casting flaw. The worn surface, with its brown patina, bears little of the gold inlay it once held.

The average of five analyses of four separate areas is given below.

Copper	Zinc	Lead	Tin
72.2% ($\pm$1.4)	17.1% ($\pm$0.1)	3.8% ($\pm$0.7)	6.4% ($\pm$1.0)

Provenance: Purchased from Ahuan, London, 1977.

Unpublished

Notes:

1. Melikian-Chirvani 1982, no. 109; and Grube 1974, fig. 78, respectively. For a study of signed and dated pieces and an analysis of signatures, see Komaroff 1979–80. The following examples should be added to the ten signed pieces discussed by Komaroff: a jug made by Husayn ibn Mubarak Shah (Sotheby's 1983, no. 305); and a second jug made in 1468 by Habib Allah ibn Ali Baharjani in the Museum für Islamische Kunst, Berlin (Mayer 1959, p. 42; date confirmed by Johanna Zick-Nissen). The example made by Ahmad Shir Ali ibn Muhammad al-Dimishqi in 1467 (Mayer 1959, pl. XIV) is now in the Museum of Turkish and Islamic Arts, İstanbul.

2. Grube 1974, figs. 76 and 77; see also pp. 245–46 and figs. 72–81 for other Timurid jugs and vases.

3. Ibid., fig. 107.

4. It is possible that the handles were produced and added in the Ottoman capital, since a number of these pieces are still in İstanbul or were once there. Ottoman versions of these single-handled jugs, made out of diverse materials, were very popular. Similar pieces in gilt silver dating from the first half of the sixteenth century are in the Victoria and Albert Museum and the Hermitage (Allan and Raby 1982, pls. 7c and 18; and İstanbul 1983, E93). The same shape and dragon-headed handle was also produced for the Ottoman court during the second half of the sixteenth and first half of the seventeenth century. These imperial wares, housed in the Treasury of the Topkapı Palace Museum in İstanbul, were fashioned of precious materials—such as rock crystal, jade, gold, and zinc—and embellished with jewels.

5. Although rare, undecorated jugs do exist. See, for example, Fehérvári 1976b, no. 148.

6. For one of the Safavid examples see Melikian-Chirvani 1982, no. 123.

7. See note 4.

26. Small Bowl

Silver: cast and spun; incised, chased, and inlaid with gold and niello

Iran, ca. 1500–1510

Height: 3.2 cm. (1¼ in.); diameter: 11.2 cm.
  (4⁷⁄₁₆ in.); weight: 258.7 gm. (9.1 oz.)

54.115

Inscriptions (Persian)

1. Around the rim (nastaliq):

He that has the bowl in hand	آنکس که بدست جام دارد
Forever holds Jam's [that is, Jamshid's] *kingdom*	سلطانی جم مدام دارد
The water from which Khidr found life	آبی که خضر از او حیات یافت
Seek it in the tavern for the bowl has it	در میکده جوکه جام دارد
The main thread of life rest it on the Beloved	سررشته جان بجان بکذار
For it is through Him that this thread is arranged	کین رشته ازو نظام دارد
Here we are with our wine and there the ascetics	ما و می و زاهدان و تقوی
with their piety	
Let us see which one the Beloved shall have.[1]	تا یار سر کدام دارد

2. Inside the foot-ring (nastaliq):

Fifty-six misqals. *Gold: eight and five-sixths* misqals. *Silver: forty-seven and one-sixth* misqals.[2]
Owned by Aqa Rustam Ruzafzun.

ست [و] خمسین مثقال * نقره سبع [و]
اربعین مثقال [و] سدس * طلا ثمانة مثاقیل
[و] سدس [و] ثلثین * صاحبه آقا رستم روز
افزون

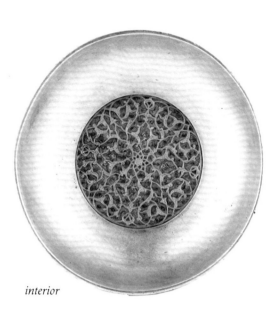

interior

base

This small silver bowl or drinking cup is among the rare examples of late Timurid silver inlaid with gold and niello, a technique popularly used in Iran during the twelfth century. Made of expensive materials and decorated in a highly refined manner, it must have been cherished throughout its existence. Its importance is attested by the name of a later owner inscribed on the back together with the statement that gives not only the weight of the piece but also the proportional amounts of silver and gold supposedly used by the artist.

The rim of the piece contains a band with eight lines of poetry placed in elongated and lobed cartouches separated by quatrefoils enclosing five-petaled blossoms. The blossoms, the borders of the quatrefoils, and the inscription panels all are inlaid with gold. The body is covered by a dense scroll composed of split-leaves rendered in gold. Behind this design is a second scroll bearing blossoms executed in niello. A thin zigzag band appears above the foot-ring, which is divided into eight gold-inlaid panels alternately filled with a floral scroll and a braided pattern. A most delicate execution makes the decoration of the foot-ring almost microscopic. The silver background was stamped with a fine ring punch.

On the inside the cavetto is plain, but the central medallion repeats the decoration found on the exterior: a gold-inlaid split-leaf scroll is placed over a nielloed floral scroll with ring matting applied to the background. The design radiates from a central rosette enclosed by an eight-pointed star with four lotuses placed in the larger units and small blossoms filling the remaining zones. Radiating stars, symbolizing divine light and traced to medieval Islamic art, were frequently used on bowls (see nos. 20 and 21).

The Freer bowl is extremely well-designed, having contrasts between unadorned areas and areas decorated with gold and niello, and between the gold-inlaid and nielloed motifs, which interlace and accentuate one another. The refinement of execution and harmonious balance of decorative themes rarely are equaled in the art of metalwork and reveal a close association with the art of Timurid illumination.

The eight lines, or four distiches, of poetry inscribed on the rim is from a *ghazal*, or ode, composed by Hafiz in the *hazay* meter. The mystical poem contains references to drinking wine from the bowl in an attempt to approach the "Beloved," who could be interpreted as either the Creator or the attainment of esoteric knowledge. The poem

187

also includes a reference to Solomon, the patriarch endowed with esoteric knowledge by the prophet Khizr, the guardian of the Fountain of Life. Solomon was thought to have been reincarnated in Jamshid, the legendary founder of the Iranian empire. Similar associations with the kingdom of Solomon and Jamshid are found in the inscriptions on a series of fourteenth-century metalwork produced in Fars (see nos. 20 and 21).

Precisely when and where the Freer bowl was made cannot be determined, but it must have been in Mazandaran, the region on the southern shores of the Caspian Sea, before 1511, at which date the later owner, whose name is inscribed on the back, is thought to have died. Aqa Rustam, who used the honorific Ruzafzun (a royal title meaning august), was the ruler of Mazandaran and had his court at Sari at the beginning of the sixteenth century. He is said to have died of shock when Shah Ismail's envoy threw at him the severed hand of the Uzbek ruler, Muhammad Shaybani Khan, trying to force him into accepting the Safavid rule.[3] Since Muhammad Shaybani was defeated and killed by Shah Ismail in December 1510, the demise of Aqa Rustam must have been a few weeks later.

The inscriptions on the foot, including the statement about the weight of the piece,[4] must have been added when the bowl came into Aqa Rustam's possession. The piece is one of the rare examples of Islamic metalwork to provide this type of information.

The Freer bowl represents the last flowering of Timurid art. This highly refined style had a strong impact on Safavid and Ottoman metalworkers. The employment of two types of superimposed scrolls—the one stylized with split-leaves and the other, more naturalistic type with recognizable blossoms and buds—became widely used on metalwork produced in the Safavid and Ottoman courts during the sixteenth and seventeenth centuries.

Technical Notes

The bowl was cast, with additional shaping of the foot executed by a spinning process. On the bottom of the bowl, a cast dendritic structure is clearly apparent when viewed under low magnification. Also present on the bottom of the bowl are a centering mark, chisel marks, and circular striations, which can be seen just inside the foot. The foot was shaped by first bringing up a slight lip around the circumference of the bottom by cutting into the metal with a chisel. This lip was then raised and smoothed into its final form as the foot by spinning.

The gold decoration on the bowl consists of thick gold sheet set into deep depressions. The goldwork stands 0.2–0.3 millimeters (0.008–0.012 inch) above the surrounding surface. The artist, taking advantage of the softness of the metal, has incised and carved the recessed decorations that cover the gold. An additional decorative element is the circular punch marks, or ring matting, used around the inlay in the center of the inside of the bowl and on the outside surface of the rim. Because points of overlap can be

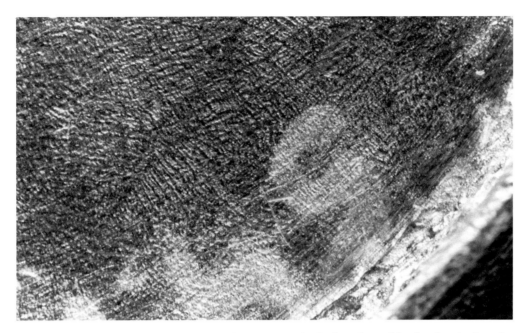

Magnified image of the foot and bottom. In the central area of the photograph, one sees the cast dendritic structure as dark lines against a lighter background. Moving toward the bottom right corner, one sees thin annular striations that remain from the spinning operation used to form the foot; chisel marks (lightest area), also remaining from the forming of the foot; and, as a blurred image, a section of the foot itself. Actual size of the area illustrated: 15 x 10 mm. (⁵⁄₈ x ³⁄₈ in.)

seen, it is evident that the punch marks were applied after the gold inlay but before the niello. The niello is basically silver sulfide, though some lead sulfide is present; the niello lies in depressions that appear to have been cut out. The inscription on the bottom of the bowl is engraved.

The inscription inside the foot appears to state the correct total weight of the bowl, but its proportions for the amounts of gold and silver are incorrect. If one takes the gold content of the bowl as 1.5% (from the X-ray fluorescence figures) and then adds the gold used as inlay, the proportion of gold stated in the inscription is still too high. Specific gravity measurements also indicate that the proportions given for gold and silver are incorrect.[5] Exact determinations of the weight of the gold and silver are not possible, and the considerable areas of niello must make up more than a negligible part of the total weight.

The bowl is in near-perfect condition. Only one small piece of gold inlay has been lost. The chased and incised details are only slightly worn.

Compositional analysis shows that the body metal of the bowl is almost pure silver. Below is given the average of two analyses of different areas on the bowl. The percentages given for the quantities of copper and lead are smaller than their corresponding confidence limits because a small number of analyses was taken and a relatively large difference (0.3%) appeared in the measurements.

Silver	Copper	Gold	Lead
96.7% (±3.5)	1.1% (±1.7)	1.5% (±0.1)	0.7% (±1.6)

Provenance: Purchased from Heeramaneck Galleries, New York, 1954.
Published: Melikian-Chirvani 1976a, pp. 25–27.

Notes:

1. Melikian-Chirvani 1976a, pp. 25–26. The translation of the sixth line, missing in the reference, has been added here.
2. According to A. H. Morton, who deciphered the inscription, the statement is in the *siyaq*, or accounting script, in which numerals are represented by ciphers deriving from the Arabic words for them. For the sake of clarity, the ciphers have been written out and the copula added where necessary.
3. Melikian-Chirvani 1976a, p. 27.
4. The weight of the bowl more or less corresponds to the statement on the foot-ring. Since one *misqal* is the equivalent of 4.6 grams (Wulff 1966, p. 62), fifty-six *misqals* equal 259.8 grams. The proportional amounts of silver and gold, however, are incorrect (see discussion in Technical Notes).
5. If the artist had indeed been supplied with 8⅚ *misqals* (equivalent to 57.3 grams) of gold and had used 3.9 grams to alloy with the silver, which would agree with the percentage shown by X-ray fluorescence, he would have had 53.4 grams remaining. If he had then hammered this out into a disc the same size as the diameter of the bowl, the gold would be 0.28 millimeters thick, which falls exactly in the range of thickness measured. He could then have cut out the gold decoration from the disc and used it on the bowl, with considerable wastage, which would have found its way into reclaimable scrap in the workshop.

27. Candlestick

Brass: cast in sections; chased and incised

Turkey, ca. 1500

Height: 26.0 cm. (10¼ in.); diameter (base): 17.1 cm. (6¾ in.);
  weight: 1,770.0 gm. (62.4 oz.)

80.19

The base and the neck of this candlestick were produced separately and joined together by a threaded post inserted into the ring rising from the shoulder. Its decoration consists of horizontal registers filled with braids and floral scrolls; circular punches in units of threes were used as accents on the leaves, and ring matting was applied to the background.

Bands with vertical incisions resembling beading define the socket, the thick ring in the middle of the neck, the shoulder, four registers of the base, and the splayed foot. The socket, four components of the neck, and the shoulder are adorned with loosely drawn scrolls with intertwining stems bearing large split-leaves. The upper register of the base has a braid, which is repeated on the foot. The second register contains a series of overlapping leaves. The next two zones employ the same scroll used on the neck; in the widest register, the elements form five units radiating from a roundel.

This boldly designed and executed candlestick belongs to a rare group of early Ottoman metalwork. There is an almost identical brass piece (fig. 66) in the Victoria and Albert Museum.[1] It is also decorated with braids and scrolls but has a more pronounced shoulder. The motifs used on both candlesticks reflect the artistic vocabulary employed during the reign of the Ottoman sultan, Bayezıd II (1481–1512), and are comparable to themes found on bookbindings, ceramics, tiles, and architectural decoration. These themes were based on the designs produced in the imperial studios in İstanbul, the capital of the empire.

Ring matting used in the candlesticks in the Freer and Victoria and Albert Museum appears on a third brass example, which has a cup-shaped shoulder and a band of inscriptions in addition to floral designs.[2] Other brass candlesticks in the series are unadorned but retain the same shape (an articulated tall neck and flared base); several of these examples have tulip-shaped sockets.[3] The same type of candlestick was produced in both tinned and gilt copper.[4]

A few of the candlesticks are dated, which enables us to establish the development of early Ottoman metalwork. An undecorated brass piece with a tulip-shaped socket is inscribed with the date 1499 and the name of Husayn Agha, the official in the Galata district of İstanbul[5]; two others were made in 1540 for Suleyman Pasha, the Ottoman governor of Cairo[6]; and a fourth bears the date 1576.[7] Considerably larger versions of the same type of candlestick, made in gilt or tinned copper as well as silver, are found flanking the mihrabs of several sixteenth- and seventeenth-century Ottoman religious buildings and mausoleums. Among the dated tinned copper examples are one made in 1657 and a pair inscribed 1683.[8] The most spectacular pair, found in the mausoleum of Sultan Ahmed I (died 1617), was produced in silver and has a pierced socket.[9]

It appears that the shape of the thirteenth- and fourteenth-century Turkish candlesticks (see no. 19) was slightly elongated in the following years. Examples produced around the turn of the sixteenth century were either decorated with chased and incised motifs, such as on the Freer example, or unadorned except for tulip-shaped sockets. The plain

66. Brass candlestick
Turkey, ca. 1500
(London, Victoria and Albert Museum, 91.1.586)

type continued to be made throughout the seventeenth century; brass was replaced by both gilt copper, which has almost the same color but was less costly, and tinned copper, which gave the appearance of silver. Silver, it seems, was produced exclusively for the court.

The threaded post attaching the two parts of the Freer candlestick is also found on other early Ottoman examples. It is difficult to explain why such a laborious device was designed when simple soldering would have served the same purpose. Even though the dimensions of the existing pieces do not match, it is conceivable that the candlesticks were produced in large quantities and assembled after being cast. Brass was a valuable material and was frequently melted down in later years to make new objects. A number of early Ottoman candlesticks might have faced the same fate.

Technical Notes

The two pieces making up the candlestick appear to be basically cast, although cracks in the top of the neck and around the foot of the base suggest that further shaping, which strained the metal, was done in these areas after casting; perhaps the metal has cracked where it was thinned excessively in a turning or polishing process. The base is apparently composed of two parts: the shoulder with the threaded post, and the cylindrical body of the base. A thin join line between the two parts, running just inside the edge of the shoulder, is apparent on X-radiographs.

What appear to be mold marks run along the inner wall of the tubular neck. Surface marks on the inner walls of the base also appear to echo the casting process and the shaping of an extremely plastic material. Most notable among these marks are raised impressions of fingerprints which, it seems reasonable to assume, reproduce impressions left in the inner mold used for the casting of the base.

The rough, irregular interior walls of the candlestick are in marked contrast to the smooth, highly finished exterior surfaces. The fine linear decorations are chased, with the exception of the concentric lines that separate the various design bands; these lines appear to be incised, and they were applied after the chasing had been completed. The majority of the chasing was done with two tools, a triangular-ended tracer and a ring punch.

The condition of the object is good, although the surface is somewhat worn. In some areas the design has been rubbed away.

Six areas on the neck, shoulder, and base were analyzed; an average of the results is given below.

Copper	Zinc	Lead	Tin
81.9% ($\pm$1.5)	16.5% ($\pm$1.1)	1.7% ($\pm$0.5)	not detected

Provenance: Purchased from Axia, London, 1980; gift of the James Smithson Society.
Published: Allan and Raby 1982, pl. 22.

Notes:

1. Melikian-Chirvani 1975c, fig. 1; and Allan and Raby 1982, pl. 15a.
2. Allan and Raby 1982, pl. 15b.
3. Melikian-Chirvani 1975c, figs. 3–5; and Allan and Raby 1982, pls. 15c–d, 35, 38, and 40–42.
4. Allan and Raby 1982, pls. 33, 36, and 37.
5. Ibid., pl. 40.
6. They are in the Museum of Islamic Art, Cairo. Wiet 1932, nos. 4395–96 and pl. XXXV; and Melikian-Chirvani 1975c, fig. 3.
7. Allan and Raby, 1982, pl. 15d.
8. Ibid., pls. 36–37.
9. These are owned by the Museum of Turkish and Islamic Arts, İstanbul. One of them bears a dedication to Ahmed I; the other contains the name of Sultan Murad IV and the date 1640, obviously inscribed some twenty-five years or so later. İstanbul 1983, E256.

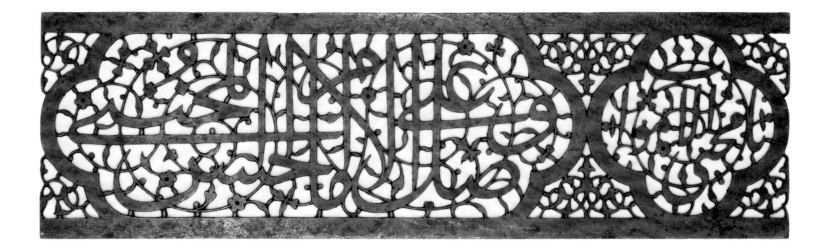

28. Rectangular Plaque

Steel: cut from forged sheet; pierced

Iran, 16th century

Height: 7.8 cm. (3¹/₁₆ in.); length: 27.0 cm.
  (10⅝ in.); weight: 162.8 gm. (5.7 oz.)

39.45

Inscription (Arabic, naskhi)

Oh Reviver of the dead. Accord your protection to the prince. Verily how excellent [is] *the Reviver.*	يا محيى الاموات و مل على الأمير اما لحسن المحيى

The plaque, which is a fragment of a larger piece, contains a quatrefoil and a lobed rectangular cartouche enclosing naskhi inscriptions placed over a floral scroll bearing lotus blossoms and five-petaled flowers. The interstices are filled with a second type of scroll composed of split-leaves.

    The inscriptions indicate that the plaque was once used in a funerary context, either on doors and windows of a mausoleum or on its furnishings.[1] Similar plaques are thought to come from a mausoleum called Darb-i Imam in Isfahan dating from the sixteenth century.[2] Rectangular cartouches with the same types of scrolls appear on an extraordinary pierced-steel ruler (fig. 67) with a central panel bearing an inscription that states it was made in 1588 by Muzaffar al-Murtada ibn Kamal al-Din al-Husayni.[3]

195

67. Pierced-steel ruler
Made by Muzaffar al-Murtada b. Kamal al-Din al-Husayni
Iran, dated 1588
(Cairo, Museum of Islamic Art, 15409)

The date on the ruler indicates that the naturalistic and stylized scrolls, used simultaneously to contrast and accentuate one another, were a part of the Safavid artistic vocabulary by the last quarter of the sixteenth century (see also nos. 29 and 31).

Technical Notes

The plaque appears to have been formed from a forged sheet of steel. Slight irregularities in the thickness and the rather rough surface appearance give the impression of a forging process. The fretwork shows the use of drills, saws, and files to create the openings, particularly on the back of the plaque, where less finishing was done. A description of modern work of this type is given in Wulff.[4]

The condition of the plaque is good. X-ray fluorescence analysis of the plaque does not indicate the presence of elements other than iron.

Provenance: Purchased from Beghian, London, 1939.
Unpublished

Notes:
1. A pierced plaque thought to be from the tomb of Shah Tahmasp was once owned by Beghian and exhibited in London in 1931. This may be the same piece as the Freer example. London 1931, no. 278G.
2. Harari 1964–65, pl. 1389.
3. Ibid., p. 2514 and pl. 1390E.
4. Wulff 1966, pp. 72–73.

29. Rectangular Plaque

Steel: cut from forged sheet; pierced and chased

Iran, 16th–17th centuries

Height: 4.0 cm. (1⁹⁄₁₆ in.); length: 7.2 cm. (2¹³⁄₁₆ in.);
  weight: 12.5 gm. (0.4 oz.)

40.8

This small rectangular plaque is decorated with a dense overall design. In the center is an eight-lobed oval cartouche bearing a split-leaf scroll; the surrounding area is filled with a second type of scroll, which employs lotuses and five-petaled blossoms with long curving leaves that have serrate edges. Only one side of the plaque has been finished.

Similar pierced-steel plaques were used as architectural decoration and on furnishings, such as boxes, chests, and cupboards made for both religious structures and residential buildings.

This pierced plaque is made from a thin sheet of steel. The openwork was executed with only a drill and files. A circular punch was used to embellish the five-petaled flowers, which comprise the only decorative element besides the openwork. There are no openings or appendages that would suggest the use or the manner of attachment of the plaque. The condition of the plaque is excellent. Only iron is indicated by X-ray fluorescence surface analysis.

Technical Notes

Provenance: Purchased from Beghian, London, 1940.
Unpublished

30. Circular Ornament

Steel: cut from forged sheet and hammered;
  pierced and overlaid with gold

Iran, 16th–17th centuries

Diameter: 4.7 cm. (1¹³⁄₁₆ in.); weight: 6.4 gm. (0.2 oz.)

40.9

Inscriptions (Arabic, naskhi):

In the name of God, the Compassionate, the Merciful.	بسم الله الرحمن الرحيم

The eight-lobed medallion with circular openings between the lobes is decorated with a concentric scroll bearing lotus blossoms and leaves. Placed over the scroll is the *basmala*, the phrase that appears at the beginning of each chapter of the Koran. The inscriptions and the band framing the medallion are overlaid with gold.

The holes around the plaque must have been used to affix the plaque with nails to an architectural element or furniture. The *basmala* is a popular pious evocation, and this plaque could have been used both in religious and secular context.

An almost identical medallion (fig. 68) appears in the center of a pierced-steel roundel in the al-Sabah Collection in Kuwait.[1] It has the same diameter but contains twelve lobes and is inscribed with the words "rely on God in all matters." The function of the roundel is uncertain; it may have been designed as a filter or screen for a brazier, incense burner, washbasin, or lamp. The Freer medallion appears to have been the centerpiece of a similar object.

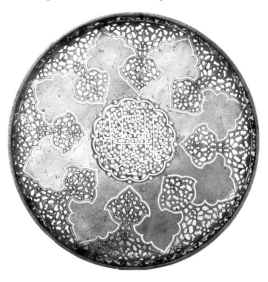

68. Pierced-steel roundel overlaid with gold
Iran, 16th–17th centuries
(Kuwait, National Museum, Dar al-Athar al-Islamiya Collection, LNS 137 M)

During the Safavid period gold-inlaid or -overlaid steel reached the height of technical perfection. The delicate and refined execution of pierced scrollwork was unequaled in any other period. A few sixteenth- and seventeenth-century pieces contain the names of the artists. These include a compass made by Mahmud; a ruler (fig. 67) made by Muzaffar al-Murtada ibn Kamal al-Din al-Husayni in 1588; a plaque for sharpening pins made by Kamal al-Din Mahmud in 1696; and two beggar's bowls and a belt plaque made by Nur Allah.[2] The name of one seventeenth-century artist, Hajji Abbas, appears on a group of objects that include an animal-headed mace, figurines of birds, and several water-pipe and beggar's bowls.[3] The inscriptions on one of the beggar's bowls dated 1606/7 state that Hajji Abbas was the son of an armorer, suggesting a close relationship between the artists who produced steel objects and the makers of arms and armor.[4] The same refined execution is found in the ceremonial weapons and armor of the period.

Technical Notes

The plaque is constructed from a thin, slightly convex sheet of steel. This sheet is regular in its thickness; it seems most likely that the plaque was cut from a larger forged sheet and hammered into its final shape. The openwork was executed with drills and files. From the back side of the plaque, the openings begin as conical shapes, becoming narrower as they near the front surface and more irregular in outline. The irregularity was caused by filing, which achieved the variously shaped lacunae of the design.

X-radiography reveals fine cross-hatched scratches on the surface of the iron underneath the gold; the gold was hammered onto the cross-hatching to secure it. Unlike inlay, which is set into recesses, the gold was applied by an overlay technique whereby the gold is set on top of the underlying metal and stands distinctly above the surrounding surface. Fine gold wires or sheet cut into thin strips and set parallel to one another were used for the overlay. An apt description of modern work of this type occurs in Wulff.[5]

The condition of the plaque is excellent. Surface analysis of the iron using X-ray fluorescence techniques did not indicate the presence of other elements.

Provenance: Purchased from Beghian, London, 1940.
Published: Harari 1964–65, pl. 1390H.

Notes:
1. Jenkins 1983, pl. 136. The diameter of the roundel is 13.8 centimeters (5⁷⁄₁₆ inches).
2. Harari 1964–65, pls. 1390D–F and 1394C.
3. Ibid., pls. 1393A and C; Mayer 1959, pp. 19–20 and pl. I; Berlin 1971, no. 608; and Allan 1982a, no. 26.
4. Allan 1982a, no. 26.
5. Wulff 1966, pp. 72–73.

31. Axe Head

Watered steel: forged, pierced, and inlaid with gold

Iran, 16th–17th centuries

Height: 7.8 cm. (3 1/15 in.); length: 15.9 cm. (6 1/4 in.);
  weight: 156.7 gm. (5.1 oz.)

40.6

Safavid arms and armor are renowned for their superb workmanship and refined decoration, which are exemplified in this small axe head.[1] A screw-pin and nut at the back of the piece must have been used to attach it to a tall shaft. This example appears to have had a ceremonial function and was most likely carried by a halberdier during parades and festivals.[2]

The steel is delicately watered. The thin blade was originally inlaid with gold. The remains of the gold design on one side indicate that the decoration consisted of cartouches with scrolls bearing blossoms. The thickened four-sided end with the screw-pin has a pierced eight-lobed medallion with split-leaf scrolls on all four sides. The same combination of two types of scrolls are seen on other contemporary pieces (see nos. 28 and 29).

The axe head is made from watered steel, but in this case one sees something different from the typical water pattern having thin, sinuous lines. Here the light areas resemble isolated narrow pools within a dark matrix.

The procedure necessary for producing a water pattern is not entirely understood, but there is a general belief that this surface pattern reflects the inherent structure of the steel ingot from which the axe head was forged.[3] The ingots that are believed to have been used to make objects of Islamic steel having a water pattern are a material known in Europe as "wootz." Wootz was traditionally a product of the state of Hyderabad in India.[4] The particular method of smelting used in this region was a time-consuming process employing both oxidizing and reducing atmospheres, as well as forging, to control the amount and form of the carbon in the steel. The process resulted in an ingot having a composition and structure that could be exploited to produce weapons with adventitious qualities. Blades forged from wootz were hard enough to give an extremely sharp edge and yet not brittle. The combination of qualities of watered steel, together with its appearance, is caused by a fine mixture of pearlite and cementite in the steel.[5] Cementite, an iron carbide, is the light material in a watered steel. Pearlite, which appears dark in watered steel, is composed of iron and iron carbide. The application of acidic solutions during the finishing process brings out the contrasting appearance of the pearlite and cementite.

Technical Notes

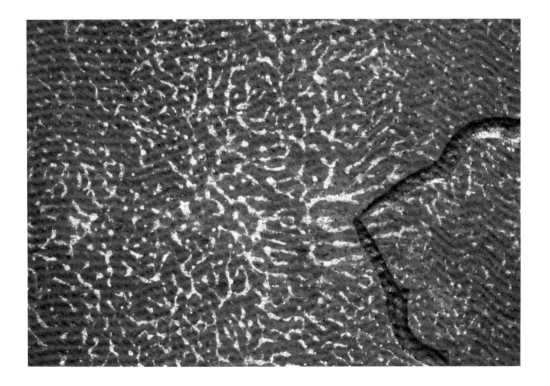

Photomicrograph of the blade showing the water pattern. Actual size of the area illustrated: 25 x 17 mm. (1 x $^{11}/_{16}$ in.)

The normal pattern on watered steel (see nos. 34, 35, and 38) is much more linear, however, than the pattern seen on the axe head. The latter looks as if it were created by crystal formation caused by slow cooling from the molten state. Dendrites can be seen, which imply that the metal was cast. Since the cast structure is clearly visible, we can infer that the steel of the axe head has been little deformed from its cast state. Light forging at a relatively low temperature must have been used in forming the axe head and welding together the various parts. Otherwise, the structure of the metal would have been altered and the water pattern would no longer be present.[6]

X-radiography shows that the back of the axe head is a block of steel that extends to the edge of the pierced design. No water pattern is apparent on this piece, or on the screw-pin and nut. The lack of a water pattern on these parts indicates that a different steel was possibly used, or that etching to bring out the pattern was not applied.

Fine, pierced fretwork decorates the four sides of the hollow end of the axe head opposite the blade. This piercing was most likely executed using drills and files. The linear design that decorates the blade was chased. Faint traces of gold inlay lying in shallow recesses are present on one side of the axe head; there is no evidence of inlay on the opposite side.

Besides the loss of inlay, there are a few spots of rust on the axe head. Iron and trace amounts of manganese were the only elements indicated by X-ray fluorescence analysis.

Provenance: Purchased from Beghian, London, 1940.
Unpublished

Notes:
1. A pierced axe head in the Beghian Collection exhibition in London in 1931 appears to be the same piece as the Freer example. London 1931, no. 275F.
2. For ceremonial axes see Stöcklein 1964–65, pls. 1430F and 1431B and D. Axes made by an eighteenth-century Iranian artist are discussed in Melikian-Chirvani 1979d. For Mamluk axes see Nickel 1979.
3. Smith 1960, p. 16.
4. Maryon 1960b, p. 53.
5. Ibid., pp. 55 and 58.
6. Smith 1960, p. 16; and Yater 1983, p. 8.

32. Comb Back

Steel: cut from sheet; chased and inlaid with silver
  and brass; originally tinned
Iran, 17th–18th centuries
Height: 6.2 cm. (2⁷⁄₁₆ in.); length: 7.7 cm. (3¹⁄₁₆ in.);
  weight: 44.2 gm. (1.6 oz.)
40.4

Inscriptions (Arabic, naskhi):

The congregation, the obedience, the religion, the hour of judgment.	الجماعة ٭ الطباعة ٭ الدين ٭ الساعة

This arch-shaped hollow piece, used as the back of a comb, was made in two parts and soldered together at the sides. A plaque with teeth would have been inserted into the sheath at the bottom and secured with a pin.

A band with four inscription panels is placed along the outer edges; the center is decorated with a loosely executed floral motif. Brass appears in the strips framing the two parts as well as in the leaves flanking the inscription panels. Silver is used in the four-petaled flowers between the inscriptions and in the central floral motif. The latter is composed of symmetrically arranged large curving leaves placed around a lotus blossom. Floral scrolls appear behind the deeply cut inscriptions.

This piece indicates that during the Safavid period even functional pieces for personal grooming were decorated with contrasting inlays and pious inscriptions. The comb was well used and several areas have lost their inlay.

Technical Notes The comb back was made from sheets of steel 0.75 millimeter ($\frac{1}{32}$ inch) in thickness. The edges of the back sheet were bent forward and soldered with soft solder to the back of the front sheet. The surface of the comb back was originally tinned with a lead and tin mixture.

The surface was further embellished with silver and brass inlay and chased decorations. The metalsmith executed the inlay by first incising or engraving an outline of the area to be inlaid. The inlay was then cut to the appropriate size and applied, with the edges of the inlay being beaten into the outline. Punch marks were then added on top of the inlay to further secure it. Thin sheet was used for all the inlay, with the exception of the horizontal brass line near the bottom of the comb back. Here, the inlay is relatively thick and wire was apparently used.

The deep, recessed areas of the inscription were made by chasing, and in one case the sheet has been perforated. Additional tooling, such as cutting or filing, may have been used to further define the raised and recessed areas. In addition, the central areas lying between the inlay have been slightly recessed; the exception is a narrow border that surrounds and delineates the inlay.

Besides the lost inlay, the deterioration of the tinned surface and the rusting of the underlying metal has altered the appearance of the comb back over time.

Provenance: Purchased from Beghian, London, 1940.
Unpublished

33. Comb Back

Steel: cut from sheet; chased and inlaid with silver and brass;
  originally tinned

Iran, 17th–18th centuries

Height: 6.2 cm. (2⁷⁄₁₆ in.); length: 11.0 cm. (4⁵⁄₁₆ in.);
  weight: 57.0 gm. (2.0 oz.)

40.5

Inscriptions:
Not deciphered

Employing the same shape, technique, and materials as the previous example (no. 32), this comb back also is decorated with a band of inscriptions placed around the semicircular central portion. Brass strips with chased strokes frame the two units. The inscription band is divided into four panels by a lotus blossom and a pair of five-petaled flowers. Another five-petaled blossom appears in the middle of the lower unit and is linked to a cartouche, which encloses the round opening used to secure the teeth. A scroll with large blossoms fills the rest of the area. Portions of the silver inlay used in the inscriptions and floral motifs have fallen out through years of wear.

The decorative repertoire is highly derivative and is based on inscriptions and floral scrolls that date back to the formative years of Islamic art. It is difficult to assign a specific date to the piece since dated or datable examples of this type of ornament are not known.

Technical Notes   There is only one difference in materials and construction between this comb back and the one previously discussed (no. 32). Here, the front sheet was bent over and soldered to a flat back sheet; for the other comb back, the front sheet used was a flat plate. The two comb backs also are similar in their state of preservation.

Provenance: Purchased from Beghian, London, 1940.
Unpublished

34. Dagger and Sheath

Blade: watered steel; ribbed

Handle: walrus tusk; inlaid with gold wire and black organic material;
  attached to tang with silver studs; tang is sheathed with gold and set
  with rubies, turquoise, and green glass

Guard: silver; chased and inlaid with niello

Sheath: wood with silver chapes; chased and inlaid with niello

Iran, second quarter 17th century

Length (max.): 30.0 cm. (11¹³⁄₁₆ in.); width of guard: 6.0 cm. (2⅜ in.);
  weight of dagger: 301.9 gm. (10.6 oz.); weight of sheath: 191.8 gm. (6.8 oz.)
58.15

Inscriptions (Persian, nastaliq)

On the tongues of the locket:

Although it is a handful of bone, the handle of your dagger is world conquering.	کرچه یکمشت استخوان باشد قبضه خنجرت جهانکیر است

The dagger and sheath are executed in precious materials and reveal a highly refined technique. The watered-steel blade is ribbed and slightly curved. The handle consists of two pieces of walrus tusk, which extend beyond the tang and are secured to it with a single pin that projects on either side with a silver roundel enclosed by a petal-shaped

detail of sheath

detail of sheath

mounting. Each side of the handle is framed by a thin band of quatrefoils and contains a central medallion linked on its vertical axis to two cartouches; these units are filled with floral scrolls, and additional sprays of leaves are placed around them. The semicircular inner faces of the projecting upper portion of the handle are embellished in the same manner and have a central cartouche enclosed by floral motifs. Gold wire, worked into flat strips, each with a central groove, outlines the medallions and cartouches, and appears in the central part of the scroll in the medallions; a black organic compound is used for the remaining motifs. The tang is covered with gold sheet and encrusted with sixteen large gems separated by a pair of smaller ones, set into plain gold collars. The larger gems are, alternately, uncut rubies and bluish green turquoise; the smaller ones are transparent green glass. One of the larger gems and three of the smaller ones are missing.

The silver crossguard is decorated with floral scrolls composed of split-leaves, lotuses, and five-petaled blossoms. The central unit and the flat ends of the quillons, or horizontal extensions, are executed in reserve with the niello forming the background; on the quillons the scroll is rendered in niello with tiny punch marks applied to the background.

The same technique and decoration appear on the silver chapes of the sheath, which itself is made up of two pieces of wood with an opening in the center barely wide enough to accommodate the blade. The central portion with the exposed wood must have been originally covered with textile or leather. The lower chape terminates with a teardrop boss; the upper joins the locket, which has two tongues with inscriptions. The two sides of the sheath contain slightly different decorative techniques. In the front, the lower chape is divided into two units; the top unit, upper chape, and triangular section of the locket below the tongue use niello for the main theme, whereas the

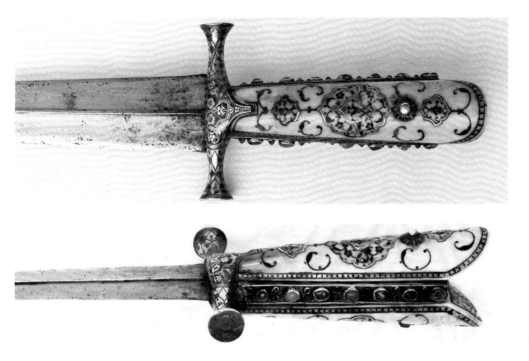

detail of handle

detail of handle

bottom unit of the lower chape employs niello in the background. On the back, the decoration on both chapes and the inscriptions on the two tongues are reserved on niello. This side has a small loop that extends from the upper chape and must have been used to suspend the dagger from the belt, if so desired (see nos. 35 and 38 for similar loops for attachment).

The maker of the Freer dagger and sheath has employed an extensive variety of materials and decorative techniques, producing a precious object that was worn like a jewel by the owner. This type of dagger, having a bifurcate pommel, is of Mughal origin and frequently appears in seventeenth-century imperial portraits, particularly those representing Jahangir (1605–27). An album painting (fig. 69) in the Freer Gallery depicts the emperor with a similar ivory-handled dagger tucked into his belt.[1] Some of the Mughal daggers with bifurcate pommels dating from Jahangir's reign were made of jade or rock crystal and sumptuously encrusted with rubies, emeralds, and sapphires.[2]

The same type of dagger was also popular in the Safavid court, as can be observed in the portraits of Shah Abbas (1587–1629). A group of these portraits were made by Bishan Das, an Indian painter who accompanied Khan Alam (Jahangir's ambassador) to Iran between 1613 and 1620. One of the paintings, in the Museum of Fine Arts in Boston (fig. 70), represents the shah and the ambassador, both of whom have daggers with bifurcate pommels tucked into their belts.[3] Several other Mughal portraits of Shah Abbas as well as those made by Riza, the Safavid court artist, depict the ruler wearing a similar dagger.[4]

69. *Jahangir Entertains Shah Abbas*
Gold and color on paper
India, ca. 1618
(Washington, D.C.,
Freer Gallery of Art,
42.16)

detail

detail

70. *Meeting of Shah Abbas and Khan Alam*
Gold and color on paper
Made by Bishan Das
India, ca. 1650
(Boston, Museum of Fine Arts, 14.665)

Even though the inscription on the Freer example includes the word *jahangir*, meaning world conquering or world conqueror, the dagger was not necessarily made for the Mughal ruler, Jahangir, who took this honorific as his reign name after he ascended the throne. The same wording appears on other Iranian daggers, together with the reference to the material of the handle (bone).[5] The technique and style of decoration found on the silver crossguard and the chapes indicate that it was produced in the Safavid court. The delicacy of execution recalls the late Timurid silver bowl (no. 26), suggesting that this type of stylized and refined decoration resembling manuscript illumination persisted for a long time (see also no. 35). The same floral scrolls appear on imperial Safavid arms and armor and luxurious objects made for the court.[6]

Technical Notes

The slightly curved blade with its thin, prominent rib running from the hilt to nearly the point, has a fine water pattern similar to that of the Mughal dagger (no. 38). Between the handle and blade is a silver guard decorated in the same manner as the silver of the sheath. X-ray diffraction analysis of the niello on the sheath indicates that it is argentite, a silver sulfide. The niello on the guard shows, in addition to argentite, the presence of a lead sulfide, galena.

For the handle a multitude of materials was used. The tang of the blade runs the length of the handle and forms its core. On both sides of the handle, in narrow strips along the upper edge, one can see a marbled effect, which is found on the interior of walrus tusk and is quite distinctive. The effect distinguishes walrus tusk from elephant ivory or other similar materials that could have been used for the handle. Beneath each side of the handle, against the tang, are thin sheets of a gray, soft metal resembling lead. These sheets of metal would seem to serve to fit the sides of the handle securely against the tang.

The dagger and sheath show considerable wear. A wide opening runs along the edge of the wooden core. The silver chapes are scratched and worn and some of the niello is missing. On the handle of the dagger, some of the inlay and a small chip from the edge have been lost.

When the dagger came into the Freer collection, the blade had a matte, silvery surface with numerous pits and scratches. The water pattern was not evident. Heavy rust at the junction of the blade and handle suggested that the blade might have become severely rusted at one time and could have been subsequently cleaned and polished. The quality of the dagger, and comparison with other contemporary weapons, suggested that a water pattern may once have decorated the blade. A small area was etched with ferric chloride, and the pattern appeared. It was then decided that the historically and aesthetically correct appearance of the blade could be restored; the water pattern was developed by etching, which brought back the blade to its original appearance.

The analysis of the blade does not indicate the presence of elements other than iron. Analysis of the gold band on the handle indicates the presence of silver and copper. Copper is also present in the silver alloy used for the guard and sheath.

Provenance: Purchased from Kevorkian Foundation, New York, 1958; formerly in the Holstein Collection.

Published: Holstein, no. 90, pp. 190–91 and pl. LVIII.

Notes:

1. It is also represented on a second album painting in the Freer Gallery. Beach 1981, nos. 17c and 18b.
2. London 1982, nos. 416–17.
3. Beach 1978, no. 36; see also p. 111 for a list of portraits of Shah Abbas attributed to the same artist.
4. The portraits by Riza and his followers are discussed in Robinson 1972.
5. It appears, for instance, on an unpublished example in the Metropolitan Museum of Art, New York, acc. no. 96.5.138. I am indebted to David Alexander for providing this reference.
6. See, for example, the daggers published in Ivanov 1979, figs. 61–63; a steel mirror in Welch 1973, no. 44; and a jeweled bottle in Harari 1964–65, pl. 1380.

35. Dagger and Sheath

Blade: watered steel; forged and ribbed

Handle and sheath: watered and forged steel on wood core; chased and inlaid with gold; silver filigree set with garnet on pommel

Made by Taqi(?) in Shiraz

Iran, dated 1191 A.H. (1777 A.D.)

Length: 38.0 cm. (14^{15}/$_{16}$ in.); width of guard: 5.5 cm. (2^{3}/$_{16}$ in.); weight of dagger: 301.9 gm. (10.6 oz.); weight of sheath: 191.8 gm. (6.8 oz.).

39.44a–b

Inscriptions (nastaliq)

1. Handle and sheath (Persian):

In the time of the reign of the Zand emperor,	در زمان دولت خاقان زنو
The just king, ruler, heir to Dara,	شاه عادل داور داراسی فی
Khan of the world, favorite of Ali,	خان عالم مظهر لطف علی
Master of the time, lord of the sea and land,	سرور دوران خدیو بحر و بر
Glory of the craftsmen, helper of the lowest [impoverished].	فخر استادان نصیر ارذلان
Oh Taqi[?], that chief of artists,	یا نقی آن قدوه اهل هنر
Made in Shiraz a beautiful dagger	ساخت در شیراز خنجری زیبا
As a crescent with pearls dropping from its blade.	چون هلالی زآب آن چکو کهی
He said its date: beginning of wisdom and lofty praise.	کفت تاویخش سر خردی و لاف
For the sun, the crescent [is] as a belt of pearls. 12.	آفتابی را هلالی کمر در

---

2. Center cartouches on the handle (Arabic):
Koran XL:44 (front) and LXV:3 (back).

Executed with the finesse of a manuscript illumination, the handle and sheath of the dagger are decorated with floral motifs and calligraphy. The pommel of the handle has a silver-filigree panel with traces of gilding; in the center is a garnet, now broken, set into a beaded ring and collar. Each side of the handle shows three cartouches with inscriptions: the upper and lower are written in Persian against a floral ground; the center, containing a Koranic verse, appears on a plain ground. Between the cartouches are a pair of gold multipetaled blossoms, resembling peonies, rendered in relief. The remaining areas are filled with gold-inlaid floral scrolls bearing delicate leaves, lotus blossoms, and other flowers. The steel blade, delicately watered, is ribbed.

The two sides of the sheath also have the same decorative layout. Around the opening is an oval cartouche that has inscriptions and is flanked by floral motifs reserved on gold. Below are six linked cartouches alternately filled with split-leaf scrolls and inscriptions. The central cartouche has been scraped; it might have contained the name of the patron, which was removed at a later date. The interstices on the front are alternately decorated with gold floral sprays and pairs of reclining deer or birds placed against blossoming branches. A scalloped band with trefoils frames the outer edges of the front. The interstices on the back have loose, gold scrolls; the lowest cartouche is devoid of decoration. At the tip is a teardrop terminal. Between the first and second

detail of handle

cartouches is a loop with a ring, which was used to attach the dagger to the belt.

The Persian poem on the dagger, read first around the handle and then around the sheath (beginning with the upper cartouche on the front of the handle and terminating with the lower cartouche on the back of the sheath), contains ten lines, or five distiches, rendered in the *ramal* meter. The poem states that the dagger was made in Shiraz during the Zand period by an artist named Taqi or Naqi. The date is given in the phrase "beginning of wisdom and praise," which is seen in the last distich; the inscription follows the *abjad* system, in which each letter has a numerical value. When totaled, the numerical value of the phrase equals 1191, that is, 1191 A.H. or 1777 A.D.[1] This date falls within the reign of Karim Khan (1750–79), the first ruler of the short-lived Zand dynasty. Since the artistic production of that period is not well known, the Freer dagger is an important piece, establishing Shiraz, the capital, as a center of metalworking.

The poem praises the unidentified Zand ruler as being the heir to Dara, or Darius, referring to the region of Fars where the Achaemenid king held court. There is also an inference to the patron's Shiite beliefs in the phrase "favorite of Ali." The artist describes the curved shape of the dagger as a "crescent" and compares the watering on the blade to a "belt of pearls." The digits ("12") placed at the end of the poem may indicate an inventory number (see also no. 36).

The same materials, techniques, and decorative themes were used on a second dagger and sheath (fig. 71), dated 1770/71, now in the British Museum.[2] This example, also made during the reign of Karim Khan, has rendered the date in digits and contains ten lines of nastaliq poetry on the handle and sheath and a verse on the blade. Technical and stylistic similarities between this example and the Freer dagger indicate that they might have been made in the same center.

Daggers with curved blades became fashionable in Iran around the fifteenth century and have continued to be produced to the present day. Those dating from the Safavid period were richly inlaid with gold, enamels, and gems. The Freer dagger indicates that the high quality of workmanship established during the sixteenth and seventeenth centuries continued in the Zand period. Other Iranian examples bear verses glorifying the object and use the word *khanjar*, meaning dagger, also found on the Freer piece.[3]

The dagger played a significant role in the court and was worn by rulers and high-ranking officials during ceremonies. Like the sword, it was a symbol of manhood as well as authority and power, and was frequently used in the representations of princely figures in manuscript illustrations devoted to court activities.

71. Steel dagger and sheath inlaid with gold
Iran, dated 1770/71
(London, The British Museum, 78 12–30 902)

217

Technical Notes

Watered steel has been used as the main material of construction for the blade of the dagger, its handle, and its sheath. The blade bears a pattern that is more typical of watered steel than is the pattern on the axe head (no. 31). The surface of the axe head shows a mottled light and dark appearance, which indicates that the steel was not deformed very much from the original wootz cake. On this blade, a steel has been created that shows thin, contrasting light and dark lines; here, the amount of forging from the original cake was much greater, causing the two phases in the wootz cake to be elongated into a linear pattern. After forging, the pattern was revealed by etching.

The sheath and handle of the dagger are both multiple-piece constructions. The sheath is made from five pieces of steel that surround a wooden core. Two pieces of curved sheet were used for the front and back; these are joined at the edge. A teardrop-shaped terminal with a short post extending into the wooden core was added at the bottom tip; these three pieces are joined with soft solder. Two other small pieces of sheet are set into the opening at the top. They serve to guide the blade into the sheath. On one side of the sheath is a small ring through which a securing cord might have been attached.

The handle is constructed in a similar manner. Two side pieces joined along the edge and applied over a core make up the main part of the handle. Two additional small pieces of sheet seal the opening where the blade is seated.

A faint water pattern is present on the sheet steel of the handle and sheath. The pattern has not been brought out as dramatically as on the blade; one must use

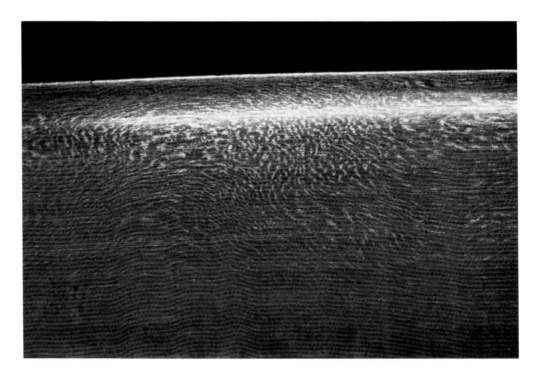

Photomicrograph of the blade showing the water pattern. Actual size of the area illustrated: 30 x 20 mm. (1⅛ x ¹³⁄₁₆ in.)

magnification to see it. The sides of both the handle and sheath are decorated with gold inlay set into chased recesses, raised inscriptions, and floral designs formed by recessing the surrounding background. No trace remains of the decoration that previously occupied the cartouches on either side of the sheath.

At the top of the handle, an ornate terminal is used. The terminal consists mainly of a flat plate decorated with filigree around a centrally mounted stone. X-ray diffraction analysis was used to identify the stone as a garnet. The edge of the terminal and the bottom of the collet are encircled by a bead pattern made from a narrow piece of chased wire or sheet.

The dagger and sheath are in excellent condition, though in a few areas the water pattern on the blade has been worn away. X-ray fluorescence analyses of the steel used for the blade, handle, and sheath do not indicate the presence of elements other than iron.

Provenance: Purchased from Beghian, London, 1939.
Unpublished

Notes:

1. In the *abjad* system, based on the Arabic alphabet, each letter is assigned a numerical value ranging from one to one thousand. The following are the values of the letters used in the inscription:

sin (s):	60
ra (r):	200
kha (kh):	600
ra (r):	200
dal (d):	4
ya (y):	10
va (v):	6
lam (l):	30
alif (a):	1
fa (f):	80
total:	1191

2. This dagger with sheath is slightly smaller, measuring 36.5 centimeters (14⅜ inches). Its inscriptions do not give the name of the maker or patron.
3. For a group of inscribed daggers from the fifteenth to seventeenth centuries, see Ivanov 1979. Other examples are reproduced in Stöcklein 1964–65, pls. 1424–27.

36. Knife

Blade: forged steel and meteoritic iron; pattern-welded and inlaid with gold

Handle: forged steel; chased and inlaid with gold

Made for Jahangir

India, dated 1030 A.H. (1620/21 A.D.)

Length: 26.1 cm. (10¼ in.); width (max.) 1.6 cm. (⁵⁄₁₆ in.);
  weight: 96.5 gm. (3.4 oz.).

55.27

Inscriptions (Persian, nastaliq)

On the tang of the blade:

There fell in the reign of Jahangir Shah	فتاده بعهد جهانکیر شاه
From lightning iron [a] *glittering precious piece*	زبرق آهن برق وش جوهری
Jahangir, [son of] *Akbar ordered from it*	جهانکیر اکبر بفرمود از آن
Two swords and this knife and [a] *dagger.*	دو شمشیر و این کارد و خنجری
In the year 1030 [November 1620–November 1621 A.D.].	سنة ۱۰۳۰ ٭ سنة ۱٦ ٭ ۱٤٦
In the year 16 [sixteenth year of Jahangir's reign]. *146.*	

The knife, beautifully designed, has distinctive lamellae on the blade, which has an umbrella (a royal emblem used by the Mughal rulers) inlaid with gold on one side.[1] The guard is decorated with naturalistic floral scrolls and also inlaid with gold. The cylindrical handle contains three large cartouches representing predators and prey placed against a floral scroll; the cartouches are linked together by a pair of smaller units enclosing a central lotus flanked by leaves. The upper and lower cartouches show a hawk attacking a duck or goose; the one in the middle depicts a lion attacking a deer or gazelle. The upper cartouche is identical on both sides; the predators in the other units face right, while the orientation of their prey alternates on each side between right and left. The flat top of the blade has a teardrop-shaped movable appendix, which is decorated with floral motifs and terminates in a trefoil. The appendix and the outlines of the cartouches on the handle both are inlaid with gold.

The tang of the blade, which extends along the handle, has six cartouches with inscriptions: the first four enclose the verses of poetry and the remaining contain the dates. The inscriptions, the borders of the cartouches, and the inventory number at the end, which follows a series of strokes, all are inlaid with gold.

According to the inscription this knife was made from an iron meteorite that fell during the reign of Jahangir (1605–27), the fourth ruler of the Mughal dynasty. The celebrated event is also mentioned in Jahangir's memoirs: the author writes that on April 10, 1621, a meteor fell outside a village near Jalandhar in Punjab, and when the piece was brought to the court, Jahangir ordered Ustad Davud to make from it two swords, a dagger, and a knife.[2] The swordmaker, finding the material too brittle, used three parts meteoritic iron and one part common iron to produce the four weapons requested by his patron. Jahangir also writes that after the weapons were made, Bi-badal K. composed a commemorative poem. Although the text published in Jahangir's memoirs differs·slightly from the verses found on the Freer knife, the same sentiments are reflected in both versions, and these four lines were either composed by this unknown poet or based on his work. The digits ("146") placed at the end of the inscriptions must refer to an inventory number, either in the imperial arsenal or in the swordmaker's shop.

detail of handle

detail of handle

Technical analyses suggest that some meteoritic iron was used in the knife. Jahangir writes that the meteor weighed 160 *tolas,* which is the equivalent of a piece five pounds in weight with a diameter of some three inches. It was, therefore, a fairly small chunk and could not be stretched into two swords, a dagger, and a knife without a substantial addition of common iron. Whether Ustad Davud incorporated only one-fourth common iron into the meteor is highly speculative. Jahangir must have believed, nevertheless, that three-fourths of the weapons were made out of this extraordinary material. Meteors were associated with supernatural powers and thought to be rare and precious, with magical qualities. They were often made into swords, daggers, and knives, in the belief that they transmitted their power and talismanic values to the owner. Of the weapons made from the meteor by Ustad Davud, the Freer knife is the only remaining piece.

The small knife with one sharp edge, called a *kard,* appears to have been popular in Iran and India during the sixteenth and seventeenth centuries.[3] Several seventeenth-century Mughal knives, a few with sheaths, have jade handles encrusted with jewels[4]; one unique example, thought to have been made in the 1620s, has a white jade handle carved as a head of a youth.[5] The *kard* is frequently depicted hanging from the belts of courtly figures in contemporary manuscript illustrations. In the collection of the Freer Gallery is an early seventeenth-century album painting (fig. 69) portraying Jahangir embracing Shah Abbas; the Mughal ruler is depicted wearing such a knife. Also in the Freer is a second painting (fig. 72) representing Jahangir entertaining Shah Abbas in which a court official is shown bearing a similar piece.[6] In both cases, the knife is suspended from a cord tied to the appendix at the top and encased in a gold sheath. It is possible that the Freer knife also had a sheath richly embellished in gold and jewels, which would be in keeping with its high value and magical qualities.

Jahangir's knife is one of the rare examples of Islamic metalwork that is extremely well documented: the date of execution and the name of the patron are given in the inscriptions; its legendary source, the name of its maker, and the author of the poem inscribed on the tang are provided in a contemporary document. This type of object, rare and precious, decorated with symbols of royalty and might (the gold umbrella on the blade, and predators and prey on the handle) would have been greatly favored by its patron, Jahangir, whose love of luxurious items and self-glorification were renowned and frequently the theme for paintings produced at his court.

Technical Notes

The forged blade of the knife displays the lamellar structure indicative of the process whereby iron or steel bars are stacked and welded together by hammering. This method of forging a blade is one variant of the process known as pattern-welding.[7] Pattern-welding yields a structure that has a surface that can be treated to give an appearance somewhat similar to that of a damascened, or watered, blade. The surface of a pattern-welded blade is essentially caused by the manipulations of the metalsmith during the

detail

72. *Jahangir Embracing
Shah Abbas*
Gold and color on paper
Made by Abu'l-Hasan
India, ca. 1618
(Washington, D.C.,
Freer Gallery of Art,
45.9)

223

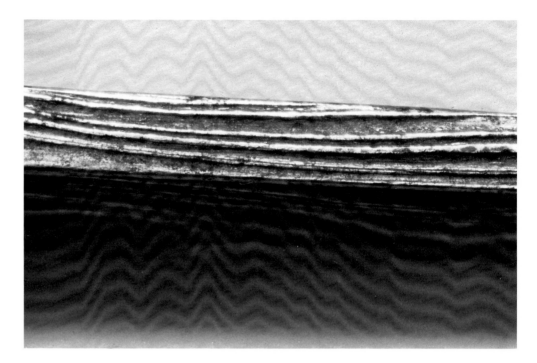

Photomicrograph of the top edge of the blade showing the layered structure. Actual size of the area illustrated: 10 x 7 mm. (⅜ x ⁹⁄₃₂ in.)

forging of the blade. With separate pieces of iron and steel, the smith could work to produce a particular pattern in his finished product. Etching the finished blade would then accentuate the pattern made by the welded strips of iron or steel.

The handle of the knife consists of at least four parts, with three additional parts making up the hinged terminal. The tang of the blade can be seen to run along the top of the handle for its entire length. Radiographs reveal that a flat, narrow, rectilinear metal insert is set into the tang, perpendicular to the flat side of the blade, to firmly seat the blade in the handle. The use of solder is not evident along the seams, nor is its use indicated by X-radiography. A bituminous material is present in some seams and a resinous material in others. These materials may have served as adhesives for joining the handle.

Gold inlay was set into both the blade and the handle. The inlay on the top of the blade was laid into circular punch marks; the punch marks are sometimes alternately placed to either side of scribed lines. The large inlay on one side of the blade shows faint traces of chased details. On the handle, the recessed areas of the design and the recesses that hold the inlay appear to have been formed by chasing and chiseling. One can find clear punch marks only along the sharp curves of the design. The inlay in one area is loose and stands above its recess; here the inlay measures 0.2 millimeters (0.008 inch) in thickness. Along the top and the bottom of the handle, the inlay has been used to conceal the seams of the separate pieces.

The knife is in excellent condition, but the gold-inlaid umbrella bears some deep scratches and appears as if it has been defaced.

Photomicrograph of the side of the blade showing the layered structure. Actual size of the area illustrated: 45 x 30 mm. (1¾ x 1⅛ in.)

X-ray fluorescence analysis of the blade indicates that some of the layers contain nickel whereas others do not. It is felt that the presence of more than 5% nickel in steel is an indication of the presence of meteoritic iron.[8] Previous examinations of the knife, and literary evidence, have suggested that meteoritic iron in combination with terrestrial iron was possibly used to make this blade. The discovery of nickel in some of the layers supports this opinion.

Provenance: Purchased from Sahami, Washington, D.C., 1955.
Published: Ettinghausen and Henderson 1981

Notes:

1. From Akbar's reign onward the royal umbrella was used as an imperial Mughal emblem, together with a throne, heart-shaped fan, and ball suspended from the coiled end of a pole. See Aziz 1947, pp. 77–106.
2. This passage from the memoirs of Jahangir is published in Tuzuk 1914, pp. 204–5; and Aziz 1947, pp. 10–13.
3. Stöcklein 1964–65, pls. 1425B–D. The latter also has a movable appendix at the top of the handle.
4. London 1982, nos. 408 and 415.
5. Ibid., no. 406.
6. Both paintings are published in Beach 1981, nos. 17b–c.
7. Maryon 1960a, pp. 25–36.
8. Forbes 1964, p. 177; Gettens, Clarke, and Chase 1971, p. 55; and Li Chung 1979, p. 278.

37. Bird-Shaped Flint Striker

Steel: cut from sheet and forged; chased, inlaid with gold,
  and set with rubies

India, early 17th century

Height: 8.7 cm. ($3^{7}/_{16}$ in.); length: 5.0 cm. (2 in.);
  weight: 49.2 gm. (1.7 oz.)

40.7

This steel flint striker shaped as a long-beaked bird has the same decoration on both sides.[1] The body, outlined with gold bands, terminates in a tail resembling a half-palmette and is decorated with split-leaves reserved on a gold ground. The curved body has three ducks or geese flying amidst sprays of twisted, feathery leaves inlaid in gold. The animal closest to the tail is being attacked by a hawk. All the ducks on one side face the tail; on the other side one of the ducks is reversed and the figure being attacked turns back its head. A chevron embellishes the upper beak of the bird; the eyes are inlaid with rubies set into gold collars. One of the stones has been crushed and the edge toward the tail is worn through use. This was obviously the surface used to strike the flint.

The design is executed in an extremely refined manner and is highly detailed, with minute lines indicating the feathers on the bodies. The subject chosen for the shape is repeated in the decoration, a whimsical feature often encountered in Islamic art (for other zoomorphic pieces, see nos. 6, 7, and 11).

The decorative themes and techniques employed on the Freer flint striker, particularly the vignettes with the hawks attacking the ducks, are extremely close to those found on the knife made for Jahangir in 1620/21 (no. 36). The position of the birds, the detailing of the feathers, and the floral background appear to have been copied from the cartouches on the knife's handle. Even the split-leaf scroll reserved on a gold ground decorating the half-palmette of the flint striker is identical to the design on the appendix of the knife. Both pieces must have been produced at the same time, possibly in the same workshop.

The same curved form appears on a second flint striker (fig. 73) now in Berlin.[2] This example, decorated with lions and hares, and predators attacking gazelles, is recorded as being 16.0 centimeters (6⁵⁄₁₆ inches) high, which makes it twice the size of the Freer flint striker. The compositions with lions attacking gazelles are so similar to those on Jahangir's knife that this example should also be assigned to India and dated to the same period as the Freer piece.[3]

Hawks or eagles attacking birds or other docile creatures is an ancient Iranian theme that symbolizes victory and power. It became a decorative motif during the Islamic period and was frequently employed on metalwork (see nos. 10 and 17). The bird, representing freedom of the soul and spirit, was also an auspicious theme in pre-Islamic and Islamic iconography.

In the Safavid period, steel, which had been reserved for arms and armor in the past, became a popular material for architectural decoration and furnishings as well as for objects such as beggar's bowls, mirrors, water pipes, surgical instruments, and ornaments including buckles and belts.[4] Often pierced and embellished with gold and silver, the items reveal a highly advanced technique and workmanship.

The same interest in producing gold- and silver-inlaid steel pieces appears in India during the seventeenth and eighteenth centuries.[5] Mughal artists generally employed these materials for imperial arms and armor, and seldom used steel to fashion the types of objects and ornaments found in Iran. The Freer flint striker is among the rare Mughal examples of the use of steel for a piece other than a weapon.

73. Drawing of steel bird-shaped flint striker
India, early 17th century
(Berlin, Museum für Islamische Kunst, I.3619)

Technical Notes

Given the two-dimensional form of the striker, it is most likely that the striker was cut and forged into shape from a thin, flat bar. The design was then chased and cut into the surface. The recesses of the design bear many tool marks, which apparently remain from the use of a chisel to remove the metal from these areas. The gold inlay has been

227

applied into rows or groups of circular punch marks. For the eyes, a hole was made through the metal and the stones were set on either side of the head and surrounded by gold. The break in one of the eyes allowed for the removal of a small sliver of the stone for X-ray diffraction analysis; the stone was found to be a ruby. The only damages seen were the wear marks and the broken eye previously mentioned.

The presence of elements other than iron was not indicated by X-ray fluorescence analysis.

Provenance: Purchased from Beghian, London, 1940.
Published: Harari 1964–65, pl. 1390J.

Notes:

1. A bird-shaped striker owned by Beghian was exhibited in London in 1931. It is likely that this and the Freer piece are the same. London 1931, no. 275E.
2. A drawing of this was first published in Sarre 1906, no. 160.
3. The theme of a lion attacking a gazelle also was used popularly in Iran, particularly on arms and armor. See, for instance, the gold-inlaid eighteenth-century breastplate in Elwell-Sutton 1979, pls. 8–11. Predators and prey were used on a flint striker similar in shape to the Berlin piece. This example, in the Museum of Fine Arts in Boston (acc. no. 16.257), is larger (21 centimeters high) and was likely made in Iran at a later date.
4. See, for example, Harari 1964–65, pls. 1389–94; Welch 1973, no. 44; and Allan 1982a, no. 26.
5. A variety of steel daggers, swords, guns, and other weapons are discussed in the section on arms and armor in London 1982, nos. 406–68; see also no. 494 for a rare steel piece thought to be a doorknocker.

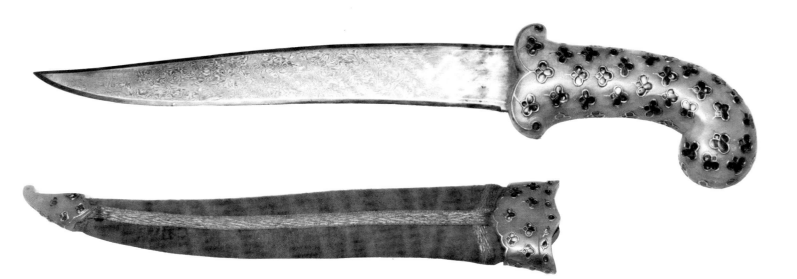

38. Dagger and Sheath

Blade: watered steel; forged and inlaid with gold

Handle: jade; carved, inlaid with gold, and set with rubies
and green beryl

Sheath: wood covered with velvet; jade chape and locket,
carved, inlaid with gold, and set with rubies and green beryl

India, 17th–18th centuries

Length (max.): 39.5 cm. (15½ in.); width (max.): 5.5 cm. (2⅛ in.);
weight of dagger: 357.7 gm. (12.6 oz.);
weight of sheath: 64.8 gm. (2.3 oz.)

1984.3

The dagger has a slightly curving double-edged blade with a refined water pattern. On one side of the blade is a cartouche with a scalloped edge outlined in gold and appended by a palmette-shaped gold-inlaid finial. Although the finial could not be identified properly, it appears to have been used as an *alam*, or standard, frequently seen on imperial Mughal arms and armor (see no. 36).

The handle has a rounded pommel, a lobed edge, and three subtle ribs on the underside to enable a secure grasp. The front and back sides of the handle are covered with randomly placed trefoils framed in gold; rubies are set in the three petals of the blossoms, and emerald-green beryls appear at the cores. A thin gold branch with three blossoms flanked by a pair of rounded leaves outlines the edge. A series of leaves set with rubies decorates the two narrow sides.

The sheath is covered with green velvet and embellished with a thin ribbon woven with silver threads that encircles the upper edge and runs vertically down the front. Both the locket and chape are of jade, carved and inlaid with gold and gems, identical in design and technique to that of the handle. The locket has a band of leaves on the top and two narrow sides, a gold-outlined scalloped edge, and decoration of two rows of trefoils. At the back is a broken ring, suggesting that it once served as a loop for the attachment of cords tying the dagger to the belt. The teardrop-shaped chape also has a gold-outlined scalloped edge and is inlaid with trefoils and leaves. This portion has been damaged and some parts of the inlay have been lost.

There exist a number of seventeenth- and eighteenth-century Mughal daggers (see fig. 74) with jade handles, lockets, and chapes encrusted with gems; their wooden sheaths are usually covered with woven fabrics, often with velvet. The majority of the handles have rounded pommels with lobed edges, similar to the one in the Freer

74. Jade dagger and sheath inlaid with gold and gems
India, 17th century
(Kuwait, National Museum, Dar al-Athar al-Islamiya Collection, LNS 12 HS)

Gallery. Many examples are embellished with gold-outlined blossoms composed of rubies, emeralds, beryls, and diamonds set into deeply carved sockets.[1] The same materials and designs were employed on other imperial objects, such as boxes, bottles, belt buckles, and archer's rings made of jade and rock crystal.[2]

Similar pieces were produced in the Ottoman court during the sixteenth and seventeenth centuries. An interesting group of daggers employ jade handles and sheaths embellished with gems, recalling the technique found on the Mughal examples.[3] These sumptuous objects, used more as decorative accessories than as functional weapons, reflect the wealth of the Mughal and Ottoman courts and the aesthetics of the patrons.

The blade of this dagger bears a water pattern similar to that of the Safavid dagger (no. 34) and is less drawn out in the longitudinal direction of the blade than the pattern of the Zand dagger (no. 35). At the handle, the blade terminates in a short, narrow tang that extends into a cavity cut in the handle and is secured by the use of an adhesive substance. On the blade just above the handle is an area inlaid with gold.

The sheath is made up of a wooden core to which a cotton cloth covering and a locket and chape of stone are applied. In addition to the cloth covering, a brocade strip consisting of silk wrapped in silver foil runs the length of one side and underneath the locket. Microscopic analysis was used to identify the silk and cotton.

The stone used for the handle, locket, and chape was identified by X-ray diffraction and hardness tests as a type of nephrite. On these nephrite pieces, the same methods and materials of inlay were used. Depressions cut in the nephrite were lined with gold foil and set with small red, green, and colorless stones. Besides providing a highly reflective surface for the inlaid stones, the soft, malleable gold was pressed in around the edges of the stones to secure them. Hardness tests and examination with ultraviolet light indicate that the red stones are all rubies except for one, which is either a spinel or, more probably, a garnet. Nothing would indicate that the different red stone is not original. X-ray diffraction analysis of some of the green and colorless stones indicate that they are forms of beryl. The dark-green stones would be considered emeralds; the others would be green beryl (being only pale green in color) and colorless beryl (also called goshenite).

In some instances adhesive or resinous materials may have been used to help further secure the gold to the nephrite and the inlaid stones into their settings in the gold. It also appears that in some instances colored substances were added on top of the gold and beneath the stones to intensify their color.

The dagger and sheath have both suffered wear and damage. Toward the end of the blade, the water pattern has been worn away. Near the handle, the end of the blade is scratched and abraded. The gold inlay lies both above and below these scratch marks, which suggests that inlay was applied after some abrasion had taken place. The reason for the blackened, pitted area around the inlay is unclear. X-radiography of the blade shows no change in the density of the blade, nor any internal flaws or voids. The thickness of the blade at this point is also constant and regular. In contrast to the blade, the handle of the dagger is in nearly perfect condition, and only one small stone has been lost.

The sheath shows greater wear. The chape has lost most of its inlay. Also, the wooden core in this area has been shattered and the fabric has been torn. On one side of the sheath, the fabric is faded in comparison with the other side. The locket has fared better than the chape, having suffered no loss of inlay. A small loop on the back of the locket, however, has been broken away.

No elemental analysis was performed on the blade of this dagger.

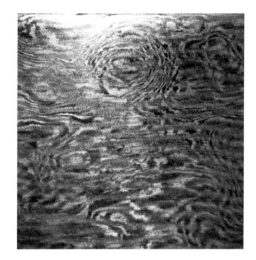

Photomicrograph of the blade showing the water pattern. Actual size of the area illustrated: 21 x 21 mm. ($^{13}/_{16}$ x $^{13}/_{16}$ in.)

Provenance: Gift of Stephen R. Turner, Winston-Salem, 1984.
Unpublished

Notes:

1. Wiest 1979, p. 77 (upper right); London 1982, no. 412; and Jenkins 1983, pl. 129. For examples with velvet-covered sheaths, see Jenkins 1983, pl. 128; and London 1982, nos. 413–14 and 418. This tradition appears to have survived up to the twentieth century; see Sotheby's 1984, nos. 454, 457, 466, and 468.
2. London 1982, nos. 304, 366, 367, and 374; and Jenkins and Keene 1983, no. 70.
3. A group of Iranian daggers with seventeenth-century Turkish jade handles and sheaths embellished with gems are published in Ivanov 1979, pls. 64, 67, 71, and 73. One of them, pl. 71, has an Indian handle but a Turkish sheath.

Sources

Works cited as references are marked with an asterisk.

Aga-Oglu 1945* Aga-Oglu, Mehmet. "About a Type of Islamic Incense Burner." *Art Bulletin* 27 (1945): 28–45.

Allan 1969 Allan, James W. "Later Mamluk Metalwork: A Series of Dishes." *Oriental Art*, n.s. 15, no. 1 (Spring 1969): 38–43.

Allan 1971 Allan, James W. "Later Mamluk Metalwork II: A Series of Lunch-boxes." *Oriental Art*, n.s. 17, no. 2 (1971): 156–64.

Allan 1976* Allan, James W. "Review Article: G. Fehérvári, *Islamic Metalwork of the Eighth to the Fifteenth Century in the Keir Collection*." *Oriental Art* 22 (1976): 299–302.

Allan 1977a* Allan, James W. "Originality in Bronze: A Thirteenth Century Persian School of Metalworkers." *Iran* 15 (1977): 156–64.

Allan 1977b* Allan, James W. "Silver: The Key to Bronze in Early Islamic Iran." *Kunst des Orients* 11 (1977): 5–21.

Allan 1978* Allan, James W. "From Tabriz to Siirt: Relocation of a Thirteenth Century Metalworking School." *Iran* 16 (1978): 182–83.

Allan 1979* Allan, James W. *Persian Metal Technology: 700–1300 A.D.* London: Ithaca Press, 1979.

Allan 1982a* Allan, James W. *Islamic Metalwork: The Nuhad Es-Said Collection*. London: Sotheby Publications, 1982.

Allan 1982b* Allan, James W. *Nishapur: Metalwork of the Early Islamic Period*. New York: Metropolitan Museum of Art, 1982.

Allan and Raby 1982* Allan, James W., and Raby, Julian. "Metalwork." In *Tulips, Arabesques and Turbans: Decorative Arts from the Ottoman Empire*, edited by Yanni Petsopoulous, pp. 17–71. New York: Abbeville Press, 1982.

al-Ush 1972

al-Ush, M. Abu'l-Faraj. "A Bronze Ewer with a High Spout in the Metropolitan Museum of Art and Analogous Pieces." In *Islamic Art in the Metropolitan Museum of Art*, edited by Richard Ettinghausen, pp. 187–98. New York: Metropolitan Museum of Art, 1972.

Ann Arbor 1967*

Sasanian Silver: Late Antique and Early Medieval Arts of Luxury from Iran. Ann Arbor: University of Michigan Museum of Art, 1967.

Art Quarterly 1969*

"Recent Accessions." *Art Quarterly* (Winter 1969): 436–37.

Atıl 1971*

Atıl, Esin. *Exhibition of Twenty-Five Hundred Years of Persian Art*. Washington, D.C.: Freer Gallery of Art, Smithsonian Institution, 1971.

Atıl 1972*

Atıl, Esin. "Two Il-Hanid Candlesticks at the University of Michigan." *Kunst des Orients* 8, nos. 1–2 (1972): 1–33.

Atıl 1975*

Atıl, Esin. *Art of the Arab World*. Washington D.C.: Freer Gallery of Art, Smithsonian Institution, 1975.

Atıl 1981*

Atıl, Esin. *Renaissance of Islam: Art of the Mamluks*. Washington, D.C.: Smithsonian Institution Press, 1981.

Avner 1974*

Avner, Sidney H. *Introduction to Physical Metallurgy*. New York: McGraw-Hill, 1974.

Aziz 1947*

Aziz, Abdul. *Arms and Jewelry of the Indian Mughuls*. Lahore: Abdul Aziz, 1947.

Baer 1965*

Baer, Eva. *Sphinxes and Harpies in Medieval Islamic Art*. Jerusalem: Israel Oriental Society, 1965.

Baer 1968*

Baer, Eva. " 'Fish-pond' Ornaments on Persian and Mamluk Metal Vessels." *Bulletin of the School of Oriental and African Studies* 31 (1968): 14–27.

Baer 1972

Baer, Eva. "An Islamic Inkwell in the Metropolitan Museum of Art." In *Islamic Art in the Metropolitan Museum of Art*, edited by Richard Ettinghausen, pp. 199–211. New York: Metropolitan Museum of Art, 1972.

Baer 1977a

Baer, Eva. "A Brass Vessel from the Tomb of Sayyid Battal Ghazi." *Artibus Asiae* 39, nos. 3–4 (1977): 299–335.

Baer 1977b

Baer, Eva. "The Nisan Tasi: A Study in Persian-Mongol Metalware." *Kunst des Orients* 9, nos. 1–2 (1977): 1–46.

Baer 1981*

Baer, Eva. "Dawat." In *Encyclopedia of Islam,* new edition. Supplement fascicule pp. 203–4. Leiden: E. J. Brill, 1981.

Baer 1982*

Baer, Eva. "The Ruler in Cosmic Setting: A Note of Medieval Islamic Iconography." In *Essays in Islamic Art and Architecture in Honor of Katharina Otto-Dorn*, edited by Abbas Daneshvari, pp. 13–19. Malibu, California: Undena Publications, 1982.

Baer 1983*

Baer, Eva. *Metalwork in Medieval Islamic Art*. Albany, New York: State University of New York Press, 1983.

Bargello 1981*

Islamic Metalwork from the Grand Ducal Collection. Florence: Museo Nazionale del Bargello, 1981.

Barrett 1949*

Barrett, Douglas. *Islamic Metalwork in the British Museum*. London: Trustees of the British Museum, 1949.

Beach 1978*

Beach, Milo Cleveland. *The Grand Mogul: Imperial Painting in India, 1600–1660*. Williamstown, Mass.: Clark Art Institute, 1978.

Beach 1981*

Beach, Milo Cleveland. *The Imperial Image: Paintings for the Mughal Court*. Washington, D.C.: Freer Gallery of Art, Smithsonian Institution, 1981.

Beard 1940*

Beard, Charles R. "Chafing-balls and Hand-warmers." *Connoisseur* 105, no. 461 (January 1940): 17–21 and 27.

Beirut 1974

Art Islamique dans les collections privés libanaises. Beirut: Musée Nicolas Sursock, 1974.

Belaiew 1918*

Belaiew, N. "Damascene Steel." *Journal of the Iron and Steel Institution* 97 (1918): 417–37.

Berchem 1904

Berchem, Max Van. "Notes d'archéologie arabe." *Journal Asiatique* 3, 10th ser. (January–February 1904): 5–96.

Berlin 1971*

Museum für Islamische Kunst: Katalog. Berlin: Staatliche Museen, Preussischer Kulturbesitz, 1971.

Berlin 1982*

Land des Baal: Syrien-Forum der Volker und Kulturen. Berlin: Museum für Vor- und Fruhgeschichte, 1982.

Binghamton 1975

Islam and the Medieval West. Edited by Stanley Ferber. Binghamton, N.Y.: State University of New York, 1975.

Birch 1974*

Jewelry from Persia: The Collection of Patti Birch. Pforzheim: Schmuckmuseum, 1974.

Bonnin 1924*

Bonnin, Alfred. *Tutenaq and Paktonq.* Oxford: Oxford University Press, 1924.

Cairo 1969

Islamic Art in Egypt: 969–1517. Cairo: Ministry of Culture, 1969.

Cairo 1969a

Islamic Art in Egypt: 969–1517—An Exhibition—Loan Objects. Cairo: Ministry of Culture, 1969.

Cameron 1974*

Cameron, H. K. "Technical Aspects of Medieval Monumental Brasses." *Archaeological Journal* 131 (1974): 215–37.

Campbell 1973*

Campbell, Sheila. "The Perfume Merchant's Bowl in the Royal Ontario Museum (970.268.5)." *Oriental Art* 19 (1973): 275–91.

Chase, Bene, Zycherman, and Westley 1980*

Chase, W. T.; Bene, I. V.; Zycherman, L. A.; and Westley, Harold. "Examination and Metallurgical Analysis of Chörten 233." Appendix A in Robert T. Hatt, "A Thirteenth-Century Tibertan Reliquary." *Artibus Asiae* 42, no. 2–3 (1980): 211–14.

Coomaraswamy 1931

Coomaraswamy, Ananda K. "Two Examples of Muhammadan Metal Work." *Bulletin of the* [Boston] *Museum of Fine Arts* 29 (1931): 70–72.

Copper Development Association 1978*

Standards Handbook: Cast Copper and Copper Alloy Products: Part 7—Alloy Data. New York: Copper Development Association, 1978.

Craddock 1978

Craddock, P. T. "The Composition of the Copper Alloys Used by the Greek, Etruscan and Roman Civilizations; 3. The Origins and Early Use of Brass." *Journal of Archaeological Science* 5, no. 1 (1978): 1–16.

Craddock 1979*

Craddock, P. T. "The Copper Alloys of the Medieval Islamic World—Inheritors of the Classical Tradition." *World Archaeology* 2, no. 1 (June 1979): 68–79.

Craddock 1981

Craddock, P. T. "The Copper Alloys of Tibet and Their Background." In *Aspects of Tibetan Metallurgy.* Occasional

236

Papers (no. 15), edited by W. A. Oddy and W. Zwalf, pp. 1–31. London: British Museum, 1981.

Craddock 1984*

Craddock, P. T. "How Zinc Was Smelted in Ancient India." *New Scientist* (March 29, 1984): 23.

Craddock and Lang 1983*

Craddock, P. T., and Lang, J. "Spinning, Turning, Polishing." *Historical Metallurgy* 17, no. 2 (1983): 79–81.

Cranston 1977–78*

Cranston, Fumiko E. "Art of Asia Acquired by North American Museums, 1976–1977." *Archives of Asian Art* 31 (1977–78): 127.

Damascus 1976*

Catalogue du Musée Nationale de Damas, by M. Abu'l-Faraj al-Ush, Adnan Joundi, and Bachir Zouhdi. Damascus: Direction Générale des Antiquités et des Musées, 1976.

Darkevich 1976*

Darkevich, V. P. *Khudozhestvennyi metall Vostoka: VIII–XIII vv* (Artistic Metal of the East: Eleventh-Thirteenth Centuries). Moscow: Akademiya Nauk SSSR, Institut Arkheologii, 1976.

Demortier and Hackens 1982*

Demortier, G., and Hackens, T. "Milliprobe and Microprobe Analysis of Gold Items of Ancient Jewelry." *Nuclear Instruments and Methods* 197 (1982): 223–36.

Devonshire 1927*

Devonshire, R. L. "Moslem Objects in the Eumorfopoulos Collection." *Apollo* 5, no. 25 (January 1927): 12–17.

Dimand 1931

Dimand, Maurice S. "Unpublished Metalwork of the Rasulid Sultans of Yemen." *Metropolitan Museum Studies* 3, pt. 2 (1931): 229–37.

Dimand 1934*

Dimand, Maurice S. "Silver Inlaid Bronze Canteen with Christian Subjects in the Eumorfopoulos Collection." *Ars Islamica* 1 (1934): 17–21.

Dimand 1944*

Dimand, Maurice S. *A Handbook of Muhammadan Art.* 2d rev. ed. New York: Metropolitan Museum of Art, 1944.

Dimand 1967

Dimand, Maurice S. "Seljuk Metalwork Acquired by the Metropolitan Museum." In *A Survey of Persian Art,* edited by A. U. Pope, vol. 14, pp. 3064–65. London: Oxford University Press, 1967.

Dodd 1972

Dodd, Erica Cruikshank. "On a Bronze Rabbit from Fatimid Egypt." *Kunst des Orients* 8, nos. 1–2 (1972): 60–76.

Dumbarton Oaks 1967* *Handbook of the Byzantine Collection, Dumbarton Oaks.* Washington, D.C.: Dumbarton Oaks, 1967.

Dunlop 1957 Dunlop, D. M. "Sources of Gold and Silver in Islam According to al-Hamdani." *Studia Islamica* 8 (1957): 29–49.

Egami 1961* Egami, Namio. *Exhibition of Persian Art.* Tokyo: Asahi Press, 1961.

El Emary 1967 El Emary, Amal A. "Studies in Some Islamic Objects Newly Discovered at Qus." *Annales Islamologiques* 7 (1967): 121–38.

Elwell-Sutton 1979* Elwell-Sutton, L. P. "Persian Armour Inscriptions." In *Islamic Arms and Armour,* edited by Robert Elgood, pp. 5–19. London: Scolar Press, 1979.

Enderlein 1973 Enderlein, Volkmar. "Das Bildprogramm des Berliner Mosul-Beckens." *Forschungen und Berichte* 15 (1973): 7–40.

Erginsoy 1978* Erginsoy, Ülker. *İslam Maden Sanatının Gelişmesi* (The Development of the Art of Metalwork in Islam). İstanbul: Ministry of Culture, 1978.

Erginsoy 1980 Erginsoy, Ülker. "Turkish Metalwork." In *The Art and Architecture of Turkey,* edited by Ekrem Akurgal, pp. 208–21. London: Oxford University Press, 1980.

Essen 1963* *Koptische Kunst: Christentum arn Nil.* Essen, Villa Hugel: 1963.

Ettinghausen 1935* Ettinghausen, Richard. "A Fourteenth Century Metal Bowl." *Bulletin of the American Institute for Persian Art and Archaeology* 4, no. 1 (June 1935): 40–43.

Ettinghausen 1943a* Ettinghausen, Richard. "The Bobrinski 'Kettle': Patron and Style of an Islamic Bronze." *Gazette des Beaux Arts* 24 (1943): 193–208.

Ettinghausen 1943b* Ettinghausen, Richard. *Metalwork from Islamic Countries.* Ann Arbor: University of Michigan, 1943.

Ettinghausen 1950* Ettinghausen, Richard. *Studies in Muslim Iconography I: The Unicorn.* Washington, D.C.: Freer Gallery of Art, Smithsonian Institution, 1950.

Ettinghausen 1956*   Ettinghausen, Richard. "The Arts of Iran at the Time of Avicenna." In *Société Iranienne pour la Conservation des Monuments Nationaux: Le Livre du Millenaire d'Avicenne,* vol. 4, pp. 132–38. Tehran: University of Tehran, 1956.

Ettinghausen 1957*   Ettinghausen, Richard. "The 'Wade Cup' in the Cleveland Museum of Art, Its Origin and Decorations." *Ars Orientalis* 2 (1957): 327–66.

Ettinghausen 1959*   Ettinghausen, Richard. "Further Comments on the Wade Cup." *Ars Orientalis* 3 (1959): 197–99.

Ettinghausen 1960*   Ettinghausen, Richard. "Takfit." In *Urdu Encyclopedia of Islam,* vol. 4, pp. 597–607. Lahore: 1960.

Ettinghausen 1964*   Ettinghausen, Richard. *Seven Thousand Years of Iranian Art.* Washington, D.C.: Smithsonian Institution, 1964.

Ettinghausen 1965*   Ettinghausen, Richard. "The Dance with Zoomorphic Masks and Other Forms of Entertainment Seen in Islamic Art." In *Arabic and Islamic Studies in Honor of Hamilton A. R. Gibb,* edited by George Makdisi, pp. 211—24. Leiden: E. J. Brill, 1965.

Ettinghausen 1966*   Ettinghausen, Richard. "Sasanian and Islamic Metal-Work in Baltimore." *Apollo* n.s. 84, no. 58 (December 1966): 465–69.

Ettinghausen 1971*   Ettinghausen, Richard. "Hilal." In *Encyclopedia of Islam,* new edition, vol. 3, pp. 379–85. Leiden: E. J. Brill; London: Luzac and Company, 1971.

Ettinghausen and Henderson 1981*   Ettinghausen, R., and Henderson, E. P. "Jahangir's 'Meteroric' Knife." In *Chhavi–2: Rai Krishnadasa Felicitation Volume,* edited by Anand Krishna, pp. 38–42. Bombay: Bharat Kala Bhavan, 1981.

Eumorfopoulos 1940*   "The Eumorfopoulos Collections." *Connoisseur* 106, no. 467 (July 1940): 42–43.

Fehér 1975   Fehér, Géza. *Craftsmanship in Turkish-Ruled Hungary.* Budapest: Hungarian National Museum, 1975.

Fehérvári 1968*   Fehérvári, Géza. "Ein Ayyubidisches Räuchergefäss mit dem Namen des Sultan al-Malik al-Adil II." *Kunst des Orients* 5, pt. 1 (1968): 37–54.

Fehérvári 1976a

Fehérvári, Géza. "A Bronze Bowl Excavated at Ghubayra." *Bulletin of the School of Oriental and African Studies* 39, no. 1 (1976): 99–105.

Fehérvári 1976b*

Fehérvári, Géza. *Islamic Metalwork of the Eighth to the Fifteenth Century in the Keir Collection*. London: Faber and Faber Limited, 1976.

Forbes 1964*

Forbes, R. J. *Studies in Ancient Technology*, vol. 9. Leiden: E. J. Brill, 1964.

Frick and Schenk 1974*

Frick, J. S., and Schenk, G. H. *Quantitative Analytical Chemistry*. Boston: Allyn and Bacon, 1974.

Gettens, Clarke, and Chase 1971*

Gettens, R. J.; Clarke, R. S.; and Chase, W. T. *Two Early Chinese Bronze Weapons with Meteoritic Iron Blades*. Occasional Papers, vol. 4, no. 1. Washington, D.C.: Freer Gallery of Art, Smithsonian Institution, 1971.

Gettens and Frondel 1955*

Gettens, R. J., and Frondel, C. "Chalconatronite: An Alteration Product on Some Ancient Egyptian Bronzes." *Studies in Conservation* 2, no. 2 (1955): 64–75.

Gettens and Waring 1957*

Gettens, R. J., and Waring, C. L. "The Composition of Some Ancient Persian and Other Near Eastern Silver Objects." *Ars Orientalis* 2 (1957): 83–90.

Ghulam 1982*

Ghulam, Yousif Mahmud. *The Art of Arabic Calligraphy.* Lafayette, Calif.: Yousif Mahmud Ghulam, 1982.

Gingerich, King, and Saliba 1972*

Gingerich, O.; King, D.; and Saliba, G. "The Abd al-Aimma Astrolabe Forgeries." *Journal for the History of Astronomy* 3 (1972): 188–98.

Giuzalian 1938*

Giuzalian, L. T. "Bronzovi kuvshin 1182g" (Bronze Ewer Dated 1182). In *Pamyatriki epokhi Rustaveli,* pp. 227–36. Leningrad: 1938.

Giuzalian 1968

Giuzalian, L. T. "The Bronze Qalamdan (Pen-case) 542/1148 from the Hermitage Collection (1936–1965)." *Ars Orientalis* 7 (1968): 95–119.

Giuzalian 1978*

Giuzalian, L. T. "Vtoroi Geratskii kotelok (kotelok Ful'da)" (The Fould Kettle: Another Kettle from Herat). *Trudy: gosudarstvennogo ordena Lenina Ermitazha* 19 (1978): 53–83; English summary: 116–17.

A. Grabar 1959* Grabar, André. "Image d'une église chrétienne parmi les peintures musulmanes, de la Chapelle Palatine à Palerme." In *Aus der Welt der Islamischen Kunst: Festschrift für Ernst Kühnel,* edited by Richard Ettinghausen, pp. 227–33. Berlin: Verlag Gebr. Mann, 1959.

O. Grabar 1959* Grabar, Oleg. *Persian Art Before and After the Mongol Conquest.* Ann Arbor: University of Michigan Museum of Art, 1959.

O. Grabar 1961* Grabar, Oleg. "Two Pieces of Islamic Metalwork at the University of Michigan." *Ars Orientalis* 4 (1961): 360–68.

O. Grabar 1974 Grabar, Oleg. "Islamic Peoples, Arts of, 4: Visual Arts." In *Encyclopaedia Britannica.* 15th ed., pp. 1001–2.

Grabar and Blair 1980* Grabar, Oleg, and Blair, Sheila. *Epic Images and Contemporary History: The Illustrations of the Great Mongol Shahnama.* Chicago: University of Chicago Press, 1980.

Gray 1938* Gray, Basil. "A Seljuq Hoard from Persia." *British Museum Quarterly* 13, no. 3 (1938): 73–79.

Gray 1940 Gray, Basil. "The Influence of Near Eastern Metalwork on Chinese Ceramics." *Transactions of the Oriental Ceramic Society* 18 (1940–41): 47–60.

Gray 1981 Gray, Basil, ed. *The Arts of India.* Oxford: Phaidon, 1981.

Grohmann 1959 Grohmann, Adolf. "Die Bronzeschale M.388–1911 in Victoria and Albert Museum." In *Aus der Welt der Islamischen Kunst: Festschrift für Ernst Kühnel,* edited by Richard Ettinghausen, pp. 125–38. Berlin: Verlag Gebr. Mann, 1959.

Grohmann 1963 Grohmann, Adolf. "Die Bronzeschale M.31–1954 in Victoria and Albert Museum." In *Beiträge zur Kunstgeschichte Asiens: In Memoriam Ernst Diez,* edited by Oktay Aslanapa, pp. 283–87. Istanbul: Istanbul University Faculty of Literature, 1963.

Grousset 1931* Grousset, René. *The Civilizations of the East: The Near and Middle East.* Translated from the French by Catherine Alison Philips. London: Hamish Hamilton, 1931.

Grube 1965

Grube, Ernst J. "A Bronze Bowl from Egypt." *Journal of the American Research Center in Egypt* 14 (1965): 141–42.

Grube 1966

Grube, Ernst J. *The World of Islam.* New York and Toronto: McGraw-Hill Book Company, 1966.

Grube 1974*

Grube, Ernst J. "Notes on the Decorative Arts of the Timurid Period." In *Gururajamanjarika: Studi in Onore di Guiseppe Tucci,* pp. 233–69. Naples: Instituti Orientalis, 1974.

Gyllensvärd 1971*

Gyllensvärd, Bo. *Chinese Gold, Silver and Porcelain: The Kempe Collection.* New York: Asia Society, 1971.

Harari 1964–65*

Harari, Ralph. "Metalwork after the Early Islamic Period." In *A Survey of Persian Art,* edited by A. U. Pope, vol. 6, pp. 2466–529; vol. 12, pls. 1276–1396. London and New York: Oxford University Press, reprint 1964–65.

Harper 1972

Harper, Prudence Oliver. "An Eighth-Century Silver Plate from Iran with a Mythological Scene." In *Islamic Art in the Metropolitan Museum of Art,* edited by Richard Etting-hausen, pp. 153–68. New York: Metropolitan Museum of Art, 1972.

Harper 1978*

Harper, Prudence Oliver. *The Royal Hunter: Art of the Sasanian Empire.* New York: Asia Society, 1978.

Hartner 1938*

Hartner, Willy. "The Pseudoplanetary Nodes of the Moon's Orbit in Hindu and Islamic Iconographies." *Ars Islamica* 5, pt. 2 (1938): 113–54.

Hartner 1959

Hartner, Willy. "Zur Astrologischen Symbolik des 'Wade Cup.'" In *Aus der Welt der Islamischen Kunst: Festschrift für Ernst Kühnel,* edited by Richard Ettinghausen, pp. 234–43. Berlin: Verlag Gebr. Mann, 1959.

Hartner 1964–65

Hartner, Willy. "The Principle and Use of the Astrolabe." In *A Survey of Persian Art,* edited by A. U. Pope, vol. 6, pp. 2530–54; vol. 12, pls. 1397–1403. London and New York: Oxford University Press, reprint 1964–65.

Hartner 1973–74*

Hartner, Willy. "The Vaso Vescovali in the British Museum: A Study in Islamic Astrological Iconography." *Kunst des Orients* 9, no. 1–2 (1973–74): 99–130.

Herz 1907   Herz, Max. *A Descriptive Catalogue of the Objects Exhibited in the National Museum of Arab Art.* 2d ed. Translated by G. Foster Smith. Cairo: National Printing Department, 1907.

Herzfeld 1936*   Herzfeld, Ernst. "A Bronze Pen-case." *Ars Islamica* 3 (1936): 35–43.

Hollis 1935   Hollis, Howard C. "A Unique Seldjuk Bronze." *Ars Islamica* 2 (1935): 231–32.

Holstein*   Holstein, P. *Contribution a l'Étude des Armes Orientales.* 2 vols. Paris: Les Éditions Albert Lévy, n.d.

Homberg 1908*   *Collection Homberg: Catalogue des Objets d'Art et de Haute Curiosité.* Paris: Georges Petit, May 11–16, 1908.

Humphreys 1977*   Humphreys, R. Stephen. *From Saladin to the Mongols.* Albany: State University of New York Press, 1977.

Ivanov 1972   Ivanov, Anatol A. "Bronzovyi tazik serediny XIVb" (Bronze Mid-Fourteenth-Century Basin). In *Srednyaya Aziya i Iran,* pp. 114–35; English summary: 183–84. Leningrad: Gosudarstvennogo ordeno Lenina Ermitazha, 1972.

Ivanov 1977   Ivanov, Anatol A. "Kubachinskii bronzovyi kotel XIV veka" (A Fourteenth-Century Bronze Cauldron from Kubachi). *Ermitazha Soobshcheniya Gosudarstvennogo* 42 (1977): 54–57; English summary: 64.

Ivanov 1979*   Ivanov, Anatol A. "A Group of Iranian Daggers of the Period from the Fifteenth Century to the Beginning of the Seventeenth." In *Islamic Arms and Armour,* edited by Robert Elgood, pp. 64–77. London: Scolar Press, 1979.

Ivanov 1981   Ivanov, Anatol A. "O bronzovykh izdeliyakh konstsa XIV v. iz mavzoleya Khodzha Akhmeda Yasevi" (On Bronzewares of the End of the Fourteenth Century from the Khoja Akhmad Yasavi Mausoleum). In *Srednyaya Aziya i ee sosedi v drevnosti i srednevekov'e,* edited by B. A. Litvinskogo, pp. 68–84; English summary: 152. Moscow: Akademiya Nauk SSSR, Institut Vostokovedeniya, 1981.

Izzi 1965*   Izzi, Wafiyya. "An Ayyubid Basin of al-Salih Najm al-Din." In *Studies in Islamic Art and Architecture in Honour of Professor K. A. C. Creswell,* pp. 253–59. Cairo: American University Press, 1965.

Izzi 1974

Izzi, Wafiyya. "Objects Bearing the Name of al-Nasir Muhammad and His Successor." In *Colloque International sur l'Histoire du Caire*, pp. 235–41. Cairo: Ministry of Culture of the Arab Republic of Egypt, General Egyptian Book Organization, 1974.

İstanbul 1983*

Anatolian Civilisations 3: Seljuk/Ottoman. İstanbul: Topkapı Palace Museum, 1983.

James 1974

James, David. *Islamic Art: An Introduction.* London, New York, Sydney, and Toronto: Hamlyn Publishing Group Limited, 1974.

James 1980

James, David. "An Early Mosul Metalworker: Some New Information." *Oriental Art* 26, no. 3 (Autumn 1980): 318–21.

Jenkins 1983*

Jenkins, Marilyn. *Islamic Art in the Kuwait National Musuem: The al-Sabah Collection.* London: Sotheby Publications, 1983.

Jenkins, Gould, and Gedecke 1981*

Jenkins, Ron; Gould, R. W.; and Gedecke, Dale. *Quantitative X-ray Spectrometry.* New York and Basel: Marcel Dekker, 1981.

Jenkins and Keene 1983*

Jenkins, Marilyn, and Keene, Manuel. *Islamic Jewelry in the Metropolitan Museum of Art.* New York: Metropolitan Museum of Art, 1983.

Katonah 1980*

Islamic Insights: An Introduction to Islamic Art. New York: Katonah Gallery, 1980.

Katzenstein and Lowry 1983*

Katzenstein, Ranee A., and Lowry, Glenn D. "Christian Themes in Thirteenth-Century Islamic Metalwork." *Muqarnas* 1 (1983): 53–68.

Keene 1981

Keene, Manuel. "The Lapidary Arts in Islam." *Expedition* 24, no. 1 (Fall 1981): 24–36.

Keene and Jenkins 1981*

Keene, Manuel, and Jenkins, Marilyn. "Djawhar." In *Encyclopaedia of Islam,* new edition. Supplement, fascicules 3–4 and 5–6, pp. 250–62. Leiden: E. J. Brill, 1981.

Komaroff 1979–80*

Komaroff, Linda. "Timurid to Safavid Iran: Continuity and Change." *Marsyas* 20 (1979–80): 11–16.

Kühnel 1939*   Kühnel, Ernst. "Zwei Mosulbronzen und ihr Meister." *Jahrbuch der Preussischen Kunstsammlungen* 60 (1939): 1–20.

Kühnel 1970   Kühnel, Ernst. *The Minor Arts of Islam.* Translated by K. Watson. Ithaca, N.Y.: Cornell University Press, 1970.

Lanci 1845*   Lanci, Michelangelo. *Trattato delle simboliche rappresentanze Arabische e della varia generazione de' Musulmani caratteri.* 3 vols. Parigi: Stamperia Orientale di Dondey-Dupré, 1845.

Lane-Poole 1886   Lane-Poole, Stanley. *The Art of the Saracens in Egypt.* London: Chapman and Hall, 1886.

Leroy 1974–75*   Leroy, Jules. "Un flabellum Syriaque date du deir Souriani (Egypte)." *Cahiers de Mariemont* 5–6 (1974–75): 31–39.

Leth 1975*   Leth, A. *The David Collection: Islamic Art.* Copenhagen: Davids Samling, 1975.

Li Chung 1979*   Li Chung. "The Iron Blade of a Shang Dynasty Bronze *Yueh*-axe." *Ars Orientalis* 11 (1979): 259–89.

Lisbon 1963   *L'Art de l'Orient Islamique: Collection de la Fondation Calouste Gulbenkian.* Lisbon: Museu Nacional de Arte Antiga, 1963.

London 1931*   *Catalogue of the International Exhibition of Persian Art.* London: Royal Academy of Arts, 1931.

London 1976*   *The Arts of Islam.* London: Arts Council of Great Britain, 1976.

London 1982*   *The Indian Heritage: Court Life and Arts Under Mughal Rule.* London: Victoria and Albert Museum, 1982.

Marschner and Wright 1978*   Marschner, R. F., and Wright, H. T. "Asphalts from Middle Eastern Archaeological Sites." In *Archaeological Chemistry 2* (Advances in Chemistry Series, no. 171), edited by Giles F. Carter, pp. 150–71. Washington, D.C.: American Chemical Society, 1978.

Marshak 1971   Marshak, Boris I. *Sogdiiskoe serebro* (Soghdian Silver). Moscow: Akademiya Nauk SSSR, Institut Vostokovedeniya, 1971.

Marshak 1972*

Marshak, Boris I. "Bronzoviy kuvshin iz Samarkanda" (Bronze Ewer in Samarkand). In *Srednyaya Aziya i Iran*, pp. 61–90; English summary: 180–81. Leningrad; Hermitage Museum, 1972.

Marshak 1978

Marshak, Boris I. "Ranneislamskie bronzovye blyuda" (Early Islamic Bronze Salvers). In *Trudy: gosudarstvennogo ordena Lenina Ermitazha* 19 (1978): 26–52; English summary: 116.

Maryon 1954

Maryon, H. *Metalwork and Enamelling*. London: Chapman and Hall, 1954.

Maryon 1960a*

Maryon, H. "Pattern-welding and Damascening of Sword-blades—Part 1: Pattern-welding." *Studies in Conservation* 5, no. 1 (1960): 25–37.

Maryon 1960b*

Maryon, H. "Pattern-welding and Damascening of Sword-blades—Part 2: The Damascene Process." *Studies in Conservation* 5, no. 2 (1960): 52–60.

Masuda 1961*

Masuda, Seiichi. "From a Trip of Archaeological Research to Iran." (Tokyo National) *Museum* 120 (March 1961): 22–24.

Mayer 1936

Mayer, L. A. "Three Heraldic Bronzes from Palermo." *Ars Islamica* 3 (1936): 180–86.

Mayer 1943

Mayer, L. A. "Saracenic Arms and Armour." *Ars Islamica* 10 (1943): 1–12.

Mayer 1959*

Mayer, L. A. *Islamic Metalworkers and Their Works*. Geneva: Albert Kundig, 1959.

Mayuyama 1973*

Mayuyama, Yasuhiki. *Chogoku bunbutsu kenbun*. Tokyo: Mayuyama and Co., 1963.

Melikian-Chirvani 1968a

Melikian-Chirvani, Assadullah Souren. "Le bassin du Sultan Qara Arslan ibn Il-Gazi." *Revue des Études Islamiques* 2 (1968): 263–78.

Melikian-Chirvani 1968b

Melikian-Chirvani, Assadullah Souren. "La coupe d'Abu Sahl-e Farhad-jerdi." *Gazette des Beaux-Arts* 71 (March 1968): 129–46.

Melikian-Chirvani 1968c*

Melikian-Chirvani, Assadullah Souren. "Le Griffon iranien de Pise." *Kunst des Orients* 5, no. 2 (1968): 68–86.

Melikian-Chirvani 1969a   Melikian-Chirvani, Assadullah Souren. "Un bassin iranien de l'an 1375." *Gazette des Beaux-Arts* 73 (January 1969): 5–18.

Melikian-Chirvani 1969b*   Melikian-Chirvani, Assadullah Souren. "Bassins iraniens du XIVe siècle au Musée des Beaux-Arts." *Bulletin des Musées et Monuments Lyonnais* 4, no. 2 (1969): 189–206.

Melikian-Chirvani 1969c*   Melikian-Chirvani, Assadullah Souren. "Bronzes et cuivres iraniens du Louvre. I: L'école du Fars au XIVe siècle." *Journal Asiatique* 257, no. 1 (1969): 19–36.

Melikian-Chirvani 1969d*   Melikian-Chirvani, Assadullah Souren. "Un chandelier iranien du XIVe siècle au Musée des Beaux Arts." *Bulletin des Musées et Monuments Lyonnais* 4, no. 4 (1969): 213–23.

Melikian-Chirvani 1969e   Melikian-Chirvani, Assadullah Souren. "Cuivres inédits de l'époque de Qa'itbay." *Kunst des Orients* 6, no. 2 (1969): 99–133.

Melikian-Chirvani 1969f*   Melikian-Chirvani, Assadullah Souren. "A Sasanian Eagle in the Round." *Journal of the Royal Asiatic Society* 1 (1969): 2–9.

Melikian-Chirvani 1970a   Melikian-Chirvani, Assadullah Souren. "Deux chandeliers mossouliens au Musée des Beaux-Arts." *Bulletin des Musées et Monuments Lyonnais* 4, no. 3 (1970): 45–62.

Melikian-Chirvani 1970b   Melikian-Chirvani, Assadullah Souren. "Un plumier d'époque timouride au Musée des Beaux-Arts." *Bulletin des Musées et Monuments Lyonnais* 4, no. 2 (1970): 265–69.

Melikian-Chirvani 1971a   Melikian-Chirvani, Assadullah Souren. "Iranian Silver and Its Influence in T'ang China." *Pottery and Metalwork in T'ang China* (Colloquies on Art and Architecture in Asia, no. 1), pp. 9–13. London: Percival David Foundation, 1971.

Melikian-Chirvani 1971b*   Melikian-Chirvani, Assadullah Souren. "Le Royaume de Salomon." *Le Monde Iranien et l'Islam* 1 (1971): 1–41.

Melikian-Chirvani 1973*   Melikian-Chirvani, Assadullah Souren. *Le bronze iranien.* Paris: Musée des Arts Décoratifs, 1973.

Melikian-Chirvani 1974a* | Melikian-Chirvani, Assadullah Souren. "Les Bronzes du Khorassan: 1." *Studia Iranica* 3–1 (1974): 29–50.

Melikian-Chirvani 1974b | Melikian-Chirvani, Assadullah Souren. "Safavid Metalwork: A Study in Continuity." In *Studies on Isfahan,* edited by Renata Holod. *Iranian Studies* 7, nos. 3–4 (1974): 543–85.

Melikian-Chirvani 1974c* | Melikian-Chirvani, Assadullah Souren. "Venise, Entre L'Orient et L'Occident." *Bulletin d'Études Orientales* 27 (1974): 109–26.

Melikian-Chirvani 1974d* | Melikian-Chirvani, Assadullah Souren. "The White Bronzes of Early Islamic Iran." *Metropolitan Museum Journal* 9 (1974): 123–51.

Melikian-Chirvani 1975a | Melikian-Chirvani, Assadullah Souren. "Les Bronzes du Khorassan: 2." *Studia Iranica* 4–1 (1975): 51–71.

Melikian-Chirvani 1975b | Melikian-Chirvani, Assadullah Souren. "Les Bronzes du Khorassan: 3." *Studia Iranica* 4–2 (1975): 187–205.

Melikian-Chirvani 1975c* | Melikian-Chirvani, Assadullah Souren. "Recherches sur l'école du bronze ottoman au XVIe siècle." *Turcica* 6 (1975): 146–67.

Melikian-Chirvani 1976a* | Melikian-Chirvani, Assadullah Souren. "Four Pieces of Islamic Metalwork: Some Notes on a Previously Unknown School." *Art and Architecture Research Papers* 10 (December 1976): 24–30.

Melikian-Chirvani 1976b | Melikian-Chirvani, Assadullah Souren. "Les Bronzes du Khorassan: 4." *Studia Iranica* 5–2 (1976): 203–12.

Melikian-Chirvani 1977 | Melikian-Chirvani, Assadullah Souren. "Les Bronzes du Khorassan: 5." *Studia Iranica* 6–2 (1976): 185–210.

Melikian-Chirvani 1979a | Melikian-Chirvani, Assadullah Souren. "Les Bronzes du Khorassan: 6." *Studia Iranica* 8–1 (1979): 7–32.

Melikian-Chirvani 1979b* | Melikian-Chirvani, Assadullah Souren. "Les Bronzes du Khorassan: 7." *Studia Iranica* 8–2 (1979): 223–43.

Melikian-Chirvani 1979c | Melikian-Chirvani, Assadullah Souren. "Bucklers, Covers or Cymbals? A Twelfth-Century Riddle from Eastern Iran." In *Islamic Arms and Armour,* edited by Robert Elgood, pp. 97–111. London: Scolar Press, 1979.

Melikian-Chirvani 1979d*

Melikian-Chirvani, Assadullah Souren. "The Tabarzins of Lotf'ali." In *Islamic Arms and Armour,* edited by Robert Elgood, pp. 116–35 and 240–41. London: Scolar Press, 1979.

Melikian-Chirvani 1982*

Melikian-Chirvani, Assadullah Souren. *Victoria and Albert Museum Catalogue: Islamic Metalwork from the Iranian World, Eight–Eighteenth Centuries.* London: Her Majesty's Stationery Office, 1982.

Migeon 1903*

Migeon, Gaston. *Exposition des Arts Musulmans au Musée des Arts Décoratifs.* Paris: Librarie Centrale des Beaux-Arts, 1903.

Migeon 1922

Migeon, Gaston. *Musée du Louvre: L'Orient Musulman.* 2 vols. Paris: Éditions Albert Morancé, 1922.

Migeon 1927*

Migeon, Gaston. *Manuel d'art musulman.* 2 vols. 2d. ed. Paris: Éditions Auguste Picard, 1927.

Miller 1976

Miller, Yuri. "Mamlyukskii Shlem" (A Mamluk Helmet in the Hermitage Collection). *Soobshcheniya Gosudarstvennogo Ermitazha* 41 (1976): 46–48; English summary: 67.

Mitchiner 1977*

Mitchiner, Michael. *Oriental Coins and Their Values: The World of Islam.* London: Hawkins Publications, 1977.

Montgomery-Wyaux 1978*

Montgomery-Wyaux, Cornelia. *Métaux Islamiques.* Brussels: Musées Royaux d'Art et d'Histoire, 1978.

Moss 1953

Moss, A. A. "Niello." *Studies in Conservation* 1, no. 2 (1953): 49–62.

Murray 1979*

Murray, Julia K. *A Decade of Discovery.* Washington, D.C.: Freer Gallery of Art, Smithsonian Institution, 1979.

Naffah and Kalus 1981

Naffah, Christiane, and Kalus, Ludvik. "Une écritoire mamelouke au Musée du Louvre." *La Revue du Louvre et des Musées de France* 2 (April, 1981): 79–89.

Needham 1974*

Needham, Joseph. *Science and Civilisation in China, Volume 5: Chemistry and Chemical Technology, Part 2: Magisteries of Gold and Immortality.* Cambridge: University Press, 1974.

Nickel 1979*

Nickel, Helmut. "A Mamluk Axe." In *Islamic Arms and Armour,* edited by Robert Elgood, pp. 149–61. London: Scolar Press, 1979.

Nicolle 1979*

Nicolle, David. "An Introduction to Arms and Warfare in Classical Islam." In *Islamic Arms and Armour*, edited by Robert Elgood, pp. 162–86. London: Scolar Press, 1979.

Nicolle 1981*

Nicolle, David. *Islamische Waffen*. Graz: Verlag für Sammler, 1981.

Ogden 1982

Ogden, J. *Jewelry of the Ancient World*. New York: Rizzoli International Publications, 1982.

Orbeli 1964–65*

Orbeli, Josef. "Sasanian and Early Islamic Metalwork." In *A Survey of Persian Art*, edited by A. U. Pope, vol. 2, pp. 716–70; vol. 7, pls. 203–50. London and New York: Oxford University Press, reprint 1964–65.

Orbeli and Trever 1935*

Orbeli, Josef, and Trever, C. *Orfèvrerie Sasanide: objects en or, argent et bronze*. Moscow and Leningrad: Academia, 1935.

Panseri 1963

Panseri, C. "Damascus Steel in Legend and in Reality." *Gladius* 4 (1963): 5–63.

Papadopoulo 1979

Papadopoulo, Alexandre. *Islam and Muslim Art*. Translated by R. E. Wolf. New York: Harry N. Abrams, 1979.

Paris 1971*

Arts de l'Islam des origines à 1700 dans les collections publiques françaises. Paris: Ministère des Affaires Culturelles, Réunion des Musées Nationaux, 1971.

Paris 1977*

L'Islam dans les collections nationales. Paris: Éditions des Musées Nationaux, 1977.

Pijoán 1949*

Pijoán, José. *Summa Artis, Historia General del Arte, vol. 12: Arte Islámico*. Madrid: Espasa-Calpe, 1949.

Pinder-Wilson 1962*

Pinder-Wilson, Ralph H. "Two Persian Bronze Buckets." *British Museum Quarterly* 24, nos. 1–2 (1962): 54–59.

Pinder-Wilson 1967*

Pinder-Wilson, Ralph H. "An Islamic Ewer in Sasanian Style." In *A Survey of Persian Art*, edited by A. U. Pope, vol. 14, pp. 3061–63. London: Oxford University Press, 1967.

Pollard 1982*

Pollard, A. M. "Analysis of Ottoman Metalwork." In *Tulips, Arabesques and Turbans: Decorative Arts from the Ottoman Empire*, edited by Yanni Petsopoulos, p. 217. New York: Abbeville Press, 1982.

Pollard 1983*

Pollard, A. M. "Authenticity of Brass Objects by Major Element Analysis?" In *Symposium on Archaeometry (23rd symposium, 1983, Naples, Italy). Abstracts,* organized by R. E. Linington, p. 97. Naples: Castel Dell'ovo, 1983.

Pope 1959*

Pope, John Alexander. "An Early Ming Porcelain in Muslim Style." In *Aus der Welt der Islamischen Kunst: Festschrift für Ernst Kühnel,* edited by Richard Ettinghausen, pp. 357–75. Berlin: Verlag Gebr. Mann, 1959.

Pope 1972*

Pope, John Alexander. *The History of Ming Porcelain.* London: Oriental Ceramic Society, 1972.

*Répertoire**

Combe, Étienne; Sauvaget, Jean; and Wiet, Gaston, eds. *Répertoire Chronologique d'Épigraphie Arabe.* 15 vols. Cairo: Imprimerie de l'Institut Français d'Archéologie Orientale, 1931–56.

Rice 1949

Rice, D. S. "The Oldest Dated 'Mosul' Candlestick, A.D. 1225." *Burlington Magazine* 91, nos. 561 (1949): 334–40.

Rice 1950a

Rice, D. S. "The Blazons of the 'Baptistère de Saint Louis.'" *Bulletin of the School of Oriental and African Studies* 13, no. 2 (1950): 367–80.

Rice 1950b

Rice, D. S. "The Brasses of Badr al-Din Lulu." *Bulletin of the School of Oriental and African Studies* 13, no. 3 (1950): 627–34.

Rice 1952*

Rice, D. S. "Studies in Islamic Metalwork: 1." *Bulletin of the School of Oriental and African Studies* 14, no. 3 (1952): 564–78.

Rice 1953a

Rice, D. S. *Le Baptistère de Saint Louis.* Paris: Les Éditions du Chêne, 1953.

Rice 1953b*

Rice, D. S. "Studies in Islamic Metalwork: 2." *Bulletin of the School of Oriental and African Studies* 16, no. 1 (1953): 61–79.

Rice 1953c

Rice, D. S. "Studies in Islamic Metalwork: 3." *Bulletin of the School of Oriental and African Studies* 15, no. 2 (1953): 229–38.

Rice 1953d

Rice, D. S. "Studies in Islamic Metalwork: 4." *Bulletin of the School of Oriental and African Studies* 15, no. 3 (1953): 489–503.

Rice 1954*

Rice, D. S. "The Seasons and the Labors of the Months." *Ars Orientalis* 1 (1954): 1–39.

Rice 1955a

Rice, D. S. "Studies in Islamic Metalwork: 5." *Bulletin of the School of Oriental and African Studies* 17, no. 2 (1955): 206–31.

Rice 1955b*

Rice, D. S. *The Wade Cup in the Cleveland Museum of Art.* Paris: Les Éditions du Chêne, 1955.

Rice 1956

Rice, D. S. "Arabic Inscriptions on a Brass Basin Made for Hugh IV of Lusignan." In *Studi Orientalistici in onore di Giorgio Levi della Vida,* vol. 2, pp. 1–13. Rome: Instituto per l'Oriente, 1956.

Rice 1957a*

Rice, D. S. "Inlaid Brasses from the Workshop of Ahmad al-Dhaki al-Mawsili." *Ars Orientalis* 2 (1957): 283–326.

Rice 1957b

Rice, D. S. "Two Unusual Mamluk Metal Works." *Bulletin of the School of Oriental and African Studies* 20 (1957): 487–500.

Rice 1958

Rice, D. S. "Studies in Islamic Metalwork: 6." *Bulletin of the School of Oriental and African Studies* 21, no. 2 (1958): 225–53.

Rietstap 1965*

Rietstap, Johannes B. *Armorial Général.* 2 vols. London: Heraldry Today, 1965.

Roberts-Austen 1892*

Roberts-Austen, W. C. *Report on the Analysis of Various Examples of Oriental Metalwork etc. in the South Kensington Museum and Other Collections.* London: Eyre and Spottis-woode, 1892.

Robinson 1967*

Robinson, Basil W. "Oriental Metalwork in the Gambier-Parry Collection." *Burlington Magazine* 109, no. 768 (March 1967): 169–73.

Robinson 1972*

Robinson, Basil W. "Shah Abbas and the Mughal Ambassador Khan Alam: The Pictorial Record." *Burlington Magazine* 114 (February 1972): 58–63.

Rogers 1976

Rogers, J. Michael. *The Spread of Islam.* Oxford: Elsevier-Phaidon, 1976.

Rogers 1977*

Rogers, J. Michael. "Review Article: G. Fehérvári, *Islamic Metalwork of the Eighth to the Fifteenth Century in the Keir*

	Collection.'' *Bibliotheca Orientalis* 34, nos. 3–4 (May–July 1977): 236–44.
Rosen-Ayalon 1972	Rosen-Ayalon, Myriam. ''Four Iranian Bracelets Seen in the Light of Early Islamic Art.'' In *Islamic Art in the Metropolitan Museum of Art*, edited by Richard Ettinghausen, pp. 169–86. New York: Metropolitan Museum of Art, 1972.
Ruthven 1934	Ruthven, Peter. ''Two Metal Works of the Mamluk Period.'' *Ars Islamica* 1 (1934): 230–34.
Salam-Liebich 1976*	Salam-Liebich, Hayat. ''A Little-Known Collection of Islamic Art.'' *Apollo* n.s. 103, no. 171 (May 1976): 380–83.
Salam-Liebich 1983*	Salam-Liebich, Hayat. *Islamic Art: Objects for Daily Use*. Montreal: Montreal Museum of Fine Arts, 1983.
San Francisco 1937*	*Exhibition of Islamic Art*. San Francisco: M. D. DeYoung Memorial Museum, 1937.
Sarre 1906*	Sarre, Friedrich. *Sammlung F. Sarre. Erzeugnisse Islamischer Kunst, Teil I: Metall*. Berlin: H. S. Hermann, 1906.
Sarre 1934*	Sarre, Friedrich. ''Die Bronzekanne des Kalifen Marwan II im Arabischen Museum in Kairo.'' *Ars Islamica* 1 (1934): 10–14.
Sarre and Martin 1912*	Sarre, Friedrich, and Martin, F. R. *Die Ausstellung von Meisterwerken muhammedanischer Kunst in München 1910*. 4 vols. Berlin: F. Bruckmann, 1912.
Scerrato 1966*	Scerrato, Umberto. *Metalli islamici*. Milan: Fratelli Fabbri Editori, 1966.
Scerrato 1967	Scerrato, Umberto. *Arte Islamica a Napoli*. Naples: Museo di Capodimonte, 1967.
Schneider 1973*	Schneider, Laura T. ''The Freer Canteen.'' *Ars Orientalis* 9 (1973): 137–56.
Schroeder 1938	Schroeder, Eric. ''An Aquamanile and Some Implications.'' *Ars Islamica* 5 (1938): 9–20.
Segall 1938*	Segall, Berta. *Museum Benaki: Katalog der Goldschmiede-Arbeiten*. Athens: Mouseion Mpenake, 1938.

Shaw and Craddock 1984*

Shaw, Thurstan, and Craddock, P. T. "Ghanaian and Coptic Brass Lamps." *Antiquity* 58, no. 223 (July 1984): 126–28.

Sherby 1979*

Sherby, Oleg D. "Damascus Steel Rediscovered?" *Transactions of the Iron and Steel Institute of Japan* 19, no. 7 (1979): 381–90.

Smirnov 1909*

Smirnov, Iakov Ivanovich. *Vostochnoe serebro* (Oriental Silver). Leningrad, 1909.

Smith 1957

Smith, C. S. "Decorative Etching and the Science of Metals." *Endeavour* 16, no. 64 (1957): 199–208.

Smith 1960*

Smith, C. S. *A History of Metallography*. Chicago: University of Chicago Press, 1960.

Smith 1972*

Smith, C. S. "Metallurgical Footnotes to the History of Art." *Proceedings of the American Philosophical Society* 116, no. 2 (1972): 97–135.

Sotheby's 1940*

The Eumorfopoulos Collections: Catalogue of the Collection of Persian Ceramics and Islamic Glass. London: Sotheby's, June 5–6, 1940.

Sotheby's 1983*

Islamic Works of Art, Carpets and Textiles. London: Sotheby's, Wednesday, April 20, 1983.

Sotheby's 1984*

Islamic Works of Art, Carpets and Textiles. London: Sotheby's, Wednesday, October 17, 1984.

Soucek 1978*

Soucek, Priscilla P. *Islamic Art from the University of Michigan Collections*. Ann Arbor: University of Michigan, 1978.

Sourdel-Thomine 1971

Sourdel-Thomine, Janine. "Clefs et surrures de la Ka'ba: Notes d'épigraphie arabe." *Revue des Études Islamiques: Articles et Mémoires* 39, no.1 (1971): 29–86.

Sourdel-Thomine and Spuler 1973*

Sourdel-Thomine, Janine, and Spuler, B. *Die Kunst des Islam*. Berlin: Propyläen Verlag, 1973.

Stewart 1967*

Stewart, Desmond. *Great Ages of Man: Early Islam*. New York: Time Incorporated, 1967.

Stöcklein 1964–65*

Stöcklein, Hans. "Arms and Armour." In *A Survey of Persian Art*, edited by A. U. Pope, vol. 6, pp. 2555–85;

vol. 12, pls. 1404–33. London and New York: Oxford University Press, reprint 1964–65.

Tait 1976* Tait, Hugh. *Jewelry through Seven Thousand Years.* London: British Museum, 1976.

Taiwan 1963* *Blue and White Ware of the Ming Dynasty.* Taiwan: Cafa Co., 1963.

Tanavoli and Wertime 1976 Tanavoli, Parviz, and Wertime, John T. *Locks from Iran: Pre-Islamic to Twentieth Century.* Washington, D.C.: Smithsonian Institution, 1976.

Tokyo 1984* *Shanghai hakubutsukan shozo Chugoku rekidai toji ten.* Tokyo: Asahi Shinbun Sha, 1984.

Tuzuk 1914* *The Tuzuk-i-Jahangiri; or, Memoirs of Jahangir.* Translated by Alexander Rogers, edited by Henry Beveridge. London: Royal Asiatic Society, 1914.

Tylecote 1962* Tylecote, R. F. *Metallurgy in Archaeology.* London: Edward Arnold, 1962.

Tylecote 1976 Tylecote, R. F. *A History of Metallurgy.* London: Metals Society, 1976.

Untracht 1968* Untracht, Oppi. *Metal Techniques for Craftsmen.* New York: Doubleday and Company, 1968.

Untracht 1982* Untracht, Oppi. *Jewelry Concepts and Technology.* New York: Doubleday and Company, 1982.

Vienna 1977 *Kunst des Islam.* Vienna: Österreichisches Museum für Angewandte Kunst, 1977.

Walters Art Gallery 1947* *Early Christian and Byzantine Art.* Baltimore: Walters Art Gallery, 1947.

Weitzmann 1979* Weitzmann, Kurt, ed. *Age of Spirituality: Late Antique and Early Christian Art, Third to Seventh Century.* New York: Metropolitan Museum of Art, 1979.

Welch 1973* Welch, Anthony. *Shah Abbas and the Arts of Isfahan.* New York: Asia Society, 1973.

Welch 1979 Welch, Anthony. *Calligraphy in the Arts of the Muslim World.* Austin: University of Texas Press, 1979.

Werner 1970*   Werner, Otto. "Über das Vorkommen von Zink und Messing im Altertum und im Mittelalter." *Erzmetall* 23, no. 6 (1970): 259–308.

Werner 1972   Werner, Otto. *Spektralanalytische und Metallurgische Untersuchungen an Indischen Bronzen.* Leiden: E. J. Brill, 1972.

Wiest 1979*   Wiest, F. Karel. "The Sword of Islam." *Arts of Asia* 9, no. 3 (May–June 1979): 73–82.

Wiet 1930   Wiet, Gaston. *Album du Musée Arabe du Caire.* Cairo: Imprimerie de l'Institut Français d'Archéologie Orientale, 1930.

Wiet 1932*   Wiet, Gaston. *Catalogue Général du Musée Arabe du Caire: Objets en cuivre.* Cairo: Imprimerie de l'Institut Français d'Archéologie Orientale, 1932.

Wiet 1958   Wiet, Gaston. "Inscriptions mobilières de l'Égypte musulmane." *Journal Asiatique* 246, no. 3 (1958): 237–85.

Wolters 1981   Wolters, Jochem. "The Ancient Craft of Granulation." *Gold Bulletin* 14, no. 3 (July 1981): 119–29.

Wulff 1966*   Wulff, Hans E. *The Traditional Crafts of Persia.* Cambridge: MIT Press, 1966.

Yater 1983*   Yater, Wallace M. "The Legendary Steel of Damascus: Part 2; How it was made in the East." *Anvil's Ring* 11, no. 2 (Summer 1983): 3–13.

Zaki 1948   Zaki Muhammad Hasan. *Funun al-islam* (Arts of Islam). Cairo: Maktabat al-nahda al-misriyya, 1948.

Zaki 1956   Zaki Muhammad Hasan. *Atlas al-funun al-zukhrufiya wa'l-tasawir al-Islamiya* (Atlas of Moslem Decorative and Pictorial Arts). Cairo: Cairo University Press, 1956.

Zalesskaya 1972   Zalesskaya, V. "Siriiskoe Bronzovoe Kadilo iz Urguta" (A Syrian Bronze Censer from Urgut). In *Sredniaia Aziia i Iran,* pp. 57–60; English summary: 179–80. Leningrad: Hermitage Museum, 1972.

Appendix I

NOTES CONCERNING THE X-RAY
FLUORESCENCE ANALYSIS

X-ray fluorescence was chosen as the analytical method because it is rapid, accurate enough for purposes of grouping and comparison with previous studies, and can be done on the surface of the object without taking a sample. Since the surfaces of most of the objects examined were quite clean, it was thought that a method of X-ray fluorescence using comparisons with known standards would yield answers adequate for the purposes of the study and for the selection of objects needing more thorough analytical tests. Previous wet chemical analyses of some of the objects provided an independent check of the accuracy of the X-ray fluorescence method used.

This discussion of the analytical method concentrates on the results found for the brass objects. The analyses of the silver and gold objects were done in the same basic manner. X-ray fluorescence did not prove to be of great use on the iron objects for the reasons stated previously in the "Techniques and Materials" section.

Experimental Conditions

The X-ray fluorescence unit used for the analyses was a DuBois 404 Object Analyzer attached to a Tracor Northern TN–1710 Multichannel Analysis System. The DuBois 404 contains a liquid nitrogen-cooled energy-dispersive Si(Li) X-ray detector with integral preamplifier, pulse processor, and detector bias/protection module. The detector has a stated resolution of 160eV at 5.9KeV (at 1000 cps.). The integral X-ray tube has a molybdenum target and was operated at 48 kilovolts and 0.10 milliamps. A two millimeter beam collimator and a 2.5 millimeter collimator on the detector generally were used; different collimators occasionally were necessary because of the size and location of the areas analyzed. Most of the measurements were taken at a standard live time of sixty seconds; when the count rate was too low, a longer live time was necessary. Low count rates were observed infrequently and were caused by the difficult geometry of the objects (which caused us to have to look into grooves, for example) or by the selection of smaller collimators for the examination of fine features. For the brass objects, under normal conditions the accumulated counts in the 8.04 KeV copper channel was on the order of 500,000.

Data was collected from the automatic RS–232C output on the TN–1710 with a Techtran 8400 Datacassette Recorder, operating at 300 BAUD, and connected to a Texas Instruments "Silent 700" Terminal; both hard copy and a computer-readable tape were saved. Labels could also be typed in from the TI–700 and put on the data recording tape at the head of the file. The data represented each of the 512 channels in the TN–1710, with the counts observed. The curve as seen on the screen of the multichannel analyzer could be reproduced exactly from the data, with adjustable scaling, as represented in figures 1A and B. The data also can be consulted later if questions come up regarding the analysis.

Figure 1A
X-ray fluorescence spectra
from the flat side (back) of the canteen
(no. 17). These correspond to analysis #3
in table 2. The spectra were regenerated
from the raw data under program control
and plotted on a flatbed plotter. Figure
1A shows the spectrum with a linear
scale for detected counts (on the vertical
axis) against energies (in KeV). Full scale
for detected counts here is 150,000. Since
the copper K-alpha peak (at 8.04 KeV)
contained 646,761 counts, it goes off-
scale at the upper margin of the spectrum.

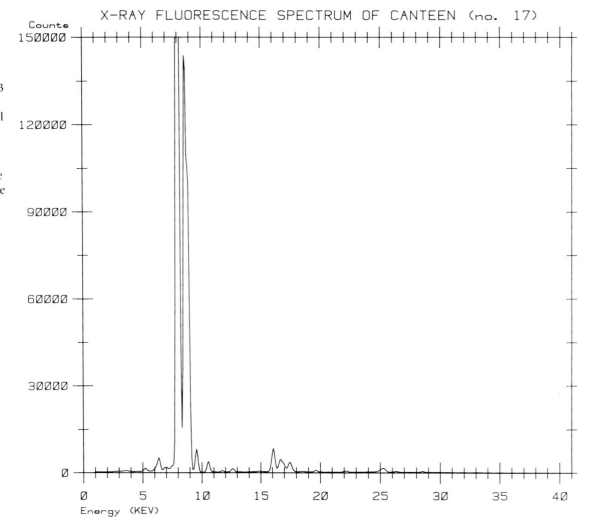

Determining the concentration present in a sample of unknown composition from the X-ray fluorescence spectrum detected by the analyzer has been the subject of much research, and many of the methods for quantification are extremely sophisticated.[1] Owing to the inherent variation in the Freer objects, with their unprepared surfaces of unfixed geometry, we decided to try a simple approach.

For the copper alloys, a large series of standards of known compositions was selected, and the X-ray fluorescence data for each was obtained under normal conditions. The standards covered the range of compositions of interest, up to 32% tin, 32% lead, 41% zinc, and 2.5% iron; pure metals also were counted. Not all standards contained all elements of interest. Many were analyzed more than once, at different times, to ascertain the amount of instrument variation. One hundred twelve full sets of counts of standards ultimately were collected.

Data Reduction

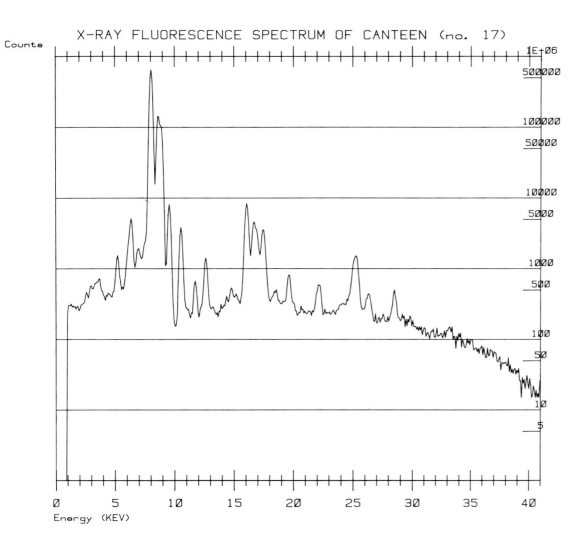

Figure 1B
This figure shows the same spectrum as 1A but with a logarithmic scale for counts. The Copper K-alpha peak remains on-scale here, but one can also see more clearly the differences in the channels with lower counts.

A number of different methods were tried in using the standards to calibrate our analysis, including methods of interelement correction and summation of counts with normalization. The method described below was the one finally used.

The channel best suited for determination of each element was selected by examination of the plotted curves for the single-element standards, by the use of wavelength tables, and by a check of some of the multielement standards to determine that the channel chosen was not greatly affected by the presence of other elements. Counts for the selected channels for tin, lead, zinc, and iron were divided by the counts in the copper channel in order to ratio each element to copper. The ratios then were plotted against the known percentage for each element in the standard, and a number of least-squares curve fits were performed using the data until a curve was found that best fit the percent-ratio data. In cases in which the composition of a standard was known to be particularly reliable, its points were given extra weighting in the curve-fitting. Final fitted curves were checked visually against the percent-ratio plots for correctness. One such plot is shown in figure 2.

Lead and iron could be fitted satisfactorily to first-degree polynomials, but zinc required a third-degree polynomial and tin required one of the fourth degree. The equations were incorporated into a computer program, which solves the more complicated function by the method of successive approximation.

Figure 2
The tin data from standards combined with curves fit to them. First-degree, fourth-degree, and fifth-degree curves are shown, with their equations. Notice how the fifth-degree curve oscillates around the fourth-degree curve.

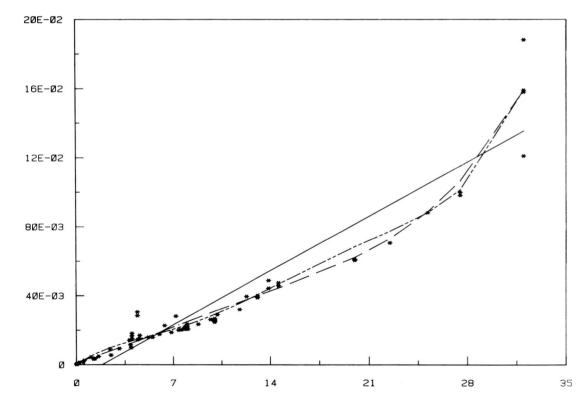

The program takes the observed counts (peak heights) for tin, lead, zinc, and iron and ratios each to the counts for copper. It then solves the equations fit to the standard curves to obtain the percentages of the four elements. The four percentages are then subtracted from 100%, and the remainder is taken as the copper percentage. Deriving the copper percentage in this way is not as reliable as a separate determination, but to determine the copper independently would have required certain refinements of the technique, which probably would not have been justified given the desire to make the determinations on the unaltered surfaces of the objects.

Because the iron content of the brass objects was rarely found to be greater than 0.5%, and owing to the possibility of surface contamination by iron-containing materials, the measurements for iron are not given in the catalogue entries. The totals for the copper, tin, lead, and zinc contents given in the entries thus generally add up to slightly less than 100%.

In the cases of the gold and silver objects, similar methods were employed but with fewer standards. For the gold objects, a preliminary examination of the spectra indicated only one instance in which an appreciable amount of any element other than gold, silver, or copper was present. This occurred in the earrings (no. 7), in which a small amount of cadmium was detected. The quantification formula thus was based on the assumption that the combined gold, silver, and copper contents totaled 100%.

The quantification of the analyses of the silver bowl (no. 26) was based on standards prepared after a preliminary examination of the spectra for the bowl indicated the presence of copper, lead, and gold combined with the silver. Here, the assumption was made that the total for the silver, gold, lead, and copper contents equaled 100%.

Following the quantification of the spectra for the objects, the percentages were averaged and the standard deviation of the results was calculated. Using the standard deviation, the number of measurements taken, and published constants used for determining probability levels,[2] known as "t" values, the confidence limits were calculated by the following formula:

$$\overline{X} \pm \frac{ts}{\sqrt{n}}$$

where $\overline{X}$ is the percentage of each element, t is the "t" value, s is the standard deviation, and n is the number of measurements. The confidence limits represent a 95% probability level. Thus, for a measurement that reads "80% (± 3)," there is a 95% probability that the correct determination lies between 77% and 83%. This applies for the area analyzed, assuming that a valid analytical procedure free from systematic error has been used.[3] Confidence limits derived by this method were found to agree closely with those calculated using the range of the measurements.

Confidence Limits

Examples of Analyses

The method of data reduction and quantification outlined above worked quite well on the standards, as one would expect, since the standards were used to formulate the method. Rather than look at how the quantification method works with standards, it is useful to examine the X-ray fluorescence results for two of the objects compared with the results obtained in previous analyses.

Wet chemical analyses for two different parts of the canteen (no. 17) are shown as #1 and #2 in table 1.[4] Each analaysis was made using 50 milligrams separated from 70-milligram samples scraped from the surface. A larger sample could not be taken, owing to the thinness of the metal, so duplicate wet chemical analyses are not available for this object.

Since the conical piece inside the center hole could not be analyzed by X-ray fluorescence, only comparisons of the analyses of the flat sheet that makes up the back

Table 1:   Analyses of Canteen No. 17

#	Area sampled	Copper	Tin	Lead	Zinc	Iron	Total
Analyses by wet chemistry, I. V. Bene, April 3, 1972							
1	Exterior, near crack (in roundel in turned edge of flat sheet)	81.7	not detected	1.4	15.2	1.2	99.5
2	Inside center hole	84.0	not detected	1.4	12.8	0.7	98.9
Analyses by X-ray fluorescence, June 29, 1983							
3	Flat sheet back, head of figure in outer band.	81.6	0.4	2.0	15.8	0.3	(100)
4	Flat sheet (back) foreleg of horse near center.	80.3	0.5	2.4	16.4	0.5	(100)
5	Exterior, in turned-up edge of flat sheet; similar to #1, above.	80.8	0.3	2.2	16.3	0.4	(100)
av.	Average composition of flat sheet (back) by X-ray fluorescence, with confidence limits, as reported in entry #17, above.	80.9 ($\pm$1.6)	trace	2.2 ($\pm$0.5)	16.2 ($\pm$0.8)	not reported	not reported
6	Domed side, sheet; in area of lost inlay, to proper left of central "Madonna" figure.	79.4	0.6	2.5	17.1	0.4	(100)
7	Seam, near analyses #6, above.	74.5	2.7	6.7	15.6	0.4	(100)
8	"Lower" bracket handle when canteen viewed from front.	76.0	−0.4	1.3	22.9	0.2	(100)
9	"Upper" bracket handle, as above.	79.3	0.3	2.6	17.5	0.3	(100)
10	Spout, on side near handle.	80.5	0.1	2.2	17.0	0.3	(100)

Table 2: Analyses of Incense Burner No. 2

#	Area sampled	Copper	Tin	Lead	Zinc	Iron	Total
	Analyses by wet chemistry, I. V. Bene, March 27, 1972						
1a	Handle, near break; first analysis.	69.08	0.31	16.58	12.31	(lost)	98.28
1b	Handle, near break; second analysis.	68.78	0.78	16.66	12.28	1.3	99.80
1	Average of 1a + 1b Confidence limit	68.9 ($\pm$0.6)	0.6 ($\pm$1.0)	16.6 ($\pm$0.2)	12.3 ($\pm$0.1)	1.3	99.6
2	Body, near handle break (single analysis only).	75.0	1.9	12.8	6.6	0.7	97.0
	Analyses by X-ray fluorescence, June 29, 1983						
3	Handle, bottom, half-way out.	59.3	2.4	30.7	7.0	0.6	(100)
4	Bottom of object, brownish area, slightly off-center.	66.5	7.6	15.5	9.8	0.5	(100)
5	Bottom of object, towards proper right side, near edge; brownish area with thin patina.	28.4	9.8	40.0	18.1	3.7	(100)
6	Lower half, side to proper right of handle, in openwork area.	75.1	6.6	13.9	3.9	0.4	(100)
7	Lower half, back side, openwork area towards proper left.	23.1	8.4	61.9	4.8	1.8	(100)
8	Lower half, flange of hinge, on proper left.	52.8	9.3	29.0	4.5	4.3	(100)
9	Upper half, flange of hinge, on proper left, above #8.	-15.3	10.2	97.7	5.6	1.8	(100)
10	Upper half, back, in openwork area, above analysis #7.	29.9	5.8	58.0	5.7	0.6	(100)
av.	Average of analyses #3, 4, 6, and 8, above, with confidence limits, as reported in entry #2.	63 ($\pm$15)	7 ($\pm$5)	22 ($\pm$14)	6 ($\pm$4)	not reported	not reported

of the body can be made. Analyses #1, #3, #4, and #5 all were done on this piece of flat sheet, which forms the back of the canteen and extends onto the outermost register of design on the front. A soft-soldered join holds together the flat sheet and the domical front.

Analyses #1, #3, #4, and #5 are extremely similar. The lead figures may be slightly overestimated by X-ray fluorescence. The iron figures, given the small amount indicated, also are in fairly close agreement; the results for iron, however, may be equally unreliable in both techniques, owing to weighing difficulties and carry-over of unwanted elements in wet chemistry, and to contamination in the X-ray fluorescence. Iron is not reported in the individual catalogue entries.

The tin figures also agree quite well in the wet chemical and the X-ray fluorescence analyses. An exception is #8, which shows a negative number for tin, simply meaning that tin is not present and the program is in error in trying to quantify it. Solder shows up in the increased lead and tin in the analysis of the seam(#7). The listing of "(100)" in all cases for the totals of the X-ray fluorescence analyses is meant to remind the reader that the percentages of tin, lead, zinc, and iron are added up and subtracted from 100% to obtain the percentage of copper. The copper percentages, arrived at by difference, are surprisingly close to those derived from wet chemistry. The brass of the two large pieces of sheet that make up the body, the spout, and the "upper" bracket handle are indistinguishable on the basis of these analyses. Some real variation can be seen in the composition of the conical filler in the hole and the "lower" bracket handle.

The situation is significantly different for the incense burner (no. 2), a highly leaded, heavily corroded brass. The X-ray fluorescence analyses of this object (see table 2) are much less reliable than those for the canteen, as can be seen by the great variation in lead content and, in fact, in all of the elements. The wet chemical samples were removed by drilling deeply into the metal. Even though only a single analysis could be performed on the sample from the body, the sample from the handle was done in duplicate and shows the sort of variation present in the wet chemical technique.

The variations in the X-ray fluorescence analyses are so broad that perhaps the only way to treat them is to reject those with copper contents below 50% and average the rest, as was done for the incense burner; for this object, confirmatory analyses by another technique was useful. The X-ray fluorescence analysis of the incense burner gave the most erratic results of any of the objects tested. Fortunately, as noted in "Techniques and Materials," only three other brass objects have similar surface conditions, which caused similar results.

Notes

1. Jenkins, Gould, and Gedcke 1981.
2. Fritz and Schenk 1975, p. 35.
3. Ibid.
4. Schneider 1973, pp. 155–56.

Appendix II

NAMES OF ARTISTS	Qasim ibn Ali: no. 16
	Shazi: no. 14
	Taqi(?): no. 35
NAMES OF PATRONS	Amir Shihab al-Din: no. 16
	An amir of Sultan al-Malik al-Nasir: no. 22
	Jahangir: no. 36
	Majd al-Mulk al-Muzaffar: no. 14
	Sultan Najm al-Din Ayyub: no. 18
NAMES OF LATER OWNERS	Aqa Rustam Ruzafzun: no. 26
	Hafiz Ali: no. 25
DATED PIECES	1210/11 (pen box): no. 14
	1232 (ewer): no. 16
	1620/21 (knife): no. 36
	1777 (dagger and sheath): no. 35

Appendix III

Thirteen of the pieces in the Islamic metalwork collection of the Freer Gallery have been excluded from the catalogue entries because they are either insignificant pieces (such as 78.48) or require further research to establish their provenance and date. One of the astrolabes (42.8) has been published as a forgery (Gingerich, King, and Saliba 1972). In order to present the complete collection, these pieces are listed and illustrated in this appendix.

08.53
Brass bowl inlaid with gold and silver
Height: 6.9 cm. (2¾ in.)
Diameter: 13.5 cm. (5⁵⁄₁₆ in.)

08.54
Brass lamp
Height: 13.8 cm. (5⁷⁄₁₆ in.)
Width: 13.3 cm. (5³⁄₁₆ in.)

42.8
Brass astrolabe
Made for Muhammad Khan Bajran
by Abd al-Aimma in 1127 A.H. (1715 A.D.)
Height: 19.8 cm. (7¹³⁄₁₆ in.)
Diameter: 12.9 cm. (5¹⁄₁₆ in.)

43.1
Gold ewer
Made for Abu Mansur Bakhtiyar
Height: 13.0 cm. (5⅜ in.)
Diameter: 9.4 cm. (3¹¹⁄₁₆ in.)

43.8
Gold medal (two views)
Diameter: 4.3 cm. (1¹¹⁄₁₆ in.)

45.6
Brass astrolabe
Made by Ustad Muhammad Zaman
in 1095 A.H. (1683/84 A.D.)
Height: 17.6 cm. (6¹⁵⁄₁₆ in.)
Diameter: 12.9 cm. (5¹⁄₁₆ in.)

50.6
Silver bowl
Made for Abu Sahl b. Tahman b. Faramarz
al-Farhadjerdi
Height: 4.3 cm. (1¹⁄₁₆ in.)
Diameter: 23.9 cm. (9³⁄₈ in.)

51.8
Silver candlestick
Made for Ispahbad Abu Mansur Rukn al-
Din Mahmud by Abu'l-Fath Ali b. Fadl al- . . .
Height: 57.1 cm. (22½ in.)
Diameter: 57.0 cm. (22⁷⁄₁₆ in.)

58.14
Gold bracelet
Diameter (max.): 9.7 cm. (3¹³⁄₁₆ in.)
Width: 5.0 cm. (2 in.)

66.6
Gold necklace
Length: 65.0 cm. (25½ in.)

66.7
Gold necklace
Length: 56.0 cm. (22 in.)

78.48
Brass ornament
Height: 5.4 cm. (2⅛ in.)
Width: 6.2 cm. (2⁷⁄₁₆ in.)

66.8
Gold necklace
Length: 38.0 cm. (15 in.)

Appendix IV

List of objects in the Freer Gallery of Art by order of accession numbers

Accession No.	Catalogue No.	Figure No.	Appendix No.
08.53			III
08.54			III
36.7	14		
39.44a–b	35		
39.45	28		
39.58	23		
40.4	32		
40.5	33		
40.6	31		
40.7	37		
40.8	29		
40.9	30		
41.10	17		
42.8			III
42.16		69	
43.1			III
43.8			III
45.6			III
45.9		72	
45.13	3		
45.14	24		
48.25	4		
49.9		73	
49.11	20		
50.5	10		
50.6			III
50.21	8		
51.8			III
51.17	13		
52.1	2		

Accession No.	Catalogue No.	Figure No.	Appendix No.
53.89	22		
53.92	1		
54.115	26		
54.128	15		
55.10	18		
55.22	16		
55.27	36		
57.3	9		
58.2		50	
58.6	5		
58.14			III
58.15	34		
66.6			III
66.7			III
66.8			III
73.4	11		
77.4	25		
77.5	12		
78.48			III
80.19	27		
80.25	21		
80.200a–b	7		
81.27	19		
82.12	6		
1984.3	38		

List of objects in other collections used as reference illustrations

	Name of Collection	Accession No.	Figure No.
ANN ARBOR	University of Michigan, Kelsey Museum of Archaeology	28801	51
	The University of Michigan Museum of Art	1965/1.182	55
BALTIMORE	Walters Art Gallery	54.457	23
BERLIN	Museum für Islamische Kunst	I.886	2
		I.2210	32
		I.3619	73
BOSTON	Museum of Fine Arts	14.665	70
		46.1135	35
BROOKLYN	The Brooklyn Museum	50.91	19
BRUSSELS	Musées Royaux d'Art et d'Histoire	E.O. 1492	56
CAIRO	Museum of Islamic Art	4463	12
		9281	3
		15043	52
		15124	37
		15409	67
CLEVELAND	The Cleveland Museum of Art	44.485	7
		48.458	33
		56.11	47
COPENHAGEN	The C. L. David Collection	27/1972	44
DAMASCUS	National Museum	A 1056	25
HAM, RICHMOND	The Keir Collection		10
(England)			60
HERAT	The Naqshibandi Foundation		40
İSTANBUL	Topkapı Palace Museum	2/2836	16
		2/2844	16
		2/2860	16
JERUSALEM	L. A. Mayer Memorial Institute of Islamic Art	M 30–68	31
		M 82–69	34

	Name of Collection	Accession No.	Figure No.
KUWAIT	National Museum, Dar al-Athar al-Islamiya Collection	LNS 12 HS	74
		LNS 82 M	38
		LNS 116 M	57
		LNS 137 M	68
LENINGRAD	State Hermitage Museum	NP–1567	5
		Z–524	21
		CA–12687	1
LONDON	The British Museum	OA 1939 3.13 20–38	27
		66 12–69 61	8
		78 12–30 682	62
		78 12–30 902	71
		91 6–23 5	39
		1878 12–30 732	65
	Victoria and Albert Museum	IS 27–1980	18
		91.1.586	66
		571–1878	43
		760–1889	58
		943–1886	64
		1191–1854	17
LUGANO	Marion Hammer Collection		24
MODENA	Galleria Museo e Medagliere Estense	8082	13
NEW YORK	The Metropolitan Museum of Art	91.1.586	48
		51.125.9	29
		57.88	26
		67.10	22
PARIS	Bibliothèque Nationale	Chabouillet 3192	11
	Musée des Arts Décoratifs	4411	9
	Musée du Louvre	E 11708	20
		MAO 331	14
		MAO 360	53

Name of Collection	Accession No.	Figure No.
	K 3435	46
	LP 16	15
	5991	54
	6034	42
	6315	36
	7428	49
	7880–118	59
SAINT THOMAS Mr. and Mrs. Everett Birch Collection		30
SHANGHAI Shanghai Museum		45
TEHRAN Archaeological Museum	11625	28
TIFLIS Museum of Arts	I/5	4
The Museum of the History of Georgia	MC 135	6
VIENNA Österreichisches Museum für Angewandte Kunst	Go. 81	63

Special Acknowledgments for Reference Photographs

Figs. 1, 4–6, and 21: courtesy of Anatol Ivanov, State Hermitage Museum, Leningrad.

Figs. 2 and 32: courtesy of Staatliche Museen Preussischer Kulturbesitz, Museum für Islamische Kunst, Berlin.

Figs. 3, 12, 37, 52, and 67: courtesy of Abd al-Rauf Yusuf, Museum of Islamic Art, Cairo.

Figs. 7, 33, and 47: courtesy of The Cleveland Museum of Art, Cleveland (fig. 7: purchase from the J. H. Wade Fund; fig. 33: Edward L. Whittemore Fund; fig. 47: John L. Severance Fund).

Figs. 8, 27, 39, 62, 65, and 71: courtesy of the Trustees of The British Museum, London.

Figs. 10 and 60: courtesy of Edmund de Unger, Ham, Richmond.

Fig. 16: courtesy of Filiz Çağman, Topkapı Palace Museum, İstanbul.

Figs. 17, 18, 43, 58, 64, and 66: courtesy of the Board of Trustees of the Victoria and Albert Museum, London (figs. 17 and 43: from Melikian-Chirvani 1982; fig. 66: from Allan and Raby 1982).

Fig. 19: courtesy of The Brooklyn Museum, New York; Gift of the Guennol Collection.

Figs. 22, 26, 29, and 48: courtesy of The Metropolitan Museum of Art, New York, New York (fig. 22: Douglas Dillon Gift and Rogers Fund, 1967; fig. 26: Harris Brisbane Dick Fund, 1957; fig. 29: Gift of Alistair Bradley Martin, 1951; fig. 48: Bequest of Edward C. Moore, 1891).

Fig. 24: courtesy of Marion Hammer, Lugano.

Fig. 25: from Berlin 1982.

Fig. 28: from Ettinghausen 1964.

Fig. 30: courtesy of Mr. and Mrs. Everett Birch.

Figs. 35 and 70: courtesy of the Museum of Fine Arts, Boston (fig. 35: Samuel P. Avery Fund; fig. 70: purchased by M. Victor Golonbew of Paris through Walter Gay and R. Meyer-Reifstahl, June 4, 1914, income of Bartlett Fund and special contribution).

Figs. 38, 57, 68, and 74: courtesy of Dar al-Athar al-Islamiya Collection, National Museum, Kuwait.

Fig. 40: from Melikian-Chirvani 1979b.

Fig. 41: courtesy of A. S. Melikian-Chirvani.

Fig. 51: courtesy of Kelsey Museum of Archaeology, University of Michigan, Ann Arbor.

Fig. 56: courtesy of Musées Royaux d'Art et d'Histoire, Brussels; copyright ACL Bruxelles.

Fig. 61: from Gyllensvärd 1971.

Fig. 73: from Sarre 1906.

Library of Congress Cataloging in Publication Data

Freer Gallery of Art.
  Islamic metalwork in the Freer Gallery of Art.

  "Exhibition held at the Freer Gallery of Art, Smithsonian Institution, Washington, D.C., September 27, 1985–January 5, 1986"—T. p. verso.
  Bibliography: p.
  Supt. of Docs. no.: SI 7.2:Is4
  1. Art metalwork, Islamic—Exhibitions. 2. Art metalwork—Washington (D.C.)—Exhibitions. 3. Freer Gallery of Art—Exhibitions. I. Atıl, Esin.
II. Chase, W. T. (William Thomas) III. Jett, Paul.
IV. Title.
NK6408.9.F73   1985   739'.0917'6710740153   85–40502

ISBN 0–934686–54–8 (pbk. : alk. paper)
ISBN 0–87474–249–8 (Smithsonian Institution Press :
                    pbk. : alk. paper)